To Ellen,

May your own voyages with Thistledown Rising lead you on internal journeys that brim with mystery... and hope.

Sean Friedlund.

DECEMBER 2004

Thistledown Rising

A Memoir
by Sean Redmond

Published by:
Thistledown Rising Productions

First Edition, October, 2004

ISBN 0-975319-49-3
LC #2004104219

Although this is a memoir, the names have been changed in most cases. Also, some of the characters are composites of several people the author knew in his youth. These characters are not intended to represent any one person, living or deceased.

COMP Designation: Original work

All illustrations and cover art are by Anne Cunningham
Editing by Faye Quam Heimerl of Whistling Swan Writing
Cover design and page layout by Eric Brearton, Kiva Communications

10 9 8 7 6 5 4 3 2 1

Printed at Sheridan Books, Inc. Ann Arbor, MI

*To Mother on the eightieth anniversary of your birth,
with all my love; to my niece Melissa "Sierra Mist"
Benton in her news anchor career; and to the twins.*

Table of Contents

Thistledown Rising

While each of us wanders our own inward path,
     We search mighty grimly and wearily laugh.
Then suddenly gathers our hope from despair,
     In radiant moments when hearts do repair.
Along inward paths we hear nary a sound,
     Save one soft and solemn: a puff of the down.

The thistledown wafted, just danced floating by,
     It first barely wiggled, then plumed to the sky.
A treasury of puffs drew nigh; I was enthralled,
     By their majesty, splendor and hope aptly called.
One viewing such wonders could not be thrilled,
     At sights such as these, with hearts reverently stilled.

Now oft in a tranquil mood as I recline,
     My thoughts rising freely and nearly sublime;
The thistledown in my mind's eye does appear,
     Just drifting with mystery, of which I revere.
And then with glad tidings I'm so greatly imbued,
     My cares lift to heaven, sweet dreams there to view.

Thistledown Rising: Windswept O'er Heartland Prairies

"That which comes from the heart touches the heart."

—*Samuel Taylor Coleridge*

$\mathcal{P}$rologue

Although most folks believe thistles are noxious weeds, I reckon they're far more than that. Have a seat, and let me explain. Thistles aren't just prickly eyesores bordering dusty lanes or scattered along too-dry pastures. Oh sure, as a boy I squinted at them with lowly thoughts of their mischief, ugly and sprinkled with dust. After all, if the cows wouldn't eat them, they couldn't count for much, right? I was wrong. I know that now, that thistles are far more than weeds, now that I see them in a new light. I feel it in my bones. A shadow of their wonder flutters in the air, drifting over still pools. Their hardscrabble wisdom echoes inward, humming inside any who might listen.

I declare, thistles look mighty different after all of the changes of my blustery childhood on an eastern Kansas farm. Most everything that I knew then is now long gone. Stubborn winds and a bunch of lessons surged over Kansas prairies, teasing me into becoming someone new. That new me holds thistles in high regard! Many of my boyish ideas have retired. That's all right, seeing how change uproots most everything. But change has not uprooted all that I fancied. Of all the questions I asked and all the ideas I challenged, one stands taller and stronger now than it did back then. Even now, I sense hope endures, even as familiar faces and places fade from memory and from view. Hope alone may be enough. All's well.

As I said, most everything changed in my youth on an eastern Kansas farm of the 1960s. The land, dusty lanes, power lines, water supply, telephones, and fences became strangely new. I barely recognize them, and that's just for starters. Mostly, the people I knew changed, some of them for the better and most of them forever: now long gone. And I may have changed the most of all. As I said, I now hold thistles in high regard. That prickly menace became my guardian in the Kansas of my youth. While that had been true all along, I needed to see it for myself.

I wish you could have seen for yourself my childhood home. It lay smack on the border with Missouri. I wondered whether a flighty grasshopper perched on a fence post at the east end of our pasture might be able to spew tobacco juice into either state. That might happen, provided the winds proved favorable.

Our farm nearly straddled the state line, just as the time I spent as a boy lay sandwiched between two times: between two different periods. Grown-ups spoke of changing times, of how one period ended as another one began. At age four I mistook what they meant by the word "period." The only kind I knew came at the end of a sentence. You see, Dad had taught me to read before I finished my fourth year, and he kicked in a bunch of lessons on punctuation to boot. As I ripened to age four, I knew all about periods, long before I knew they are also spans of time. Armed with my tiny punctuation mark, I reckoned folks spoke about sentences, not about time. So whenever I heard how one period ended while another one began, I pictured two periods cradling a brief sentence, one with words blown into italics. I fancied Kansas winds blew the letters in those words, and those italics showed me both words and time pass quickly. Grown-ups often spoke of how times had changed: gone with the wind. Did Kansas winds tease out old periods to commence new ones?

As a boy I imagined that old times teetered in the balance and then gave way to the new, like an aged chestnut tree. It groans in the wind after its trunk has been chopped through most of the way. Protesting and moaning, the tree crashes to the ground—provided healthy gusts prevail. During the time I spent as a boy on a Kansas prairie, the tail end of a time long ago made way for our time coming. Dad told me how it was. When we moved to our farm on New Year's Day of 1960, the roads were narrow dirt lanes sprinkled with gravel. Wickedly rutted, the dirt roads washed out with most cloud bursts. Downpours made up in size and strength for what they lacked in numbers. Our old-timer lanes soon retired, heralding a new period.

Our dirt roads became well-groomed and graded gravel roads nearly twice as wide as we had known. Even after fussy storms pounded down to break up a dry spell, those gravel roads usually held. They did not wash out. As the 1960s ended, earth movers smoothed the dusty lanes that skirted rolling hills, later themselves leveled.

Sprinkles of gravel lined rutted dirt roads surrounding our farm. Gravel wore thin enough to remind me of the lime we dusted on clayey soils. That lime helped the plants soak up minerals. Lining the dirt roads, sturdy plants pouted in ditches even during dry spells. When folks mowed them, they often dulled or broke blades. We called thickened stumps left after mowing "old pokes" for painfully clear reasons. Those pokes grimaced in ditches, gathering dust showers and dirt for company.

Most folks reckoned pokes were about as ugly as they were tough.

Tarnished barbed wire and weathered fence posts lined our dirt lanes. Weeds grew all around, often threading themselves between the wires, as if the fence was a trellis. The fence posts soon gave way to metallic ones, triangularly shaped and notched. Fresh barbed wire bound posts into fences. Those wires glinted in afternoon sunshine. Were rich city folks on land next to ours showing us how their new fences were special? Did they mutter the same about themselves?

Power lines to carry electricity also dangled from wooden poles hewn from pasture trees stunted by dryness. The wires rested on cross beams nailed to the tops of poles, a few of which toted metal boxes to manage details of electricity. Soon, humming overhead lines twenty feet high on aluminum monsters carried electricity. Those lines pushed out makeshift wooden poles. Those metallic wonders demanded new right of ways through fields.

Telephones were hand cranked and connected by wispy lines resting on telephone poles, often the same ones holding power lines. Those poles were splintered and forked above the crossbeams to form two scrawny pointed pieces, like serpents' tongues. The sputtering and crackling sounds on those makeshift lines reminded me of a diamondback rattler vibrating to strike. At three spots on each pole ceramic spools held phone wires. Sometimes cracked and as weather-beaten as poles themselves, spools were fastened by rusty nails which left ochre streaks.

Party lines and hand-cranked telephones with funnel-shaped metal tubes to speak into gave way to rotary dial phones and private lines. Our hand-cranked phones passed into history before I reached age four! Gazing from the kitchen door, I wondered at our new black phone as it rested at eye level on our round table draped with a white bib in the southwest corner of our kitchen. I admit my mouth drooped open, like a widder woman's pig. Our new phone needed rest, what with all the magic it worked. Why, it let people hear each other from a distance! Staring at me, it warned, "Don't touch me. I'm for grown-ups only. Stay away, boy!" Its arrival felt large, especially when I was roughly four years old and not even that many feet high.

I simply won't forget the day our hand-cranked telephone left us. Mother fussed, "I'll miss hearing those rings: two long and one short." That had been our party line code. Most folks paid little heed, and they listened in even when the call wasn't theirs. After Dad pried the box off of the wall, I wanted to hold its black listening tube to my ear. It felt as cool as a cucumber and as slick as our linoleum floor. I needed to hear if its time had passed—silent at last. Dad had sputtered, "When the line is disconnected, it goes dead." Did death mean being pulled from what's known: from whom we love? Did death mean "disconnected", as it had for our hand-cranked telephone? Did death's silence leave only still memories?

Bolting, I ran outside to scoop up two fistfuls of dust. I pounded back into the kitchen, grasped that fool phone, and sprinkled dust all over it. I'd seen something like that done at a funeral once, the box being lowered.

"What in the Sam Hill are you doing?" Dad asked with a puzzled frown.

"Well, if the line is dead, I'll use dust to get it ready. Then, we need to bury it, right Dad?" He flashed a half-smile, and he sauntered out of the kitchen. The porch echoed his muttering. I'll wager he felt happy and sad, and that confused him. Otherwise, he'd have stayed. And I needed to ask him if hand-cranked telephones dry and shrivel when dead, the way plants do when they're mowed . . . the way crops do when harvested. As a boy I thought of death as shriveling, dryness, and silence. Did it mean all of that on top of being pulled away from what I knew?

Speaking of knowing things, if anyone knew the land, Kansas farmers did. They thought about the land in clumps or sections, each one a square mile or 640 acres. When anyone asked about our neighbors, we rambled on about who lived in our section. Numbering six when we moved in on New Year's Day of 1960, our neighbors blossomed to twenty before the 1960s gasped their last breath. No doubt about it, time and place hung in the balance. The Kansas of my youth now rests in my mind as an artifact of a time that changed suddenly, maybe too suddenly.

As a boy in Kansas, I saw soft-spoken streams gurgling up from ancient springs. Waters oozed over green algae. Mosses slithered in dampness. Tiny streams joined forces to craft creeks, echoing aromas of life. Bluegill, channel cats, crawdads, and bullfrogs floated there. Then, these wonderful creeks made way for progress. Crews blustered in to gouge trenches and lay city water lines. They dynamited their way across the land, and they spoiled our menagerie, rending deep and jagged trenches for hard, white plastic tubing. But there was no call for that. We already had spring water to fill our cisterns. Their trenching looked like someone fancied a dull knife to gut channel cats, which he then left on the bank to spoil. Was that a kind of sin? City water line crews blasted their way across the land, changing the course of creeks and the lay of the land. Bodies of dead bluegills rotted on banks of once-proud creeks, spoiled with hushed memories of life-filled stories.

Rusted and slumbering silos—a few abandoned with volunteer trees growing smack inside of them, like gigantic potted plants—yielded to line-of-sight communication towers. These also changed the land and the landmarks which proved to be novel topics of conversation in town.

The businesses in town live in my memory. Our town's mercantile slumbered with ceiling fans twirling above dimly lit rooms, fronted by rusted and curved metal siding. As I walked into that store, I heard rickety wooden planks, withered with age. An elderly couple owned our mercantile, and they watched every detail. Their wariness meant they were thrifty. Scurrying about, they wore starched white aprons which the missus cleaned daily. Mr. Hamlet called out the order, and Mrs. Hamlet recorded it in her fine script in a thick ledger. That couple knew all about us, and they offered credit when crops failed. Our aged storekeepers used clunky mechanical cash registers with separate keys for cents, dollars, and for "NO SALE."Mrs. Hamlet often smiled and held her hands behind her back. "Guess which hand, Sean?" I had spied which hand held her orange lollipop by glancing into the tilted mirror above her head. I can't forget her surprise at how I guessed correctly every time. Did she know my secret? Did she play along to make me feel grown-up?

Soon she began to ask me questions, as if she assigned herself to be the hostess of a quiz show. "Sean, what is the capital of China? Who reached the South Pole first? Give me the cubic root of 1,000," she droned. Was she only a kind jokster? Heck fire, her questions felt silly, and I reckoned she poked fun at my expense? To cloak embarrassment, I played along. I thought I needed to make some joke or play on words to amuse her. Acting puzzled, I scratched my head, gazed at the ceiling, and peered at the floor. Pawing at it with my right foot, I stammered, "Aw, shucks. I reckon the answer is . . . well . . . (looking at both of my hands and holding them up) I imagine it is ten, Mrs. Hamlet,"as I threw my hands above my head, twitching my fingers to make sure she saw all ten digits. "The answer rests in both of my hands, not just one, Ma'am" I chortled, my lips curled up and my face beaming to Mrs. Hamlet's delight. No treat dared escape my reach! She chuckled, "You're as cute as a speckled pup under a red wagon!" Her approval, not the candy, rewarded me.

That game lasted until I reached age six. By then Mrs. Hamlet tired of our silly pastime. There's no way she could've run out of questions because she toted a truckload of them. While I miss the treats I won in her games, I miss Mrs. Hamlet's kindness most of all. Her memory burns warmly, echoing my youth.

Soon, a supermarket replaced that mercantile. A builder slapped it up near US 169 highway in what had been a cattle pasture, where deer had once roamed. The Hamlets are now long gone, just as is their welcoming grocery store that made me feel like I was surely at home.

Both that "home" and that couple are gone now, replaced by kids punching away on computerized cash registers. Mrs. Hamlet's fine, swirling handwriting in thick, ruled ledgers gave way to automatic inventory systems and finally to point-of-sale scanners hooked to computers.

The adults who toiled on the land to work out their lives have ebbed away. Most of them are gone now, leaving another generation of youngsters—my generation—to fill their roles. All of the kids in my family are now well into our middle years. That includes me, and I was one of the younger children in our family. Much has changed, which isn't surprising if I remember that time and place often lay in the balance, poised to welcome a new era and to send the old one on its way. It happens slowly at first, but then it builds on itself as one period melts into another one, as swiftly and naturally as a reader may turn pages of a griping mystery. The pace of change inched along slowly enough that few noticed it until many of the familiar places and faces were no more, until I could see and feel all of their effects, until the Kansas I knew as a child had disappeared.

Whenever I consider changes in the Kansas of my youth, I hear a soft melody powered by a stately wind. That wind rustles more than words and times. It nips at grasses and weeds while bellowing over the land to breathe life into it, the way air may breathe life into a pump organ. Does the wind hint that with change may come a plan far better than we know? If I breathe deeply, I spy a tuft of thistledown wafting in the breeze, renewing hope. Like a winded runner catching my breath, I sense we're part of a mysterious melody. The notes in "our tune" depend on the ones before it. By choosing carefully, I may open up more choices for tomorrow. Options feed on the past, the way a creek feeds on tiny streams that merge to power it along its way.

Are our choices scribbled on a dance ticket in an endless dance? Do we keep time to the music to manage life's uncertainties, one framed by the Grace of Something too grand to see fully? The possibilities stretch onward. When I spy thistledown highlighted in gold against the light of a setting sun, I'm enchanted. When I reflect on the Kansas of my youth, I remember common thistles. Beguiling, their virtues aren't common at all. Thistles form tiny purple blossoms—lovely and enthralling to view. Although small, their beauty far outshines that of larger flowers. Do their blossoms reflect our dreams, beautiful yet elusive? You see, when I've reached out to touch thistle flowers, they drift away. They change into tiny white pillows of fluff, striated with fine tinsel: ethereal.

When I was quite young, Dad read to me about Mr. William Wordsworth. He mused, "The meanest flower that blows can give thoughts that do often lie too deep for tears." Thistles snugly fit his words. The thoughts those mean flowers evoked for me lie too deep for tears, perhaps too sublime to capture. Yet, I do try. Please don't hold this against me. You see, over many years I grudgingly fell in love with common thistles. How so? How could I love what most folks consider a menace? Well, have you really looked at a grizzled and gnarled thistle on a rocky hill? It's stunted, and yet it clings to life. Stalwartly it survives against all odds. Staking out a patch of ground too poor for other plants, its roots tunnel into the rocky soil. It endures. If anything show-cased Kipling's sentiments about persistence, thistles do. They held on, endured, and then hung on even longer still "when there was nothing left except the will to hang on."

Beguiling, thistles are enchanting. Unassuming yet reliable, they deserve praise. I've learned to admire them by pondering long enough to know them. You see, something even as angry and prickly as a thistle holds loveliness in its heart if I know how to find it. And I only needed to watch goats to glimpse that fact. I saw how they dined on thistles, although they're the only farm animal that had anything to do with them. Maybe goats are as stubborn and as ornery as thistles. Is that how they saw their way clear to put up with something that's mostly prickly?

Thistles hooked me, just as their spiny shafts may prick you. They're guarded by prickly points, and livestock keep a low opinion of them. But that's unfair. Well, cows might sniff and lick at thistles, but they always lurch back with startled pain. Oh yes, I've been pricked many times when I reached for a thistle's flower. That's a rude awakening, but fitting. You see, dreams often disappoint and pay us wages of pain. Then, people make a bunch of excuses, acting rough when they don't get their way. We might hide embarrassment, shielding ourselves from prying eyes whenever our plans misfire. Aren't people like thistles whenever they use their prickly "thorns" to scare away intruders?

Thistledown wafting over Kansas prairies resembles a wordless song, a vibrant melody sung by a giddy meadowlark in full-throated revelry. That melody sounds immortal. It comes and ebbs like the tide on an ancient inland sea where salt mists rose crisp and clear each and every dawn. Even when thistledown puffs away blithely into nothingness to some mysterious place, it never really leaves us. Aren't our dreams and hopes like that: lovely to behold, difficult to grasp or even to see? Yet, dreams endure. Thistledown wonder lives forever as does its melody. Our dreams and memories remain, granting immortality to the best in all of us. Hope and nature endure.

Kansas farmers did themselves proud with tall hopes that set them apart, like a lanky man who struts through fields of sweet corn. The ones I knew clung to dreams the way a feral cat snatches at and then clutches a tawny chick. Kansas farm folks endured and hoped and then endured even more. They were weather-beaten and grizzled, gnarled in stature from a lifetime of using their bodies as tools. Yet, they were not broken. Hope endures. Each season brings a fresh start to realize dreams. Each season and each generation sends a whole host of dreams and hopes wafting over the rolling prairie. The seasons repeat to offer a fresh start, one that farm folks pray to find and work to grasp, one offered to every new generation seeking it.

Like the down of a thistle, dreams are piloted by winds and rains to destinations unknown. The seeds sometimes fall on fertile soils, and sometimes they fall on rocky hills. Yet, dreams endure. And like thistles, these farmers were toughened and sinewy, ready to meet the world and to face whatever disappointments might come. Like thistledown, their dreams were managed by nature and by her endless cycles of birth, death and rebirth. And like thistles, these farmers endured and grew.

Welcome to an adventure! Welcome to the Kansas of my youth! We'll explore times and places on that rolling prairie, and I'll share with you the thoughts and feelings that came with them.

The questions we wrestled with are still mighty important even today. Much has changed with that tidal surge of time and with the torrid winds whipping across the parched Kansas prairie. Still, much more remains the same. Of all that I learned, I know for certain that hope and nature endure.

Oh, my! Will you look at the time. I need to thin a patch of thistles tucked along a hedge row. Those ornery thistles hatched a small thicket along the northeast corner in our east pasture. My sakes alive, I've let them go untended too long, and those stubborn stalks have seeped from that fence line into the fescue field. It won't take me too long since I aim only to thin the thistles. After all, I've got to leave some of them for other folks to enjoy. I aim only to thin them, to balance them, so that they don't spread out of control.

Please walk with me, and I'll share my story, this tale of *Thistledown Rising*. It won't take as long as you might think, and there are parts of the story that will sound familiar. I bet you might even recognize it, and you might reckon that some of this story is about you, too. Surprised? Don't be. Guess what, I'll warn you now that I'll spring a few more surprises on you along the way!

Listen, I'd be tickled if you walk with me to share this tale of *Thistledown Rising*. We'll stop by my garden to dig potatoes and carrots after we work in the pasture, and we'll simmer a soup. Please join me on a windswept prairie, nestled along the Kansas-Missouri line. Let's tend to thistles in the Kansas of my youth.

Come Home From Evening Pasture

"Mum, com'on Mum!" split the twilight's hush. "Mum, Mum, com'on Mum!" rippled over our pasture, teased at tall grasses, and tumbled down the valley. Dad's calls rolled down the hill to our old Redmond valley creek. The sound collided with Mum, Suzie, and her tag along Reddy. "Chum on! Hum on, Mum! It's time. We're ready!"

Dad turned an ear toward the east pasture that overlooked the valley. He listened for the dull "clunk-clank" of cowbells. Except for autumn's rustling, the air lay still. Then again, his words rumbled across our pasture and down the valley to echo from our creek. Piercing the brittleness of the autumn air, Dad leaned his frame gently forward to help wedge both his frame and his voice through the air. Dad moved with the weary skill of a rail splitter who wields a wedge to splinter logs into posts.

"Mum, Mum, com'on Mum. Chum on! Hum on, Mum!" He might just as well have called, "Come home, Mum and Suzie, to our milk barn, a creaking shed with weathered planks, limestone foundation, and rusty tin siding. Come home for evening milking.

Clank-clank, boom-bong, clang-clang went two metal feed pails, dented and split on the ends, as Dad pounded them together. He listened again. Clank-clank answered back without cowbells. Re-aiming the mouths of the pails for the angle that boomed most loudly, he pointed the pail mouths toward the creek, and he slammed them together. This time, "Clank-clank, boom-bong, clang-clang," hollered good and loud. "Come home from evening pasture!" but no sign of Mum or Suzie wafted in reply.

Dad suspected our Jersey cows nibbled grasses along the banks of the creek. That creek glided over weathered stones, and it flowed even during dry spells, owing to a faithful spring. Its waters gurgled over moss-covered stones to chill shades of green.

"Where the heck are they?" Dad mumbled, his forehead furrowing deeply as speckles of sweat collected over his upper lip.

"Clank-clank, boom-bong, clang-clang, clank-clank, boom-bong, clang-clang."

"Come on girls, I'm nearly out of time."

"Clank-clank, boom-bong, clang-clang; clank-clank, boom-bong, clang-clang; clank-clank, boom-bong, clang-clang . . ."

I delighted in this routine as I watched from my special place in the largest of our three pear trees near our garden, flanked by our king cottonwood. No more perfect place could ever be invented for a boy of four in which to lounge. There, I ate my fill of golden pears, the sweetness dripping from my chin. Can a body get drunk on such pears, the way Uncle Arthur did on Irish Whiskey? No matter. From my perch, I often trained my eyes on Dad, the barnyard, milk barn, and farmhouse.

I willed Mum and Suzie to rush home so that Dad could milk them with enough time left over to read to me. He worked the "graveyard" shift at the Santa Fe Railroad switching yard in Argentine, Kansas.

Dad banged the pails together three more times before he adjusted his bifocals. He was in his early forties, a time when many grown-ups switch to heavier glasses, but I reckoned his eyes were tired on account of staring into too-bright locomotive lights in the yards. Besides, fresh out of The University of Missouri at Columbia, he scoured stacks of papers as a high school English teacher. His eyes needed a rest.

But my eyes were strong. I don't recall a time when I couldn't read a little, and I owe that to my dad, Thomas A. Redmond.

From a slight distance, I studied Dad's face as he read silently. His eyes misted all kinds of feelings: joy and sadness, love and fear, boredom and suspense. Hope and despair flashed over his eyes more surely than any silent film star ever could. Feelings drifted over him, each one quivering and hanging like a gentle breeze that rustles tall cotton plants.

You bet I drew to him, just as if a gigantic hand beckoned me. How else could I read all that he read? Climbing onto his lap, I snuggled into Dad's left side and melted there, the way a Hershey bar puddles on a hot dashboard. Dad's mint dental floss wedged between his teeth—only half-finished flossing to grant more time to read—and his Vick's Vapor Rub spelled heaven.

First I'd ask Dad to point to each word as he read it. With my left eye, I followed his finger as he underscored sentences on the page. With my right eye, I studied his ever-changing face. After a bit, I asked him to read aloud. His emotion-drenched voice and movie-star looks guided me, and I began to register words and meanings as images and feelings. Soon, I could read and print longer words, like "adventure", "mystery", "graceful" and "gratitude".

"Clank-clank, boom-bong, clang-clang. Mum, Mum, com'on Mum," hummed back from hills, girded by gurgling rills. There was no mistaking it. Clanging feed pails meant come home from evening pasture. Mum cow and Suzie paused a moment, pregnant with control. Then, catching a second wind of obedience, they bolted toward the milk barn from pasture mists.

As I watched the creamy scene, I wondered where all of that dairy goodness began." Had it taken root in swaying grasses that our cows munched?

Watching Mum and Reddy being milked often drowsed me to sleep. Our cows felt satisfied, creasing their eyelids shut as they chewed. I did not know what was sweeter—their milk or that taste of late autumn, oozing from pear-laden branches. Closing in on my third pear, I felt its lovely juices trickle down my chin. "Why, I'll let it seep down my face. Can that feel as fine as pears taste?" Summer's flavors brimmed in those pears beneath golden skins. A few too-ripe ones—brown and bleeding— oozed juices. My arms and legs wilted, and I drifted. Stillness edged by.

I'd earned a breather in the pear tree after my day of discovery. If done properly, all that fun can tucker a boy out! I chased naughty goats that made snatches at clothes fluttering on our line. (Goats nibble on anything they take a notion to—rubber, shoes, shirts, and even thistles.) Our goats grew partial to cotton, and any goat stalking a full clothesline walked through high cotton. Next, I shooed three greedy geese away from the cucumbers, spinach, and the last of our pole beans. I was alone in this, as I often was and even preferred. The six older kids were in school, and my sister Julie played house and helped Mother clean. Next, I hightailed it to the creek, a mere quarter mile east and in my whole other world.

Grown-ups had long ago ceased pleading for me not to scramble down to the creek alone. "You're too young to be there alone. Please don't go there by yourself. Wait for one of your brothers or sisters to hold your hand, to take you there." That made no sense to me. What, hold my hand like a baby? Why, I was nearly grown—four years of age (and going on forty.) Besides, our creek beckoned for me to explore, and by no means was I waiting for someone to hold my hand. There I skipped flat shell stones across the surface of our deepest water hole. It lay tucked in a wide spot in the creek, and a mighty cottonwood guarded its east flank with a thicket of gooseberries camped around its trunk. Bluegills and channel cats floated through sleepy pools smelling of rich ooze. Rotting branches swirled in the pool. Ferns and shell fossils nestled in limestone and shale along the creek's banks. Those stones called out to me, "Scoop us up! Fill your pockets, and take us home." I obliged, my pockets bulging.

As I skipped a few more shales across the water's surface, I was distracted by a finely veined and creased dark rock. Another rock snatched my attention, one with a rounded lump of a shell from a time long past—nearly one hundred million years ago, according to my oldest sister Janice's earth science book—when Kansas was part of a shallow, inland sea. Was that an image of a time long ago when Kansas lay at the bottom of a shallow inland sea? Are fossils a kind of image in stone, just as are reflections on a rippled surface, or echoes from metal pails clanging at milk time?

Yet another row of stones with funny imprints on them caught my eye. Naturally, I tried to stuff more treasure into my pockets. I needed to ask Dad if these were fossils, the value of each one vaulting with Dad's weary "yes". Shucks, I asked the same question about *each* rock, even the rocks that looked nearly the same as the previous one. Excited glances have a way of blurring details, don't you know!

Snapping turtles snooted their pointed beaks and devil-red eyes at anything that came near the creek. I spotted one sprawled at the water's edge, and I charged toward it to have a closer look. It hissed at me, warning, "Stay away . . . or else." I knew enough about powerful snapping turtle jaws to comply. Twin fires of danger loomed in its eyes.

The creek became my wonder-filled laboratory that day, and I didn't know how long or far I'd traveled to explore it. My stomach sure did. It begged me to reconsider and head home from my "far and distant" land. While I commenced to pick my way back along the creek, a hawk—my raptor scout—floated overhead. He waited for my signal to make a meal of a field mouse or of a dead channel cat.

Along the way I spotted a few bull frogs, croaking and wallowing in syrupy mud along the creek bed. One frog hid itself by padding over mud, faintly lined with bird tracks. It waded into water until only its eyes and snout peeked out of the water. That meant it could swim away faster with its webbed feet if a little boy tried to grab it. Guessing right, it escaped. I hadn't come close enough to snatch that frog before it made a watery escape.

I drew a piece of limestone with a shell rising from it out of my pocket. The fossil smelled of salt from the ancient inland sea, and I was no longer aside a puny creek. No, this creek was my gigantic sea. Monstrously large fish with razor-sharp teeth swept through its swirling waters. Channel cat and blue gill minnows became prehistoric monsters in search of prey.

All the while as I splashed along the banks of my inland sea, I flew in pursuit of another fool frog. Still more minnows glided through rippling waters, and each one swished back a request for me to hold still. Crawdads scurried toward the bottom, their tails curled as they scooted to hide. Water spiders skittered over the sea surface, rocketing protests.

Wait a minute: the earth rumbled and trembled. That tingled my spine, meaning only one thing—and it wasn't grazing cows. (Mum, Suzie, and the rest of their species wouldn't evolve for many millions of years). No, this meant a starved and thirsty brontosaur, searching for ferns and water, grumbled toward marshland. I knew to run away, seeing as how I did not fancy being swept up or mashed. But where?

My scout "kee-yer"ed to signal my way out of danger, and we both traveled for days before we rested—all right, maybe it was only twenty minutes. I was creeping near our family's cave when I was startled by a "thud" and violent twitching from the spirea bushes. What was that?

With a quickening pulse, I froze and waited for the intruder to show itself. Then, it broke out of the bushes and darted behind a birch. Spinning around, I caught a glimpse of a bony tail. Wasn't that an ankylosaur? Partially hidden, it stared back at me, and I knew that the dinosaur with its bony plates and spikes wanted my help. Heck, it didn't wish to wait for a chance to club me with its tail. I knew too much, and I could help it escape—that much we both knew. For a better view of its tracker (maybe a T-Rex), I climbed the pear tree above the spirea bushes.

There! There it was again below me! Squirming for a view, I lost my balance and crashed into the bushes, my eyes full of business. Leaping up, I felt the small hairs on the nape of my neck stand to attention. Then, before you could say "Jack Robinson", I bounded toward our cave—oh, all right, our house—to report.

Rounding the rear of our house, I misjudged my speed, and I tumbled into a headlong pitch on our lawn. My feet and legs didn't get the message that I'd stopped running, and they ground away while my arms groped to right myself. Reaching the porch screen door, I clawed it open.

"Mother!" I yelled. "Mother! Guess what?"

I must have been quite a sight, what with my shirt torn in three spots and my pants covered in chlorophyll stains, my chin bleeding, and my reddened face streaked with dirty sweat. Mother turned from the stove. Her face darkened.

"Have you boys been fighting again? What did I tell you about that?"

My brother Mark, nine years old, and I had "gone at it" the past week. Our fracas commenced after I'd watched Mark skate down the sidewalk north of our house a dozen times, and I didn't fancy making it a baker's dozen. Each time, he skated he flared his arms for balance as he curved around Mother's iris bed. (When he crashed, he plowed up what remained of her prized bulbs.)

"You're plain spoiled if you don't watch me skate!" Mark snapped. Then "whack" a plastic bat splatted me upside my head.

"Oh yeah? You're a towering sissy!"

The rest is history. Mark dragged me outside and across the grass. Once released, I put up my dukes. Mark swung at me but missed. When I swung back, I didn't miss, but pummeled him with my wicked right— training complements of Grandfather Kearney—and bloodied his nose. Dad had to break us up before I really did Mark in. Poor Mark, beaten up by a runt like me!

"Sean?" mother asked.

"No, we weren't fighting!"

"Well, what then?"

I could only flutter my fingers around my mouth and chest. My mouth opened but no words squeaked out. Then I sputtered, "Dinosaur . . . an ankylosaur! He thudded his tail against the pear tree and I fell out of the tree, but don't worry 'cause I'm all right. Not rightly sure how long I scared it away, but its gone now. You ought to have seen it! Scales plastered all up one side and down the other, its tail coated with thorns! And he looked set to attack, but I stood real quiet so he wouldn't know I was alive, and you know ankylosaurs have better night vision than day vision, and it was day so it thought I was dead, but I didn't want to take any chances so I–"

"That's nice," Mother said. She'd gone back to her cooking about the time I got to the creature's scales. "I'm glad you weren't hurt. Now, get ready for supper."

Supper? That was everyday fare! Who could be calm enough to eat at a time like that? How could anyone be calm when it came to dinosaurs?

Flitting toward the bathroom sink to scrub my hands, I thought, "Heck NO, that just isn't normal."

"Mum, Mum, com'on Mum!" Dad's voice boomed through those still evenings, echoing more loudly now as if he's uttering those words still. From where I perched, I spied the flicker of light reflected from Mum's cowbell. Soon I heard its "clunk-clank" as she and Reddy trekked homeward.

"Clank-clank, boom-bong, clang-clang," sounded from Dad's pails, echoing from the valley, girded by gurgling rills.

"Chum on, hum on, Mum! Come home from evening pasture. Hum home, girls. I'm weary, and night awaits!" His graveyard shift loomed closer.

The clanking and shouting ended with Mum and Suzie lumbering up to the barn and into their stalls, as it had for as long as I could recall.

Dad, Paul, and sometimes Mark did the honors, seeing as how I was too young. I left my tree to claim a spot on a hay bale up front and center. I watched the cows rocking side to side, chewing their cud to the two-count rhythm of milk streams striking a metal pail. Our meowing barn cats sidled up to the cows, the errant squirts hushing them. That warm, rich goodness had been harnessed from the energy of our rustling grasses, I reckoned.

I was often lulled to sleep by Mum and Suzie's swaying, back and forth, back and forth, back and forth, back and . . . I wonder if that moving lullaby worked its magic on the cows, too.

To Hear Dad Tell It

"Sean, let me tell you how I came to buy the farm . . . , so to speak," Dad often said. Maybe I was one of the few who could tolerate listening to "the story" yet one more time.

"During the week after Thanksgiving of 1959, I drove my 1950 Dodge thirty miles south of Kansas City to view the farm, one that a buddy at work mentioned. A midday fog of icy mists shrouded the fields and weathered farmhouse, not much to view even on a clear day. During the 1950s the farmhouse stood empty. The last tenants had packed up and left for Kansas City two years before President Truman left office. A local farmer, William Knuckle, tended the fields planted in corn, milo, and alfalfa. He shared in one third of the crop for his trouble. The rest of the harvest went to the landowner, Dr. Giles, an orthopedic surgeon living on Ward Parkway in Kansas City, Missouri, just over the state line." Dad inhaled deeply to launch a description.

"Dr. Giles' home was neatly painted, a white clapboard ranch-style, quite fashionable. A twenty-foot high pole held a flag fluttering in the breeze. Well-tended beds of petunias and marigolds lined the red brick sidewalk leading to his front door of stained glass and wrought iron. Inside, an alcove with white marble flooring led to a solid mahogany staircase. It began with an angel carved in its newel post, which stood guard over an alabaster vase that rested on an inlaid table of Pyrenees oak. A winding staircase led to the second floor where velvet curtains danced on evening breezes and fluttered over the mahogany wainscot lining the walls."

No doubt about it, Dr. Giles' Ward Parkway home looked nothing like the vacant house that rested on his eastern Kansas farm, some thirty miles south of Kansas City.

"Although Dr. Giles didn't need the money, he turned red in the face and his breath came in hard, angry puffs every time his tax man told him his farm had lost money, and that was nearly all of the fifteen years since the war. Dr. Giles had started practicing medicine in Kansas City after the war ended. He figured he had time to tease profits out of his farm. The ground was mostly clay strewn with limestone and shale. The clay soils sucked up fertilizers, and the harvests were meager. No matter how long he waited and wished for a profit, his farm either lost money or barely broke even during good years. Dr. Giles wondered what to do with his farm, one which he had first loved to own and then yearned to sell. After years of patience, he decided to unload it in a package deal. Sighing with relief, he knew the time had come to be done with it for good." Dad paused to regain his breath, wheezing through all that in less than two minutes.

"When my aunt Margaret left me a legacy, I had my down payment in hand. How I dreamed of becoming a gentleman farmer! With my best poker face, I low-balled Dr. Giles. To my surprise, the good doctor threw up his arms and said yes, his shoulders slunched and his face red with bother." So, Dad became the welcomed buyer wile Dr. Giles played the harried seller. With a few strokes of the pen, the deed was sealed. Dad had himself a farm. Grinning, he fancied himself a gentleman farmer at last!

"Sean, the farm came as is with 320 acres and all of the buildings on it. I wetted my lips as I peered at a few tin-roof sheds, two grain silos, and a milk barn with its loft to store hay. I could already taste the rich milk from a herd of Jersey cows."

Dad huffed, "The empty farmhouse, first built in 1890, was enlarged in 1900. It sat on the farm's southern boundary. Most of the house looked like someone might be persuaded to live there—although the roof leaked considerable—provided they had a powerful imagination. Oh sure, several panes of glass went missing from the rows of windows on each of two floors, and a few holes punched in the floor offered rodents easy access. Not to worry! Well placed throw rugs could plug the holes gnawed in the kitchen and living room floorboards. Maybe those fury residents wondered what I meant by intruding on their home. 'Why can't they leave us be?'"

Dad sighed, "I thought like a country farmer, like a genteel country squire who might earn a living from the land. I didn't guess how the land can be an uncertain host. Nature promised nothing. A few years of crop failures and a skidding cattle market wiped out my equity. Nature ruled. She directed the wind, the sun, and the rains. I couldn't gauge her mood from year to year. Anyone who thinks nature is a willing ally tempts bankruptcy." As he finished that thought, Dad stretched out his hands into space. His gesture reminded me of the empty homes from other farm failures.

Dad told me how Mom and he viewed the farm and its abandoned farmhouse that first time on New Year's Day 1960. Mother's parents, Grandmother and Grandfather Kearney, joined them on that trip. "My, what a fixer-upper," gasped Grandmother Kearney in a tense voice, already grown gravely with age and smoking.

"Just imagine its possibilities," Mother declared, her heart soaring with the dream.

"We'll give her a try," mumbled Dad, his confidence shaken a bit by the prospects of all the unending work. That would be a grueling grind at best, and the sudden shock of reality had set his mind in motion. A powerful case of purchaser's regret shook him. His mind quaked.

"You'll need a plan, Tom," offered Grandfather Kearney. He knew too well about planning, hard work and steadfastness. He knew all too well about planning, perhaps better than most. Grandfather Kearney had been the chief clerk of the Missouri-Pacific Railroad in Osawatomie. Plans and numbers swirled in his mind.

The Land

So began our family farm on the eastern edge of the Kansas prairie. It rested on a section of eastern Kansas scrunched up with frayed hills, worn by the wind and rain since the last ice age. The land had crinkled into rolling hills, like a rug bunched up on a linoleum floor. So began my boyhood home nestled on a Kansas farm at the edge of a teeming prairie, drenched with life. Our farm hugged smack on the Kansas-Missouri border, as if it lay poised in the balance.

When I thought about our farm hugging the state line, I remembered seeing a tightrope walker balanced on a high wire in a dusty, big top circus tent. That image of the walker carefully balancing on that rope stuck with me, just as that walker clung to the rope. He impressed my mind, just as surely as the rope must have impressed his feet.

I imagined that tightrope walker also used a balancing rod on his wire stretched high above the Kansas-Missouri border. If the walker fell, he might have teetered into either state. I guessed the walker did fall, and that he did tumble into Kansas. With his fall came a thud that sent clouds of dust airborne. It swirled with blow dirt. Likewise, I sensed our farm could have found its way into either state, but restless Kansas winds had their say. They sent it toppling into Kansas.

"Land of the Southwind People"

Each day the Kansas winds framed our lives. On fair days, prevailing winds toted a bit of Missouri's real estate back onto our farm. On poor days, those winds became rebels and shot our soil right back to Missouri. The soil swished back and forth as if whisked by a gigantic broom. That dust and dirt became fine, difficult to see with untrained eyes, and easy to ignore by trained ones that saw daily negotiations between winds and soils.

The wind sucks up dust from the broken prairie like a thirsty vagabond. Wind-strewn dust and dirt became very fine, visible only if viewed in a great consort of particles that swarmed like a mass of angry locusts. That dirt, called blow dirt by some, is finer than "frog's hair." It could and did settle just about anywhere. One day as we helped a neighbor raze a derelict frame home on a farm he had purchased, I saw layers of silt packed on insulation—yellowed newspapers—crinkled with age. When we reached to pull out the boards and paper, the fine dust puffed away into nothingness.

This is the Kansas I knew, "the land of the Southwind People." To help the crops grow, we tapped spring water that wept up from deep in the earth and seeped over moss-covered stones. I imagined the stones luxuriated in cooling moisture. These gentle sounds help define the Kansas I knew as a boy.

The Kansas of my youth was a community of small, thirsty farms scattered along gently rolling hills. It was a time and place now long forgotten, if indeed anyone else dared to remember it. It was a place of hand-cranked telephones and of party lines, of ice cream socials, and of doctor's house calls. In that Kansas, windmills pumped sparkling water from musty wells to fill dark cisterns. That Kansas was a gentle place where neighbors really cared for each other, like the Knuckles, the Crockers, and the Finesses. I felt connected with nearly all of the families and friends, just as I felt connected to the wise old wind. That sense of belonging, of feeling warm inside, is what I most remember about small town Kansas.

The sounds of both wind and water frame my memories of that time and place. Above all, the whistling sound of the wind whipped across the prairie. I can still picture the rusted metal blades of windmills twirling faithfully. Their haggard forms, stooped and rusted from years of toil, framed moaning sounds. Groaning sounds voiced their tales of service, sounds muffled by the moist prairie grasses that stretched with the winds. Soon those twirling marvels sipping water from deep aquifers gave way to electric or gasoline pumps. I knew at once that I would miss those wonderful clanking towers that had quenched my thirst.

Winds spoke to me in the early mornings, whispering tales of adventure as fresh and as real as the dew that clung to the moistened prairie grasses. I imagined the sound of the winds echoed the stories and dreams of all who lived there. I only needed to strain a bit to listen and to hear them, to hear them fully, just as the tall stem grasses strained to punctuate and to record each tall tale. Those stories seemed glamorous and sassy, enlivened by the winds.

The tales were more than sounds—far more than language. The stories appeared as thoughts which created memories from my imagination and feelings. I cannot describe those feelings fully, although I recall I felt full and part of something grand. Winds and grasses drenched my brain with thoughts that made me feel I was part of a fine life. I felt honored. Mostly, I felt like I belonged, that I was part of the stories and the feelings, and that the stories and feelings were a part of me.

Farming

Although those magical feelings framed my youth, times were tough. Folks struggled. Just as our farm straddled a state line and the time lay folded between two periods, farmers labored to make ends meet. Farms hung in the balance and depended on the weather. Even families with two incomes worked to solve money problems. Our family did what we could with what we had: too much wind, dryness, and bills. We tried most anything, and some things we tried more than once. Acre-sized gardens, homemade clothes, and economy-sized everything blunted our money woes. Dad hired on as an engineer for The Atchison, Topeka and Santa Fe Railroad in 1952. He worked the extra board for overtime premiums which grew richly on graveyard shifts from 11 p.m. – 7 a.m.

I remember our neighbors' hands, especially those of Mr. Finesse who raised wheat, milo and potatoes. He never seemed to stop working. His hands grew leathery with work, even though he sometimes wore a pair of cloth gloves. I saw how his hands commenced to split with deepening lines surrounded by calloused patches of yellowish-brown skin. Specks of soil clung to fissures in his toughened skin, reminding me of the soil after a powerful drought.

The soil meant food, and Kansas farmers fancied talking about the land, the weather, and farm prices. They covered droughts—the dry spells when the ground ached for moisture. They talked about how the wind sucked water out of the land, how the sun and wind blistered it. Soon, the ground dried into crispy patches with blossoming cracks. Soil crinkled along the cracks to form tiny clay patches baked by the sun—calloused by the dry wind. I imagined that the land shriveled to signal that crops might fail again that year.

During one drought that lasted two seasons, the land went through a bunch of changes. The crops welted first, turning shades of brown. Next, the sturdy weeds and pokes suffered. Finally, the plants simply withered on the stalk. Their loss meant less ground cover. That meant the wind could tote the soil about the landscape as easily as a small child pulls a Radio Flyer. The land shriveled and darkened the wind's color. The farmers sighed with the land and joined in a common prayer for water. Another crop failure hung in the balance. A few more days of searing sun and wind might shroud the horizon with dust clouds, the only things blooming in a drought. A few more days like that could end that season's crop. A few years like that could humble any prosperous farm and send its owners into an early retirement (or to another career). Livelihoods and the land hung in the balance. Kansas farmers worked endlessly, prayed tirelessly, and hoped unceasingly.

In years when the rains came, people walked faster and stood taller. Worry eased from their eyes and furrowed brows. Harvest became a celebration. In those years, we gathered the fruit of the land and of our work. That made us feel cozy inside, and I sensed we became part of the farm or that the farm became part of us—I don't know which. A full feeling in the pit of my stomach told me things would be all right, at least that year. We tended the land and imagined we were its lords. Yet, the land and the weather had more control over us than we ever guessed possible. I suppose the land and the plants became our stewards. We simply did not know it.

I sensed that farmers served as caretakers of the land. Their devotion wowed me. To work the land, they made do with what they had. What they did not have, they improvised. Magically, baling twine and burlap sacks became 'mend-alls' for garden gates and hoses. We made do, making things right. We did what he had to do, and that meant we did all right.

Neighbors

Our neighbors were decent Kansas country farm folks with little money. Most were gentle people who learned too soon who they were, perhaps too soon to know they could become someone different. Maybe they could reach their dreams, which were often all that they had each morning as they glimpsed stark daylight. Dreams were all they had as they toiled in smothering heat, their drenched brows plastered by bits of dust, hay, or blow dirt.

A local potato farmer, Mr. Finesse, grew the most delicious spuds! It's useless to try to describe their meaty flavor, rich enough to make my mouth water. When I saw him walking in his dusty coveralls and inspecting the fields, I pictured a plate of steaming tators over his head like a halo. Their heat wafted on the evening air.

As he ended his grinding day of sweat-stained labor, Mr. Finesse lifted his eyes to view a clear Kansas night sky, to cast his wishes upon a shooting star.

Watching him one afternoon, I wondered what he was thinking. Would another dry spell eat up his crop? Would he hang on long enough to start fresh? Would his dreams be fulfilled before time and place felled him? When gone, would anyone remember he'd been there? I sputtered, "Yes, I'll remember him!" How could I forget his quiet dignity and works of art growing in that sandy soil? When I remembered him, my words could echo his talents. And if I told a story about him, people might know him provided the story read well.

Harvest Moon

The image I most recall of my youth is a low-hanging harvest moon, casting silvery shadows on a rolling prairie. Its beams sent soothing bands of solace to the land and people, as if to bind up festering wounds. The bewitching spell it casts hasn't faded. Rather, it has strengthened with time. As I recall gazing at a the silvery harvest moon, I felt like I saw a threshold to some other world unknown to the human mind. Maybe the folks there beamed back at us, wishing us success and sending us their hope. You know, I could not forget that old harvest moon, shining on brightly, even had I tried.

The Homes and Farms

The Kansas of my youth was a landscape dotted with rambling farm-houses silhouetted against the prairie's twilight sky. My, the beatings those farmhouses took from the relentless sun, wind, and rain! Oftentimes ramshackle, those homes interrupted the prairie haphazardly. I imagined the winds had gotten a little carried away as they surged in strength mostly from the west. They spewed homes across the country-side—sometimes at the end of a lonely dirt road, and oftentimes where two dusty lanes with no names crossed.

Our farm lay divided right down the middle by a small valley first carved during the last ice age. Well, the very front end of a rebel ice floe provoked the valley by teasing at soft limestone and shale that dwelt in those parts. The deed looked as though the hand of a frozen colossus gouged out the valley. Rainwater meandered there to form a well, where waters rested from their weary journeys. When refreshed enough to spring forth, those waters surfaced to power our creek. That flowing wonder fussed to complete the work which the ice began. Bit by bit, amidst swirls and eddies, our creek added to the valley's depth, toting bits of sand and dirt that became reluctant hitchhikers on lengthy trips through our county and to points beyond.

My childhood home was that farm nestled on a rolling prairie. It lay 6 miles from the nearest town. I can still see the drowsy streets of that town. Sturdy vehicles gyrated over its rounded, worn stones and bricks to hum rhythmic melodies. The tires echoed tunes as they played over the cobbled streets. This reminded me of the way musicians play a familiar, seasoned instrument.

Blow Dirt

One day when I was not yet four years old, I saw a stranger driving a Cadillac, polished and glinting in the morning sun. I also saw dust clinging to its running boards and along its white walls. The stranger's face looked anxious and lonely, as if he craved adventure, yearning to experience the world. The man slowed his car and waved at my brother Mark and me as he turned onto the south road leading from our farm into town. I watched clouds of dust settle down in his wake. To this day I wonder if the stranger found what he craved.

Clouds of blow dirt swirled and puffed around the vehicles, covering them in a fog. I can still taste the grimy earth and fell it cake my face. The blow dirt wedged between my teeth. If I blew my nose, I saw the dust had plowed up my nostrils, leaving trails of subtly nuanced ochre in gritty streaks, striated in charming patterns. The blow dirt's inimitable scent mingled with its textured flavor, arousing my curiosity. From where did it hail? Could it be more than blow dirt? Could it have been carried from points unknown by a gleaming Cadillac, piloted by a lonely soul touring the country? I felt full inside when I imagined that I would never know the answer to that question, still shrouded in mists of time, dust, and blow dirt. Mysteries soothed me.

Mr. Bentley's City Folks

Sights linger longer if they mean something. For me, the images meant a sense of community. I felt connected to all our friends in the Kansas of my youth. I imagined we were all one family just doing our best to endure. I remember old Mr. Bentley, a widower who lived one mile south of our farm where the creek ran southwest in the county. Mr. Bentley told me, "Son, we're the ones who do all the living and struggling. City folks come to build a summer home and stay for a spell. Their children might last for a summer or two. Then, they leave." I reckoned he didn't care much for city folks. As far as he knew, country folks were the ones who kept right on living and trying as we lived our trying lives.

Abandoned or Lost?

Mostly, farm families in our county were lean in numbers but rich in spirit. I reckoned that the lonely stranger might wish to visit with Mr. Thomas Curtis, who'd lost his farm after two corn crops failed. The Curtis home stood empty, silent and slumbering. It reminded us what might happen, and it showed visitors what had happened. If that traveling stranger passed by and spied that empty farmhouse, he might have wondered, "What happened?" The Curtis' home once teemed with children, laughter and frowns, gingham dresses and curls, worried glances and hopeful stares. Activity had mobbed that home, and that showed in the worn door sill and frayed screen door on the front porch. The screen door once opened and shut as rapidly as ceiling fans spin. Now as dead as a coffin nail, the farmhouse stood empty. Winds whistled through its stone fences and foundation to send a mournful rale that echoed down the valley. That reminded me of the sound unhealthy lungs make when filled with fluid, wheezing for air.

The stranger might scratch his head, wince, and ask, "Where did they go? What became of their dreams, their lives, and their hopes? Would the same thing happen to other families?" Well, I knew that only God's Grace kept us from losing our farm. Surely, our neighbors and our families were extensions of ourselves. In Kansas we truly were, as Alexandre Dumas mused, "One for all and all for one."

The isolation of wide-open prairies scared some folks. In 1848 when my great grandfather settled in Indiana, he told his new bride that the lonely prairie reminded him he was no longer at home in Ireland. He was no longer where he could depend on his parish and pub for reassurance. In the Kansas of my youth, we country folks aimed to look out for each other. Naturally, we found ways to socialize. We held country bazaars, church picnics, and dances on hard wood floors in the spring and fall. I imagined my great grandfather knew he needed friends each time he listened to the howling winds, quite the teacher!

Rains and Winds in Charge

Evening rains often caressed the pastures and the fields where Indians once lived. The rains first danced on the soil before quietly mixing with it. That formed a sticky paste, oozing with coolness and a pleasure to touch. Seeds loved that fertile silkiness. Did they groan with pleasure in the richness of nature's patet? Alive with smells, the land wafted a thousand scents that drifted from it whenever rain soaked into it, releasing nature's aromas. A dozen scents wafted sweet and fresh from the newly plowed fields.

On stormy evenings, my family melted with cooling relief. The evening wetness soothed all of us following a day of winds that bellowed from the northwest like a blast furnace. This duet of rains and winds swept over the land to refresh and to caress it.

Raindrops trickled down our farmhouse windows, shimmering in the light from our driveway. The flickering light hung at the top of a gnarled old pole—not really a pole, but an ancient maple tree stripped of its branches, fulfilling its final purpose. The light cast eerie shadows on our farmhouse walls as it shone through the branches of a spidery walnut tree which whispered tales long forgotten, tales of hushed secrets held dear by people long since gone.

On the second floor of our farmhouse, lace curtains fluttered in the evening breeze. The curtains danced approvingly, as if in a primeval mating ritual. The storm strengthened, and the wind hummed through the cold, broken stones. The stones had been stacked into fences and barn foundations. Like everything else, they began to crumble with age. Now, the wind's song echoed a mournful, eerie melody as it whistled through stones.

Fields Under an Inland Sea

The fields stood where long ago lived an inland sea teeming with life. Some 200 million years ago had lived strange, unfamiliar creatures—fishes and reptiles, corals and sea anemones. That was so long ago that only footprints remained of a once mighty, ancient menagerie. Untold seasons passed. No one could say how many creatures came, lived, and were no more. The inland sea fled to leave a vast plain. The duet of winds and rains brought life, a rich mixture of plants and animals, to the barren landscape. The land waited patiently for nature to write new chapters in its story of life. Her tools were time, wind, rains, and the sun. Each served her well.

Countless generations of fish and sea plants lived and perished. They floated down onto the sea bed to decay. There, domes of limestone and of silt formed to entomb their rotting remains. Gas and oil deposits under those domes were small in size but large in number. Their meager size meant that not too many people wanted to tap them, and most deposits were left undisturbed.

Along with the oil and gas lay fossils—ancient ferns, and fish to delight children who explored these hills near The Ten Mile and Wea Creeks.

"Dad, is this one a fossil?" I yelped with wonder, pawing at Dad like a restless pup.

"Yes, yes. It is a fossil," he muttered again without looking at the specimen, number 1,000.

"Dad, are there dinosaur bones here?" I asked in a hushed voice betraying my excitement.

"No, Kansas was an inland sea. No land dinosaurs lived here. Plesiosaurs, perhaps." He explained. I repeated my question to quench my thirst for discovery.

Our Valley

In the valley ran a small brook, a creek, really. It gurgled up from deep within the ground to pour over moss-covered rocks along the hillside. The water had fallen to the earth long ago, and the earth trapped it. The waters had waited patiently to spring forth. The water that flowed over the surface was only a small ripple compared to the aquifer running below it.

The freed waters fed our creek which flowed even during droughts. Patiently, the creek did its work. It aimed to gouge out a creek bed with waters that coursed along the valley. Our creek water swirled with sand and silt. The murky water carried countless particles of debris which had become hapless, reluctant hitchhikers in its teeming waters.

Ancient sandstone and limestone formations filtered the water as it bled to the surface, powered by artesian pressure. At certain spots the creek paused to form small, cool pools where bluegill, channel cat, tadpoles, and crawdads floated.

Prehistoric Prairie

I often puzzled how life had changed over billions of years. Lounging in a mulberry tree with my face spackled in shades of blue and purple berry juice, I gazed across the prairie. My favorite daydream was to see all of the life that lay shrouded in the grasses. I saw grasshoppers and gophers, prairie dogs and hawks, field mice and garter snakes, ants and termites. I compared the animals in my panorama to the unfamiliar ones of 20 million years ago. After studying them in a science book, I knew their names. I compared them to the 'Big Pig' porcine carnivore dinohyus. I also compared them to a chalicothere with its weirdly comical body like a rhino, head like a horse, and clawed feet resembling those of a three-toed sloth.

Then, I imagined back still further to 100 million years ago when Kansas was part of an inland sea. I saw the fish and the corals, the giant horseflies, and the shell fish. The sun danced on the rippling waves striking the shores. Those waves shone with the splendor of a thousand diamonds shimmering at noontime, while the fields in the early morning stood pregnant with dew that cast a dazzling spectacle of reflected light. The swaying prairie grasses reminded me of the undulating waves in that ancient sea, moving back and forth—unceasingly.

Our Creek

Rain from evening storms powered our creek, which swelled with growing anger and darkness. The winds strengthened and shifted out of the south. A peal of lighting and a crack of thunder completed nature's portentous ensemble. As the rains ran off the rocky hills toward the creek, it swelled into a wicked torrent. Small animals sought higher ground; the animals in the fields huddled together. Some borrowed shelter beneath a row of hedge trees along the southern perimeter of a fescue field.

The Kansas of my youth lives in a patchwork of birth, storms, and rebirth. It is a story as old as time itself. The sounds of the rain and wind whirl as clearly as they did then. If I close my eyes, I may hear them again.

A Fine Dawn to View

After supper came prayers, usually a decade of the rosary. Then came bedtime. In the dawn of my childhood, Mother told me, "Now, Sean, it's time you slept in your own bed."

At first I missed the peace of Mother's luxurious double bed and her rhythmic breathing. Those familiar comforts made me feel protected, which suited me just fine! Feeling a bit cheated, I tried to be big about it. Exiled to the "boys' room" where my two older brothers slept, I began to jabber to anyone who would listen. I bragged about my freedom there. Switching on the lamp next to my new bed, I told myself, "I'm the boss here. I'm in charge." As I glanced around the room, I imagined that all of its wealth belonged to me. "Just look at all this truck!" I declared. Throw rugs next to closets smelled of mothballs, and school books rested on a desk brimming with notes and who knows what! Next to the desk and against the west wall stood a wooden dresser that creaked when Paul opened its drawers. Those drawers were laden with bunches of secrets, forbidden to view. "Don't you touch any of it!" Mark barked at me. To them, I was a small intruder—the new kid. Age and rank carried authority, leaving precious few rights for me. That did not matter, not really.

My brothers stored much more than clothes in those dresser drawers. I knew it. Did they hide slingshots and yo-yos, slinkies, and spit wads ready for flight? Coin collections, including a few Indian head pennies, beckoned to me with piercing war hoops and cries. A warm hand wafted across my forehead, begging me to explore. "Come see these goodies, here for you!" As I walked past the drawers, I showed no interest, mostly because Mark and Paul stood there with folded arms. They watched me the way a hawk watches a field mouse. My eyes wavered a bit as I passed the dresser with pretended disinterest, the way a hound ignores a downed bird until his master commands "fetch".

Then I said to myself, "Now hold on. Today is Sunday, and tomorrow

Paul and Mark are back in school. Why, I'll sneak in to explore the dresser then." My idea made me feel grown up and excited. Then, curiosity deflated like a punctured balloon. Knowing I could explore the drawers at will seemed no fun at all. I never did look through that dresser, which I suppose proved sound judgment on my part. That would be no fun, no show at all! Instead, I thought I'd find a heap of things to keep me busy in "the boys" room." For starters, I could go through school books on the desk, which was not off limits.

I reasoned that all of these treasures would still my mind for quite a spell. I guessed wrong. Much sooner than I had hoped, I grew both bored and lonely. These feelings blossomed mostly at night when I missed Mother's bedroom and the sound of her breath. So, on the nights when Dad worked the graveyard shift, I waited until our farmhouse slumbered. Then, I scampered into Mother's room while I took care on the patch of creaky boards near her door. Under the cover of night, I crawled under Mother's bed covers.

Grandmother Kearney declared, "Sean, you are like a coon hound pup that is lonesome for his mother. He whines and fusses to find her. When he snuggles up against her, her heartbeat calms him." That wouldn't be the last time that Grandmother compared my actions to those of a hound.

Memories of my "secret" nighttime voyages remain crisply etched in my mind. I cleverly tiptoed over the planks of our wooden second story floor to avoid grumbling, creaking boards near her bedroom door. Those sounds might betray my trek. My night vision must have been strong, seeing how many carrots I ate. You see, carrots were my favorite vegetable, best gnawed fresh from the garden, the bits of sandy soil still clinging to their flesh. The wind whistled through chinks in our attic roof. That melody sounded like it came from a harmonica player who is partial to mournful melodies.

Since the ladder to our attic rested outside Mother's bedroom, I needed only to listen for the wind's humming near our attic ladder. I knew that bats are guided by sonar in darkened caves. Janice told me so, her knowledge fresh from a science book. A scent of moth balls oozing from the attic also led me there. Winds on a Kansas farm in the pitch dark brew ancient-smelling bouquets of blow dust, mothballs, and musty timbers. One whiff told me I neared my goal—mother's second floor bedroom. Groping in the night, I felt the entrance to her bedroom. I tested that spot by running my fingers along the door sill, its welcoming pine trim sanded and varnished smoothly.

I folded myself into Mother's soft bed where stillness engulfed me. Melting in comfort, I felt as if I'd voyaged to another world. I inhaled redolent scents from flowers below her open window and from her lilac perfume. I focused on nighttime sounds wafting through her east window. If I decided it suited me, I gazed into my darkened kingdom. I entwined myself in those sights while I lay wrapped in Mother's comforter.

Nature sang. A whippoorwill lamented will's punishment, and a barn owl hooted. Was that a brown thrasher? Did a western meadowlark wish to serenade? Their calls swirled, drowsing me to sleep. "Come see some of my wonders, unobserved," they said. Seeing as how the bed was as high as the window sill, I needed only to move my head to peer eastward over the barnyard.

As I gazed out of Mother's bedroom window into the inky stillness of the night, a gust of wind caught my tangled forelocks, brushing them aside. My eyes strained to see what lay before me in the pitch peacefulness. A sliver of light from the crescent moon glinted on the corrugated tin roof of our chicken shed, and the faint light showcased our barnyard. A few barrels stood there with metal fasteners girding them. Large containers filled with fresh water reflected the moonlight. Each morning our chickens guzzled that water. I wondered if anything might happen if the chickens drank the water at night with the moonlight reflecting off it. "Would they gain special powers from the moonlight? Would those beams seep through their feathers to light up the barnyard?" Heck, I knew that couldn't happen. "Or, could it?"

Our family's half-breed hound lay snoring on the packed dirt near our chicken shed, our fence tools propped along its walls. My brothers leaned the tools against the shed after using them to make fence. Moonlight colored our dog's outstretched paws and muzzle with silver. He lay there slumbering. His chest rose and fell with a tired, two-count rhythm. His legs rested loosely in front of him, tipped by mighty mud-packed paws. Next to those paws lay a savory bone for his evening gnaws.

My eyes flitted from the familiar barnyard back into the ebony soup.

While I saw a few outlines of mulberry trees and bushes, most of the scene lay buried in inky repose. My eyes played tricks on me, registering eerie sights that I knew had not been there by day. Bits and pieces of light wiggled or vibrated rhythmicly . A faint humming leaked in to join them, and then the bits and pieces of material began to vibrate more energetically. They moved in an orderly manner. No doubt about it, I had not seen *this* by light of day. So, I just lay there to study them. The moonbeams cast comforting strands of light, like bandages to help heal a wound. My wound grew from a burning thirst to explore and to understand small pieces of my world. Could the moon help bind up my wound by giving me some idea of the world's secrets?

Might I glimpse more of that other world some day?" Excited by mystery, I fell even more deeply into reverie.

"Am I seeing a glimmer of another world? What do all of the dancing bits of light mean?" I asked. The lights tightened with each vibration, like tiny pieces of thread from Mother's spools on top of her Singer sewing machine. The strings came alive and danced with life. Then, as rapidly as they came, they faded from view. Next, I spied the familiar barnyard, reassuring me.

Peering out the bedroom window, I wondered about the dancing lights. Then, I thought about the birds on a Kansas farm, about all the winged songs in flight. I dreamt those birds serenaded anyone who'd listen with songs and stories of folks long gone. Did song birds bear important messages for any who might listen?

For most of the night, I must have drifted off to dreamland, where all that I had seen mixed with all that I imagined. Oftentimes I slept for no more than five or six hours. Then, just before dawn, I usually awakened. I thrilled to the pre-dawn air, sights, and sounds. Their magic sent quivers of delight through my body. "I must not go back to sleep," I said as I struggled to stay awake.

I peered eastward with the morning winds, eastward to catch Aurora's glimmers. First, I fixed my gaze on muted ocher and taupe puffs that softened the still blackness. Next, I saw mauve and raspberry shards pierce verdant ebony. My mouth watered because those colors reminded me of raspberry cobbler that Mother made. I smacked my lips to welcome that heavenly flavor. Warmth and flavor radiated to soothe me, and I basked in delights.

The night grudgingly yielded, offering dim outlines of fences and of dirt roads with no names. It surrendered to errant sparkles as light shimmered on ponds. Sunlight muscled its way through sleepy arbors to find ribbons of water in the creek. The light beams slowly showcased prairie grasses dancing in the morning breeze. Fowl appeared strewn in languid flight, while squirrels scampered along sturdy branches. Those branches harbored western meadowlarks twittering with news of another miracle—news of a new day dawning!

Smokeless breeze revived restless leaves on aged sycamore trees. The leaves whispered and yawned. The trees outlined fields, skirting creek beds and tiny sylvan shores. To view it all seemed like pretend time. Yet, there I was, awestruck and slack-jawed. Peace lived.

I don't know how many times I strained to stay awake to witness those spectacles of night before dawn and of the dawn's first light. Usually, try as I might, sleep slipped in. I stirred to powerful morning beams pouring over my startled eyes. Sometimes, though, I won. I saw the views unfold. Even so, I lay so tired that sleep ran a close second, nearly winning the foot race. On those mornings, my mind flitted between wonder on one hand and sliding back into dreamland on the other. Then, I asked myself, how much of what I felt were only dreams, how much of it was nature, and how much of it came from curiosity that welcomed each moment. Maybe someone focused on problems might miss the show.

On the mornings when I drifted back to sleep, I awakened to find Mother gone. After getting up, I often waited at the head of our stairs for Mother to haul me down to the ground floor. I don't know why that seemed so important. Maybe Mother had a lot to do. I craved my fair share of attention before all of the kids stirred for the day, stirring things up.

Sometimes, I walked down myself, though, to measure my world. It seemed new. Even things familiar felt and looked askew. For example, I leaned up against the balustrade to see how much larger I had grown. "I'm growing," I said. As I grew, both my world and I had changed. I guessed that sometimes as an observer changes, his world might change as well. Maybe reality depends on how we choose to view it. Do we need to improve the way we see our world?

"Will you just look at that!" I told myself. I pointed at molding along the wall and noted how small it looked, now that I *towered* over it by an inch or two. Why, just last fall, I had barely been level with it! I patted the loyal woodwork and smiled. You know, I grew to love that panel, and I recall it fondly.

"Wow, I must be a big boy!" I boasted, thumping my right fist against my chest triumphantly. Ordinary objects felt fresh and new.

On the mornings when I didn't drift back to sleep, I asked Mother to take me with her when she went downstairs. For some reason, she imagined I still needed my rest. So, she placed a blanket over the kitchen table. From the table, I watched Mother scurrying about her chores. First, she turned on the electric heaters to coax life back into the kitchen. Slowly, the heaters grumbled to attention. Soon, convection currents leaked outward from the wall-mounted units. Hopping down from the table, I huddled against one of those heaters. Made of a glasslike material, each heater held a small metal grill over its glass plate to prevent burns or shocks. I plastered myself against the metal grill. "I must look like a tree frog clinging to a tree," I giggled.

During the winter months, Mother asked me to get ready for a trip to check on the sheep. Just as surely as I lurched forward to don layers of clothing, I became a Mercury astronaut. The gloves connected to a string lining became a life line to my orbiting space ship. My promised adventure more than paid for leaving that redolent kitchen.

I was glad to go outside where I faced the stinging wintry morning air. Mother was a nurse, and she knew that some of the ewes needed help delivering, particularly those she suspected of a breach birth. Occasionally, the ewe did not survive. Her back might be broken, and then she'd die.

If Mother couldn't save the ewe's life, she'd say, "Sean, she was too tired and cold. It's up to us to raise her baby." She whispered to the dead ewe not to worry. "Madam, we are on the job, and everything will be fine." Then, Mother asked me to help her use rags to begin cleaning the orphan lamb. We squeegeed mucous and slime off of its face so it could breathe and see.

Why, the first thing you knew, we no longer had a blind, trembling orphan—just an orphan shaking violently. Then, Mother said, "Sean, please bundle up our baby to keep it warm." The baby lamb peered up at me as if to say, "Thank you!" It stopped trembling. If I placed the bundle down, it began shaking even faster, needing to catch up for any lost time for shaking.

After bundling the little darling, we trudged back to the kitchen: cozy and inviting. As we hurried up the sidewalk, I spied the kitchen's golden glow, which felt warm. Walking into our kitchen, Mother plopped the orphan into a box near the open door of our kitchen stove. Our stove warmed the tottering newborn. It breathed rhythmically in slumber. Mother told me how scent is important to form a bond between a ewe and her baby. The other ewes didn't adopt orphan lambs because they smelled funny. They knew which one belonged to them, based on the special scent of their baby.

Now, it was my turn to ask questions. "Mother, how do the ewes know to accept only the lambs matching their scent?" Well, she looked me right in the eyes and said, "Sean, it is instinct. Long ago, nature decided that the mother sheep needs to care for only their own babies. So, nature trained them to use their sense of smell to tell them apart. That way, the mother cares for them better than if she spreads her effort over other babies."

Her words made sense. "I see. It's like when I'm making pretend money from folded newspapers. When I count the cash, I bundle it. If I choose only C-notes, it is a lot easier than if I make tens or twenties. I don't want to spread myself too thin. After all, there is not so much of me to spread around," I grinned as I stretched to stand on my tiptoes. I coyly prompted her to realize I had grown some. Soon I might even pass for one of the big boys.

Mother gazed at the baby lamb and then at me. "I suppose it is similar," she mused. "But where in the world did you learn what a C-note is?"

"Oh, I have my sources, Mother. You see, I'm nearly grown, so I have my sources!" I boasted. In reality, I was only four years old.

As Mother worked with the orphan lamb, I needed to ask her something. "When we were in town the other day, you remember I pointed to a crude sign with the misspelled words. You know, the ugly ones? It said, 'NIGER, don't let the son sat on y'urn bak." Our Sheriff boasted how he had placed the sign there. It kind of scared me."

"Yes, it's disgraceful."

"Do you reckon our sheriff pushes others away because he doesn't have enough time or money to help anyone who doesn't look like him? Is he using instinct, telling him to care for only his own kind?"

Mother paused for a second. "NO! The sheriff isn't using instinct. His mind is sick, hot with a fever born from fear and self-loathing! It is his choice. Learn from his mistake, and never give way to fear. It has fevered his mind.

"All right. But what made his mind sick?"

"Do you remember when you had the flu? I stayed up all night cooling your face and body with a washcloth. Well, your fever was caused by tiny soldiers in your body working feverishly to defend you from an attack of germs—a virus, really." I remembered the weird dreams that night.

She continued, "The sheriff has another kind of virus. It's fed by his own shame. That makes him lash out at anyone who is not like him. His fever can't be broken with cool water. His fever will be broken with understanding and love. When his fever breaks, he'll have sweated out a bunch of poison,"

"Really?"

"Sean, just imagine how drenched his nightshirt will be."

I giggled as I thought about old folks scurrying around town in drenched night shirts. "That's funny, Mother. Tell me more."

Then, I stopped laughing. I knew about fevers, for I had fought a doosie just a month earlier. "Thanks. I'll remember what you said. I feel sorry for people sick with fear."

Mother smiled. "You are right to feel sorry for them, just as you would for anyone with a disease of the body or of the mind. Fear makes both their victims and themselves miserable. Everyone loses. You know, the victimizers are also victims of their own folly."

Nervously, I stood up to paw at the floor with my right foot. I dragged it in symmetrical patterns as I searched for an explanation. I answered, "Well, Mother, I think it is sad because they must be in terrible pain. I imagine they are doing the best they can," I guessed.

I turned my head slightly askew, squinted my right eye, and glanced to one side. Tightening my lower jaw, I formed a mental picture. "I think they are part of us, and we are part of them." I imagined that we all need to help our town leaders fight the sickness that tormented their minds.

Mother whispered, "That's right. We're all part of the same big slice of life. Things don't merge because they are already together. A power controls it all. It is up to us to see. That means all things are part of the same wholeness . . . a stillness."

"Why can't we see clearly?"

"Our filters get all fouled up. Love heals us by clearing our eyes."

Mother's words made sense, even to the mind of a child. I blinked as I recognized their power. "How can I respect my elders if they are wrong?" I wondered.

Mother explained, "You respect all people and all life. Remember to be especially kind and make allowances for adults with feverish minds. Love everyone. That will cure our ills. Remember, folks are doing their best. It's just confusion and fear that pushes them to evil. You can respect someone even if they are afraid and confused. Your love may be just what heals them," she declared.

Mother reached to brush my tangled curls as she continued. "Love them. Love will heal their brokenness," she declared. Hope shimmered.

Glancing at the wall clock, she said, "Think about it, and we'll talk about it tomorrow. For now, we need to help this baby lamb and finish our work. She sacked lunches and shuttled everyone to parochial school. The kids will be up soon. Don't be surprised if they are cross."

Later, we tried to bottle-feed the orphan. I can remember trying to get it to take the nipple. Sometimes, we coated our hands with the milk. Along with a nipple, we used our milkdrenched hands to prime its mouth. We worked on its sucking instinct to teach it to feed. Usually this worked, and it did that morning as I I taught a trembling orphan to feed. Then, I knew my little pal would be all right. I smiled as I watched it gulp milk.

Each morning Mother went straight to work. She began making the breakfast and sack lunches. You can't believe the work needed to launch a small army of children! She also begin making plans for the day. Mother ran a small cleaning products business, ran our household, and worked part time as a nurse at the State Hospital on weekends. Then, my sisters cared for us youngsters. A few times she asked an older sister to help with sack lunches. Once she asked Janice to make egg and jelly sandwiches. Well, Janice obliged but did not make two different kinds. Instead, she mixed the two toppings into one weird hybrid. My stomach turns at the thought!

Sometimes after dropping the kids off at Wea's parochial school, Mother, Julie, and I drove six miles south to town. We ran errands.

In town, businessmen scurried about selling dry goods or services inside shops fronted with wondrous signs swaying gingerly in the wind. The curious clanking of the freely floating signs wrought a den with a rhythm that relaxed nerves frayed by care and toil. A hushed, squeaking serenade of the signs created a rhythm to muffle the relentless sound of the wind. Its music calmed anyone pestered by vexing problems, economic or otherwise.

I saw professional folks clamber about offices to complete the day's work. I recall Dr. Gately's waiting room couch with its large brass tacks holding together worn leather upholstery. That upholstery was so slick that children clung like a tree frog to the couch to stay on it. Only adults could support their bodies with both legs planted on the floor. Who knows how many anxious minds were calmed by that couch for all the years since his father, the town's "first" Dr. Gately had given him the couch as a graduation gift from medical school.

Old Dr. Gately, age 85, still ran a full-time practice. His withered hands had grown thin-skinned and bruised with age. He looked worried when a needle bent on a toddler during a vaccination. "Oh, Lordie!" he exclaimed. "Let's try again." His patient had tensed up, and the needle bent. Dr. Gately and his patient weren't enthused.

One day, as Mother and I left Dr. Gatley's office, I heard the town's wooden walkway creaking as it grumbled to attention. The walkway stood elevated for access to the raised stone, brick, and wooden buildings. Despite our dry climate, flooding occurred. We needed the raised fronts.

Mother relished walking with me along that wooden sidewalk. A glow in her eye and a certain cadence of her feet told me so. We would be fine, and she wanted all of our neighbors to know so. Walking with Mother made me feel special. Walking eases cares slowly, step by step, to leave imagination running free.

We passed the stucco town mercantile fronted with corrugated awning, a bit worn and rusted. Its weathered edifice hinted of age. Crinkled, plain paper lined shelves and display cases. Next to a dented coke machine with thick metal sides stood a grizzled meat counter holding piles of gristly cuts, a bit darkened in the musty air. Next to the meat counter loomed shelves of neatly stacked dry goods. The clerk, wrapped in his crisply starched apron, dutifully dusted the displays. On the floor a 32-gallon pickle barrel rested next to a cracker barrel. Folks lingered there for their cracker-barrel visits. Heat blew through the forced-air ventilation system, and it warmly greeted me through metal gratings near the front door. As I entered, I stepped over a worn welcome mat.

The Proprietor, Mr. Hamlet, was the third Hamlet generation to own and manage the store. He used a pad and sheets of carbon paper to record the orders which he posted to thick, green ledgers. He knew the locals. He knew all this and more! What he didn't know, Mrs. Hamlet told him. You see, she knew a lot, owing to how often she eavesdropped on our party line whenever business slowed. Mrs. Hamlet then plied me with questions so that I could "earn" an all-day sucker. I felt funny taking the candy from her for answering easy questions, but I suppose I earned it every time.

My family traded on a handshake with the Hamlets. It was all right when we fell behind on our account. Mr. Hamlet knew and cared for his neighbors.

Next came Mr Daniels' barber shop with its rotating red and white column. Both stories and hair did fly freely there! Mr. Daniels spun a tale or two as he snipped hair, snatching years off the way folks looked. Alongside his shop lay the sleepy town paper. Its editor slumped in a swivel chair as he lay drowsing over a copy of the Thursday Herald edition. He needed time to contemplate—and to nap—over this special 8-pager! In it lay wondrous news of socials, of suppers, and of invitations from lifelong friends. All of this ruckus still amounted to newsworthy events in town.

At the end of the street, I heard the clacking of a tin sign fronting the town bar where folks shared whiskey and conversation. Electrical bulbs on wispy cords of Xmas lights fluttered above the bar. They flickered and swayed in the early morning breezes during the Season. The Chief of Police intended to throw a switch to turn them off daily, but oftentimes he had no time to do even that. Visiting and food sopped up most of the free time he had. Nearly any time during the day, I could spy him glued to his stool at the town cafe, the greasy spoon with its glowing orange neon light by night. Well, those Xmas lights burned without stopping throughout the Season.

Isn't it strange how meandering lights often subtly change colors depending on the viewing angle?

Once back at the farm, I actually missed all of those lucky little hellions who studied secrets in school. Why was I banished to a swirling world of daydreams? Why must I read all alone.

I often wandered outside, my eyes squinting in the sunshine. "Help,

help," I heard Julie crying one day. She had been trapped between the chicken shed and fence. Julie was cornered and terrorized in the barnyard by a goose, strutting and thrusting her beak at her. The goose hissed with hot breath, and its evil, reddened eyes might shame any demon dragon. It hopped on top of a hay bale.

"Help me, please," pleaded Julie as tears streamed down her face. She cowered in the corner next to cows grazing nearby in the pasture.

Well, I began to scheme to outwit that goose. I thought that mean old goose might be a bunch like our sheriff. I guarantee he would have attacked a child like Julie simply because she did not look like him. Then, I thought the bird might be distracted by food. So, I dashed into the chicken house for a tray of grain, which I brandished at the goose. It worked. The goose darted from Julie and toward the food and me. I tensed. By this time, I was angry, and I had just about enough of that threatening fowl. My thoughts raced.

After I lured that goose into the chicken house, I slammed the door behind it. I could hear cackling and hissing behind the door. It was not pleased. Still, because it had grain for consolation, its uproar ceased.

I ran to check on Julie, I asked, "Are you all right?" She looked shaken, not hurt. I wiped her streaming eyes with tissues. "I'll be all right."

"I don't like that mean old goose!" Julie exclaimed.

"I reckon we need to walk around the barnyard to calm our nerves," I said. We skirted the barnyard and walked one block north of the house. Our non-septic waste water collected there. Adjacent to this slough lay a derelict foundation, which was all that remained of an old utility shed. Next to the foundation rested the remains of an abandoned tractor. Julie and I climbed up on the metal seat, which was perched on a support made of one massive metal rod bent to hold the seat in place. The seat was designed for shock absorption, cushioning any driver who was brave enough to steer the monstrosity.

As we tried our hand at all of the rusted levers and knobs, we fancied ourselves masterful farmers plowing the fields. We prepared for spring planting. Each of us grew impatient waiting for the other to finish their turn on the tractor shell. At first, we imagined that it would be the source of endless delight for us. Why, we might be taking turns all day at the controls. Well, that lasted for about fifteen minutes, and then we grew weary. We wended our way back to the house. After all, play time has its limits, self-imposed or otherwise.

Believe it or not, about noon time I began to bug Mother. "When will the kids return? Is today special with a light schedule? Shouldn't we start now to Wea to pick them up so that we are not late?" I pursued. It's hard to imagine how I might miss those hellions, even though they had their moments.

After fetching the kids, we did our chores and took a quick supper. Then, I watched my siblings do their homework. I usually pouted, saying it was unfair that I was not in school doing the same kind of homework. My brother Paul sardonically snapped, "Oh, you're lucky not to take all of this endless crap!" He barked, "Don't fret. Your time will come soon enough," he taunted with a jeering lilt in his voice. Still, my heart ached when I knew I had been left out of their studies.

Then, it was time for another decade of the rosary and for bed. That meant taking a bath and brushing my teeth. I owned a large yellow toothbrush with the form of a bear molded on its handle. I grew partial to that old toothbrush, and I protected it from anyone who dared use it. I couldn't use another brush! I often reminded everyone which brush I owned, and I grew frustrated that no one could remember what I said. I was the youngest, yet I was the one telling everyone else what was what when it came to toothbrushes! Maybe I wanted to boost my own identity. After all, I was only four years old. For me, owning a special and precious object (like my yellow, bear-handled tooth brush) helped me feel unique.

Then, it was off to bed with my routine question, "Will Dad work the graveyard shift?" If the answer was yes, I planned another stealthy trip into Mother's bedroom.

Day of the Coyote

I honed my role as "baby of the family" for four glorious years before Leo and Greg happened along. That meant plenty of time to form kinships with babies, human or otherwise. Oh, I passed *some* of my time with siblings. For example, a few times Paul drilled me through a 36-piece box of crayons to ensure I knew the names of each color. Every time we hit upon pink, he shook his head, calling it "the forbidden color". I called it "a whopper" so as not to utter its name. Oh, I often watched Mary as she swayed gently in her easy chair. Whether she read or simply rested, I could count on her silent lightness, as if in Holland Vermeer himself was fixing to paint her. And Julie and I often worked on ways to foil our old nemesis—that nasty gray goose with reddened eyes and hot breath. While I guessed playing with human youngsters was all right, I much preferred the company of barnyard animals.

At first, whenever Mary milked our goat Gertrude, I sat by Mary's side to lap up all of Gertrude's gaminess. That was before I knew that goat milk tasted like an insane man conjuring trouble. But I also knew that sitting next to Gertrude and her kids at milk time meant I might be special, too. Why, they could nibble at anything and come away unhurt. (Was I as blessed?)

In the corner of our shed, chicks nestled under heat lamps. Their light yellow fluffiness thrilled me, cheeping innocent hope. I could stare at them until I nearly forgot where I was—just to hear them. We'd crafted an enclosure of tin to tuck them in with warmth. I had to wonder if their cheerfulness, which they lost when they grew up, was too much to pay for learning to fly. Their once hopeful feathers turned into a mottled gray or even stark white.

Well, you already know about the lambs, the orphaned ones my specialty. They were gentle and kind, and I reckoned any feathers must be rough by comparison. Those babes suckled their bottles at feeding time, stilling my heart. Can anything that tender and peaceful be real?

Although my goat, chick, and lamb friends were hauntingly dear, my duckling friends were my be-all-to-end-all. One evening I caught sight of Mother Duck waddling by, her babies in tow. Those three "special" ducklings became my favorite friends, and their memory nips at me still. Heck, my sunshine-feathered pals were company of choice day or night. I was partial to their crisp "peeps" that shrilled to an emergency level whenever they lost sight of their mother, and I positively wilted to the pitter-patter of their minuscule paddling feet. How they propelled themselves along at marvelous speeds, those sprightly tugboats! And what compares to their waddle? Their sassy tails swished to and fro in a rhythm that only those yellow sprites could muster. Oh sure, gossipy women in town aimed to rival them, their mouths moving faster than the south end of a duck. But they were no match for my ducklings.

One morning a mission swept me away, one of love for my ducklings. My sister Mary told me ducks were born with a love and a talent for swimming. I was riled, seeing as how my ducklings didn't show even an *interest* in swimming, much less a love or talent for it. Naturally, I reckoned they needed someone to lead them to water before they might take to swimming alone; I would be that someone. Even though that role was reserved for the Mother Duck, didn't she need nudging or even considerable help?

I filled Mum cow's water bucket, crafted of weathered metal thick and slumbering, with cistern water. Leaving two inches unfilled, I didn't wish to overflow the bucket. Water was precious and not to be wasted. Besides, I reckoned my ducklings might splash out a few inches. So, I left room at the brim. Then, I scooped up my friends from their straw-lined box, and I headed for their new swimming pool. They didn't go quietly. "Peep, peep, peep—"

Mother Duck frowned at my horseplay, sassing me something fierce. She threw a hissie fit the likes of which might have put to shame Patty Duke as Helen Keller in "The Miracle Worker".

How ungrateful, I thought. Wasn't I doing her babies *and her* one big favor?

Not caring for my kindness at all, she kept right on hissing, rivaling the likes of salt mists that attack rock-strewn shores pounded by waves.

"Here you go," I said all adult-like, "You need to soak." I set each duckling on the water's rippled surface. "Then you'll take to swimming. Did you know President Roosevelt soaked in mineral pools so that he could walk better?"

I suspect they didn't give a hoot about President Roosevelt's mineral baths. But they sure peeped up about this swimming hole. In a wink, all of that peeping speared from being only slightly miffed to fast and shrill.

Using Mother's take-charge tone, I purred, "Don't worry, you'll take to water soon enough."

As their swim instructor, I patted myself on the back: fine job. Then, I rewarded myself with being lured away by heady blossoms in our apple tree west of the cistern. Hadn't that tree been promoted to lead a parade of wise men who cast a spell over anyone who drew near? Did it work wonders on anyone foolish enough to edge near, the way poppies drowsed the gang on the Yellow Brick Road? Only it wasn't sleep that wafted over me. No, a series of plays and stories came on, and each one needed my attention. Sprawling under the tree, I took to rehearsing lines from stories that I'd adapted: Captain Hook visits a limb factory, Alice mixes her potions just right, and Wyatt Earp rounds up space alien outlaws in space suits and all. Miraculously, six shooters were more than a match for their death rays. "Did you reckon you'd get away with it?" I asked in my best western drawl. "Let me tell you something, buster. You moseyed into the wrong town today. When I meet up with the sheriff I'm let him know—"

"Why in the hell didcha drown the ducklings?" It was my oldest sister Janice, age fourteen.

Jolting upright, I heard myself crack, "Draw, partner."

"What are you doing? Why didcha drown the ducklings?"

"Huh?" Although I didn't know what "drown" meant, I did know from her voice that it must mean a wagon load of trouble.

"Just look at what you wrought, you rotten little boy! You killed them all three!" Janice hurled a limp and silent duckling at me. It struck my leg before it tumbled alongside my right big toe.

"This is not some make-believe mumbo-jumbo! You drowned our ducklings!" Janice had just washed her hair. Tiny strands of her dark bangs clung together, framing her seething eyes.

I "drowned" them? I "killed" them? Hmmm. The sunshine had left my drenched duckling's feathers. When I peered into its eyes, I knew something wasn't right. They appeared plastic, like those of a doll, open but eerily unseeing.

"Look at me when I'm talking, you freak!" Janice's legs jerked like those of a spastic hen, and her feet clawed at the ground as if she was fixing to roust out some tasty worms. "You've killed them. Don't you get it? Say something!" Her cackle melded with that of our chronically ornery Rhode Island Red rooster. He'd tromp out in a mist of feathers to spur anyone who so much as looked at him funny. Then, he'd rear forward to make a snatch at a peanut butter and honey sandwich that I dangled from my right paw. Frightening—

Killed—killed—where had I heard that word before? Dad and I had found the shredded body of a sheep in our field, but I didn't know what that meant. Had coyotes aimed only to bathe the sheep with kisses, but somehow they lost their wits? And look what happened . . .

"Coyotes got it," Dad said before shaking his head. He shoved his hands into his pockets. Later, Mother told me coyotes hunted only sick or weak sheep. They let the strong ones be.

"Say something!" Janice cackled. I'd been staring at who knows what.

"Look, a coyote must have gotten them," was all I mustered.

"A coyote? A coyote? In a bucket of water?"

A shiver bolted down my spine. "Can an animal stop living when it's in water?" I asked Janice. "Is that what drown means?"

"Of course! What else can it mean? That they free-styled it to a hair dresser for a new hairdo? Come back to earth for once. They sucked your water into their lungs, and everyone except you knows they can't do that and keep breathing." She clenched her right fist in rage, her knuckles whitened.

I grimaced, knowing that my babies were dead—gone—on account of me. But how? I'd only plopped them on top of the water, and that ought to be all right. Water helps people, vegetables, and trees grow. Right? It heals people, like the way it fussed to help President Roosevelt a bit so that he might walk a little. (Well, maybe it was the brace and all the help from his boys, but it looked as if he grew stronger.) Water *ought* to help my ducklings learn to swim. It can't stop life—or could it?

Mother Duck staggered in circles, quacking dolefully. "What happened to my babies? I can't hear my babies." Misty-eyed, she waddled up to me. Spying her baby at my feet, she poked at it with her bill. "What in the Sam Hill did you do?" she positively bawled at me.

My eyes drifted down, my chin sinking south. I stared at the ground, and she stared at me.

"Oh no you don't!" Janice yelled. "You're not gonna play dumb. Not this time. What the hell is wrong with you?" Then she swung at me. I looked up fast enough to dodge her hand, but I lost my balance, thumping my head against the apple tree's trunk—and I mean hard. It smarted some, but I'd felt much sharper pain than that—being accident-prone and all. Rubbing the back of my head, I gathered dampness on my fingertips, and I lifted it to my tongue. A salty taste of injury loomed.

"Serves you right," Janice said. "You're lucky I wasn't trying to hit you."

Just then I felt a prick of a new "kind" of hurt: loss. I must have been sobbing because Janice jeered, "Why, you little baby. You drown ducklings and act like a zombie. Then, you bump your 'wittle' head and what do you do? Cry."

Why was I sobbing? I wanted to think about that, but Janice's scolding bushwhacked me. I needed time to let my thoughts percolate. So, I did what came natural. I tuned her out. Maybe I could join my precious ducklings one last time . . .

Oh, my wonderfully fluffy friends. I had such plans for you. You were going to follow me on hikes. You were going to swim in the creek with me, and sleep by my side at twilight. You were going to quack melodies to me. (I couldn't bring myself to touch the duckling at me feet.) My careless daydreaming killed you. I can't help it—daydreaming I mean. It drifts over me in waves. Do you know daydreaming? And now you're gone. I grabbed for you, and you vanished.

I'd seen the down from cottonwood take flight, and when I asked Mother about it, she let on how it aches to heave up to parts unknown. It leaves on a voyages, grand and mysterious. She explained, "It's the same way with dandelions and thistles, too. Thistledown vanishes when you reach to touch it, especially if you try to hold onto it. Best let it be. Let it drift where it may."

"Yes, Mother."

"Although thistles are prickly, their down is fluffy. But we can see it only at a distance because we don't own it. Thistledown isn't ours to control. Like most wild things, it's best left to take off on its own."

"How do we know for sure to leave it be?"

"All of its fluffiness tells us so."

"Where does thistledown drift?" I asked Mother.

"I like to think it searches for a secret place to land." Likewise, I guessed maybe my ducklings floated away to some secret place, too. Where else could they be?

I decided to find thistles. Finding a clump of purple flowers, I wasn't about to give them a chance to twitch away, leaving me. No way. Why, with my eyes stuck on them, I walked right up to those flowers. Cupping my fingers around the thistle flowers, I heard myself say, "ouch!" That darn thistle shoved its prickers into me! How could I win? Either the down flies away, or thistle thorns bite me. Oh, what a morning!

"You're hopeless," Janice bellowed. Then, she stomped back into the house. Her ranting didn't end, though. "Mom, you'll never guess what your nitwit little boy . . ."

Within minutes Dad sauntered onto the porch and over to me. I didn't have the heart to move. He rested his hand on a branch above me.

"Are you all right, Sean? I heard what Janice spouted about you in the kitchen, and—"

"Oh— I'm fine. Well, . . . maybe not."

Dad waited.

"I felt sure I was helping them. Really, I did. Ducklings ought to know how to swim. How could I have been careless enough to kill my friends?" My chin rested on my chest, and I couldn't bear to face Dad's disappointment.

"Well, this helping business sometimes throws adults off, too."

"Really?"

"Yep. Take what happened to your Uncle Jim. When his doctors collapsed his bad lung, they certainly thought they were helping him, possibly saving his life. He died anyway not long after his surgery. I don't think they helped him, not a smidgen. In fact, their so-called help may have killed him. Who knows? I sure don't."

Dad gave this some time to settle.

"I *do* know that sometimes our best intentions backfire, and then we're left scratching our heads. By the way, that's a nasty bump on yours."

"What? Oh, it's nothing. I'm okay. Well, maybe Uncle Jim drowned, like my ducklings."

"Like your ducklings, he couldn't breathe. That much is true. But I think he may have really died of a broken heart."

I pictured his heart hitting the counter top where it snapped in two.

"The love in his heart was too large for this world. It had to break open to free his mountainside of love."

I'd seen a cow's heart once, and it was as large as both of Grandfather Kearney's fists put together, and then some. (He had been a boxing champion in his WWI company.) Maybe Uncle Jim's heart was like that. And wasn't there a disease that puffs out a person's head until it clouds the mind?

"Was he slow?" I asked Dad. "I mean, did his head keep growing until *it* was too large, too?"

"What . . . slow? Heck, he was powerful smart. Maybe he was too smart. His brain couldn't keep up with all of his thoughts, and so it began to crack into slivers."

"Why couldn't he share some of his extra thoughts with someone who wasn't as sharp?"

"It doesn't work that way. Anyway, Jim's mind began to crack—splitting into parts."

"That must have hurt—a lot. Dying that way must be one powerful weak feeling."

"It did hurt a lot. He suffered greatly." Dad let his hand slip from the branch and slap his thigh. He became suspended in thought. "We'd better bury the ducklings," he eventually mumbled as he ambled back toward the house.

Maybe it would have been better had the doctors left Uncle Jim alone. Why hadn't I left those ducklings be? Mother Duck was right.

Moping around the farm, I mostly whiled away the time by staring at my feet. I felt lousy about what I'd done, and I needed comfort from my other barnyard friends. But when I approached them, they seemed "different". Were they afraid of me? If so, I couldn't blame them much.

Heading toward our fescue field, I happened to spy a lone figure—an animal hunched and still—watching from about twenty-five feet away. There stood a coyote. I froze. How long had he been there? Did he pant for the chance to shred me like that sheep that Dad found? Was he studying me to learn if I was weak or strong? I didn't rightly know myself—if I was weak or strong.

For a silent moment we stared down one another. His eyes were droopy like mine. I was sad because I'd killed three ducklings, but what made him sad?

I broke my stillness. "Mr. Coyote, you don't want to eat someone like me."

"Why not?" the coyote answered.

"Because I'm careless and not much good for anything."

"You're young," he said, "but you'll learn. I hope you know you must not interfere with nature's timetable."

"I know—now. Why didn't I let the ducklings learn about water on their own? I thought I knew better than—."

"Yes, boy. Your heart was in the right place."

The weight of what I did lifted a pinch.

Then, the coyote whined, commencing to paw at the ground.

"What do you want?" I asked.

He moved a few steps nearer. Stopping, he whined louder, pawing at the earth as if he was hungry and grubbing for beetles. His paws puffed up dust.

Suddenly, I knew what was eating him. "I'd told Janice I *guessed* you killed the ducklings," I said, "not that you *for sure* killed them."

The coyote waited.

It was time for the full truth. "Mr. Coyote, I'm powerful sorry I dragged you into this mess. Yes, I told Janice that maybe you got the ducklings."

The coyote perked up his ears and bristled. Swishing his head from side to side, he looked starved for truth. Imagine a four-year-old boy blaming him for a killing he hadn't committed.

Then, the coyote shot me a wary glance. Did he warn me never again to accuse anyone falsely? Then he trotted into our fescue field.

Dad spoke of Native Americans who called coyotes "tricksters", meant to remind us that what happens might be seen a few different ways. What seems like bad luck—like breaking a leg, for example—might be the best luck of all. It might mean that you're home in bed instead of being hurt somewhere that isn't safe. Our trickster friends aim to tell us that it all depends on the way you see things. Nothing is all bad or all good.

I wondered about that. Did this coyote really know what I'd done. I had been bad without even knowing it. Had I known better . . .

Or, did he aim to trick me into learning something, the way Grandfather Kearney fancied? Is life a trickster? I wondered.

I puzzled over my question that day, and I hunger for its answer even still.

Barnyard to Platter

What a mark we wrought when we rustled up a chicken to pinch its neck in between two rusted nails that stuck out of a withered plank. One well placed chop, and off came its head! A rampaging ghost dance followed, one of a headless fowl protesting that its time hadn't come. Its limbs spasmed in meterless frenzy, and a still-beating heart pumped crimson fluid into the dust. A slowing and then ending of the dance writhed into silence and nothingness. This was death, clawing into chickens with an uneasy peacefulness. Frantic stillness loomed.

If I squint my right eye and cock my head to one side, I can see a well honed hatchet casting reflected spears of sunlight. Where once had tilted a head, heavy streaks of tepid blood spurted. Were those shards of red stained glass? Do chickens flail with liquid-stained glass pumping through their veins? After their blood pooled into a tired stillness, death lived.

Butchering ten to twelve chickens a day meant, "All hands on deck!" (And that went for me too, a four-year old.) Dad told me that while I was too young to weld an ax, I could pluck feathers. Mother saw to it that our chicken dunking water was hot enough to persuade stubborn feathers to let loose of chicken flesh. But she didn't use a thermometer. Did she own a built-in temperature gauge? She needed only to look at a steaming pot of water to know if it was heated enough, which was plenty hot! Although fresh blood stays warm for a spell, it feels cool next to steaming water grumbling its threat. Of course, we locked our hound PJ inside our downstairs bathroom so that he couldn't help. Our half-breed hound's jaws sweated to lap up all that salty, metallic goodness—something that no self-respecting hound can resist.

No chicken plucker (including me) ever forgets the odor of sticky chicken blood: pungent, metallic, but mostly salty, not really much different from human blood. Who can forget the musty scent of hot water tinged with dunked chicken feathers? Yet, while that smell felt sick, it drew me in like a misty hand—invisible. Was this the smell of minutes-old death? I aimed to ask Dad about it.

One morning I spotted Dad taking a break. The shade of our walnut tree offered rest from head chopping. Joining him, I began, "Dad, do you ever think about our chickens, about their lives? I mean, one minute, they're tromping around our barnyard in search of bugs and grasshoppers. The next minute, 'Whack!' they're missing their heads."

Rubbing his cheek with the palm of his hand, Dad thought for a moment. He stooped to pick up a fallen walnut branch, which he swished to scratch a circle into the dirt. "You're asking about cycles. Our ancestors knew them. They knew about cycles: of seasons, of ocean tides, of the moon, and of the sun. You know what a cycle is, don't you?"

"Well, maybe. Is it kind of like what happens when we plant winter wheat in the fall? We harvest it come summer. Or, I know—the way the land rests in the winter and wakes up again in the spring? Like that, Dad?" I had his attention. "And another cycle is the earth revolving around the sun once a year, and still another is the earth rotating on its axis once a day. And—"

"And," Dad interrupted, stopping me from spinning into orbit, "Our ancestors knew that life is connected to death, just as these two points connect to make a circle." He closed the circle in the dust. "Like us, our ancestors fed their chickens. Then, in turn, the chickens fed them. It's a cycle, a part of the mystery of life and death. But they didn't think about death the way we do."

"They saw it differently from our priests?"

Breathing softly, Dad sat down and gazed past the thistles that framed the swaying prairie grasses. Patting the ground, he said, "Sit with me." He picked at some dried blood under his fingernails. "Things have changed since our ancestors raised chickens. Now our culture says death is separate from life, that death is ugly and terrifying. Oh, our priest doesn't mean to scare us, but he does. Father Shudders frightens folks with his nonsense about how life and death are separate. But it's not his fault. The Church has done that for nearly two thousand years."

"Isn't it scary, Dad? I know I'd be scared to go away from you and Mother and everything that I love, never to see you again." (I was thinking about my drowned ducklings.)

"Fear of death is due to clouded vision, like looking underneath water and wondering why you can't make things out clearly. No, I say death and life are pieces of a larger mystery. We must be ready to leave our body's shell to parts unknown when death comes calling.

"Dad?"

"It's all simply a matter of timing. Both life and death are pieces of something much grander than we are. Both are parts of a giant mystery, just as shards of glass are slivers of a grand window pane that we can't see clearly or wholly when it glints in a thousand pieces."

"You mean like all the shards of red stained glass that might pump as a liquid in chickens?"

"What? You know better than that, don't you? Now, really!"

"Yes, sir. I know better." But why do you know about this mystery, while our priests don't?"

"Reared wrong, I reckon. Or maybe they've trained themselves not to see it—not to feel it, not to know it— in their innards." Dad tapped his stomach. "But I have to admit, sometimes I sense it, while other times I don't."

"Dad?"

"Sometimes I think life and death are like trains heading to California and to points beyond." (Dad knew I liked the idea of riding to California.) "Both trains are headed the same direction but along different tracks. We don't know when we're getting off one train to board another. Who knows what station stop calls us?"

"Like not having your train schedule with you, and having to wait and wait at the depot for a train to come?" I asked.

Dad laughed, "Sort of. And I think not knowing 'when' scares people. They miss seeing. They miss the lusciousness of the mystery."

"Come on, everyone likes a good mystery—don't they?" Jabbing a thumb at my chest, I quipped, "I sure do. What could be more juicy than a mystery?"

"Not everyone likes mystery, though. I reckon when people puff themselves up to be important they commence to see and to think strangely."

"Like how?"

"They might begin to think that they are the center of things, that they are the most important. But they miss the fact that they are the same as the person next door or the one clear across the planet. We're all equally important and part of one grand mystery. They miss the mystery of life and death, of how we are all connected."

"I pictured a puffed-up bullfrog wearing our priest's Sunday clothes. Silly, don't you think?"

Dad let me wallow with that. "Yes, I reckon it's silly. But please don't show any disrespect. Our leaders are doing their best, and never forget it! You know how those frogs get when they feel important. They lose their sense and make all kinds of racket."

"Priests have more sense than old bull frogs, don't they?"

"Oh, I suppose so. But sometimes they don't make sense—any more than an ornery raccoon can spit!"

"Dad, *everyone* knows that raccoons have no spit!"

"Yes, which means those leaders loose their sense of order and can't find it. That's why we need to pray. We need to pray that they feel and see more clearly."

By this time, Mother was glaring at us from the back porch, her hands resting on her hips as if to say, "Boys, time's up. If you expect fried chicken for dinner, you'd better get back to work—now."

"Well, . . ."

I quickly rose, then—big boy that I was—pulled up Dad. "Remember this, Sean. Always hold mystery in your heart."

"I sure will, Daddy. I promise."

Back at the house I joined the other chicken pluckers: my brothers and sisters. Ours was not to question why, and boy did feathers fly! Yanking the still-steaming feathers from the chickens meant that handfuls of feathers flew through the air. We piled them next to the plank where the chickens lost their heads. Most of the feathers left, while some clinged to our wet hands—even in between our fingers! They layered in coats over the fingers, growing on themselves. A sudden swish of the hand and snap of the fingers might fling away half of them. While those hitchhikers felt odd at first, I grew accustomed to them. I could let feathers pile up in three or more layers before I needed to fling away all of that stickiness.

Once cleaned, the chickens were toted to the kitchen where Mother used a gruesome, stainless steel blade to remove their guts. Let me tell you, there is nothing like the stench of fresh chicken guts—nothing! They smell like festered sulfur. Fresh sulfur smells bad, but *festered* sulfur smells mean enough to make a body heave.

Next Mother hacked the chickens in two, lopped off and threw out the clawed lower leg, then cut off the wings and breast. And was she swift! Mother could clean and chop up a chicken in less than three minutes.

After dispatching most of the chickens to the freezer, she doused "our" birds in a special coating. Then, she plopped them into a frying pan. Frying chicken oozes an aroma that is oh my . . . so tasty! It all smelled fine enough to chase the stench from our house, while still leaving enough 'oomph' to craze our appetites. Soon we'd devour a meal that'd moved from our barnyard to our platter—in under two hours!

Gazing at the steaming platter of chicken, I oftentimes wondered if some of the heat wafting from the freshly-killed chickens was left inside of them. Might life linger for a spell? But then that thought passed. I'd seen opossums and skunks devour their prey, sometimes while it was still alive! While I gobbled my chicken and smacked my lips, I wondered if that's much different from what I was doing! I also wondered if fryers recently scurrying about our barnyard (in search of bugs, worms, and grain) pass some of their busy energy to us? "That's another cycle, isn't it?" I needed to ask Dad. My legs twitched like a chicken's leg—one attached to a spritely fryer chasing after a winged grasshopper.

Yet, as thankful as I was to be eating that tasty chicken, I also felt sorry for them. They stopped living so that we could live. I wondered if anything would live on account of *my* death. While the warmth of a drum stick hung heavily upon my tongue, I muttered, "Maybe so. I sure hope so." Not knowing for sure is fine. It means the mystery lingers, as does steam from freshly killed chickens.

Dad would have said, "For in not knowing, maybe we do know at least that. Maybe that's knowing something—at least a pinch—after all." I have to agree.

Ripple a Riddle, Echo a Wish

Especially after *plucking* chickens, I often needed to escape to the creek. There I could strip off some of that salty smell. There I could explore. And every time the creek whispered to me, I wound up stuffing my pockets with pieces of shale, sandstone, and limestone. Each stone I pocketed was creased with imprints of ferns, shells, and worm-like bodies with thin slices that looked like the liner on Dad's new aspirin bottles. He called them "fossils". On this day, Dad was set to join me at the creek. So, I lined up my collection *to impress*. Arranging the first wave of my display by the kind of rock (shale, sandstone, limestone), I then divided them according to the type of fossil that slumbered there. In the first row I laid rocks with ferns. In the second row came the shells. I reserved the last row for the worm-like bodies. Then, glancing around to make sure no one saw me, I introduced myself as Professor Redmond, Chair of the Archaeology Department at the National Museum in Washington. Dad called it the "Smithsonian". I called it fun. What was good enough for Dad was fine by me, and so the Smithsonian it became. "Ladies and Gentlemen, if you'd care to step this way, I'll begin to share my collection of rare specimens. You'll be privy to wonders never before seen by humans. Imagine how we labored for your viewing pleasure, here-"

A warm hand brushed my right shoulder. "Professor Redmond, since you're a premiere fossil collector, I must ask, what's this specimen?" Naturally, it was Dad, who motioned toward a slab of shale nearly the size of a notepad. He picked it up. The imprint of a fern creased near its center.

"This old thing?" I asked, picking up the shale. "Oh, it's a fern, I reckon. But I meant to ask *you* that, Dad." I grinned sheepishly.

Feeling embarrassed, I began to flutter. I skipped a flat stone, one not bearing a fossil (of course), across the water. One skip . . . two . . . three . . . four . . . five skips. Five skips. Not shabby, but not the seven beats that I'd hoped for. "There you go, Sean," Dad said.

Still skittish, I skipped another stone. One . . . two . . . three . . . four . . . five . . . six skips. Dad sat silently as if replaying my throw in slow motion. Then, he cocked his head and looked at me. "Do you ever wonder about questions, ones you need to ask me, but you can't ask because I'm away?"

"All the time."

"What do you do with *those* questions?"

"I wait ... but sometimes waiting is almost more than I can take, especially when you're working the extra board."

"Okay," Dad whispered, "here's what you do." He motioned for me to follow him over to the west side of the water hole. Its rippled surface shimmered like a too-drunk mirror. He lofted a stone—after checking it for fossils—into the center of the pool.

"Kaplunk," the stone broke the pool's surface, rippling it from its center toward its rock-strewn banks.

"Whenever a question itches at your insides, remember this creek in this old Redmond Valley. Think now and then of these ripples."

Without meaning to, I began to hum "Red River Valley".

"From this Valley they say you are going. I'll miss you bright eyes and sweet smile. Just remember this Red River Valley, and . . ." Dad wasn't impressed.

"Sean-"

Cleaning my throat, I sputtered, "Then what?"

"Don't skip stones across its surface. Instead, gently loft one into the deepest place in the pool. Watch how the tiny waves lap at the shore. Those waves commence from the motion of the stone. Those waves reflect the stone's gentle motion."

Dad's voice made me feel like everything was holding its breath, as if all the world had stopped to wait for his words to pass. I let my mouth relax, and my chin headed south. Although he was talking about motion, it felt like stillness.

He continued, "Now notice those ripples near the creek's banks. They're different from ripples that a stone forces out when it bounces off of a rock girdled inside the cottonwood's roots. Dad tipped his head toward the cottonwood that slanted to the west with brambles of wild berries camped around its east flank.

"How are those ripples different?"

"The stone ricocheting off of the trapped stone may split into pieces, and that might hurt. You know, *wicked* things happen when stones and people begin to split into pieces. Remember that. It's sad when anything splits into pieces, and I reckon that whoever caused it committed a kind of a sin. It really hurts."

"All right, it hurts. But how are the ripples 'different'?"

"As the stone flies through the air, strikes the flat rock, and bounces into the water, its motion is unlike that of the stone *gently* dropped into the pool. That flying stone doesn't land the way it must in order to tease out the *best* ripples."

"You mean its pieces might strike the water in shallow spots? Then, it might make weaker ripples than if that same stone hit deep water?"

"Maybe . . . Yes, remember, when you lob the stone into the pool, tiny waves lap at the shore. Those waves commence from the motion of a stone. I prefer the soothing ripples in the deep part of the pool much more than the vulgar motion of a ricocheted stone—bounced off of a flat rock wedged into a trunk."

"How come?"

"First of all, that rock in the tree might not fancy little boys hitting it with a stone."

"But maybe that rock *wants* to be free to go exploring. Maybe *I* could set it free."

"Maybe. A ricocheting stone returns to us like echoes—piercing ones. But the ripples swimming on the surface are 'different'."

"How are they different?" I tried my hand at lobbing a rock into the pool, and I studied what happened.

"The stone, like echoes, returns to us through the ripples, just as the sound of clanging feed pails fly into the valley and comes back to us." Dad said. "The pails are echoed through the sound, and the stone is echoed through the motion of ripples. Take the time to *notice* the difference, to *feel* it." As Dad spoke, a warmness crept over, in, and through me. Squinting my right eye, I tried for a better view of something important in the pool. Wasn't there something grand *and* fleeting for me to notice?

Dad turned the shale over in his hands. "Son, I'm telling you this because all around us nature speaks her quiet wisdom. It echoes like these tiny waves. Imagine how each one carries a special knowledge of the stone. Just as the fossil is an echo imprinted in this shale, the ripples of the pool are echoes of the stone's motion." Dad's reassuring tone flowed from him in slow, deliberate waves. (This was *not* the way Father Shudders spoke. He voice sounded loud and *booming mad*, or at least loud and lost. Once Dad muttered, "Father is small potatoes, and few to the hill.")

Dad picked up another worn rock, and he arched it into the pool. "When a question can't wait, loft it into the Kansas winds, just as I throw this rock into the pool. The wind will tote your question to the powers that be, to those far wiser than we. You may expect an echo in good time, but not an ordinary one. No, it will be special, one to answer your question. Its echo will contain words *different* from the ones in your question. Its words will answer your question."

"Really?"

"Yes, and it will be unlike the echo of clanging feed pails that sound in the valley, wafting on evening breezes during milk time. The wind echoes answers back to us—provided we're ready to understand."

How friendly and wise the Kansas winds must be, I thought. That feeling of friendship felt like our dog PJ wagging up to me, his tongue drooping, his eyes glistening, and his back end wagging faster than the south end of a goose. He would want to play fetch right about then. That feeling of kindness slid all over me, like the Indian summer goodness of golden pears dangling from branches. Their skins are slightly bruised and ooze the sweetness of summer. Their juices dripped down my chin. Can such a flavor feel as swell as it tastes?

Dad continued, "And the answers drift with your age and with what you know. Like the ripples on this pool, they swirl and change, moving and twisting with different shapes, depending on the spot from which you choose to view them. Likewise, your answers mature and ripen as you grow."

"You mean the answer for the same questions that I feel can't wait may be different for each person?"

"Now you're getting it. Just about all answers depend on perspective. Until a person understands this, he risks insulting the mystery and wonder of 'What Is'."

"But don't you think it's hard work spying mystery and wonder? Isn't it tough trying not to insult 'What Is', whatever that may be?"

"Yes, it's difficult, but we must try. Don't you fret now. You're still a little boy. These ideas will grow clearer as you grow. Until then, the key is to catch a glimpse of the mystery without reckoning you know all there is about it."

"And what if I *do* know all about it." Was Dad saying I was a baby who didn't know anything?

"You don't know. And if you imagine you do, then in truth you're lost. All you *really* know then is that you're mixed up."

"As mixed up as a dog's breakfast?" I stomped my foot in earnestness.

The corners of Dad's mouth lifted. "*I* sure think so," he said. He teased the water with the tips of his fingers, and he stirred up tiny waves to balance the incoming ripples from the worn stone. "The time it takes to hear your answer may be long or short. Sometimes you might even forget that you asked the question," Dad said in short breaths. "But you *will* have an answer. You will, once you're ready to understand it . . . once you make a connection and know what the answer may mean." Dad's face relaxed, his eyes glistening. And he stared as if the waves entranced him. Didn't his thoughts swirl on those ripples before they nestled against the stones lining the creek bank?

"Dad, do you mean that the wind is that smart?"

"How smart?"

"Enough to tote my questions to the 'powers that be' and to move it clear across the prairie to some place mysterious? And then it knows to move answers smack back to me?"

"Yep."

"And the wind keeps track of *who* asks questions and *when* they're ready to understand the answers?" I stared hard at Dad, my right eye squinted, my head tilted to the right, and my jaw slackened.

"Well, the wind may not be quite that wise. I don't think it knows when you're ready for an answer, but it *does* know to keep saying the answer until you get it."

"How will I know when I'm ready?"

"When you catch the wind rustling and teasing stems of tall grass prairies . . . you'll know an answer when you hear the wind twitching through burr oaks, playing with its leaves. You'll feel the answer as the wind frolics through the cattails in the pond." Dad lowered his voice. "You'll hear it when the time is right for you." His wispy words sounded much like the wind itself.

"Mother says that when she 'smells' her baking cookies, it's the right time to snatch them from the oven. I don't think I'll be able to smell answers that way."

"No, but you'll 'feel' them."

Twirling one of my forelocks to tightness first in one direction and then in another, I gazed into the pool. I strained to understand and to remember Dad's words.

"Answers trickle in from all around us," Dad murmured, "from places far and near. I reckon the wind knows to pick them up and to carry them along. Did you know that the folks who lived here long ago, the Kaw Indians, knew that the winds of Kansas answered tough questions?"

"Nope."

"Yes, they knew the wind's power. As a matter of fact, the name Kansas comes from the Kaw words that mean 'Land of the South Wind People'. Winds carry knowledge of all who came before the Kaw, just as it does for all who came after them. The Kaw knew that the South Wind could answer even the toughest questions from children musing on windswept prairies, as they crouch near swirling waters. The wind tightly holds all of that knowledge, and it aches to share it with any who ask politely."

"But the wind grows tired sometimes. It stops. You know that. What happens to questions and answers when the wind isn't around?"

"If the wind seems to leave, remember it's resting for a spell. You need only ask kindly, and the winds of Kansas will come through for you." Dad handed the shale to me. "Don't stop waiting for answers. Sometimes, they'll waft into your mind when you least expect it." Grinning, he said, "You know Sean, I'd say you're one of the luckiest boys in the world."

"I am?"

"Yes. You're growing up *here*, on this special farm, on this blessed land, on this 'Land of the South Wind People'." Dad clasped my shoulder. "Now Professor Redmond, we'd best lock up the museum and start thinking about milking. Soon it'll be time to call the cows home." Dad yawned. "Chores are waiting, and there's much work before rest."

Memorial Day in a Country Cemetery

Mr. Legg huffed, "Tom Redmond sings tolerably well. But he's not one of us." He didn't spy me waiting in the shadows next to the copper and steel holy water urn with its shiny spigot to trickle refills into white stone holders. If he had, he might have hushed up. I was waiting for Dad to pull up his 1960 Dodge near the front door of the Church that rainswept morning. Attending a first Friday service, Dad and I represented our family. Mr. Legg and Mr. Henry had also taken Mass.

"Tom's a newcomer, and he's not welcomed. No one joins the choir unless his family has been in the parish for at least two generations—not even if he's Frank Sinatra."

"What about Mrs. Stoddard?" Mr. Henry asked. No one heard of her family until her daddy showed his grinning face in 1940. Why'd you let her in?"

"What . . .? Oh," Mr Legg said, waving his hand. "Who do you think paid for the statue of St. Cecilia? She did, and that short-circuits *at least* one generation of waiting. She belongs," Mr. Legg stammered as he pawed uneasily at the floor. Did even he see the contradictions?

Even after my family had been part of Wea Parish for years, we were the outsiders. Folks needed to wait three generations, be baptized in the church, and buried in its cemetery before becoming one of them.

On Memorial Day Sunday of 1962, Mother attended an Alter Society meeting after church. (This was before Memorial Day permanently fell on Mondays.) The rest of us had to wait around. With an hour to kill, Dad and the kids moseyed over to the school playground, while I high-tailed it to the cemetery with the intention of steeping in the heady scent of the lilacs there.

Wea's Queen of The Holy Rosary Church cemetery, slumbering east of the church and rectory, sat framed on three sides by a six-foot chain link fence to "keep out" grazing cattle. Lilac bushes bordered the north side. Our parish founders were pioneers who'd settled in the Wea Indian mis-

sion (thus the parish's name) long before a mason had laid the corner-
stone of the present church, circa 1895. By 1962 those founders—and
Indians—were long gone. What remained? Only their descendants, the

church, the rectory, the school, and its playground . . . and this lovely country cemetery dotted with headstones. Once Dad swished his right hand into the air, as if he was splashing holy water over the cemetery to bless it. He muttered, "Life's but a fleeting shadow, as unsteady as a late spring shower that pops up from nowhere, dumps its load, and ebbs away before we take time to feel it fully."

Ornery thistles had snaked their way in and out of the chain link fence on the opposite side of the cemetery from me. They wound up looking old and gnarly, different from the sturdy upright fence that held them. Mr. Henry, the church custodian, mowed those thistles twice a year whether they needed it or not. And still some of the ornery ones persevered and grew back year after year with tree-like stems to taunt mower blades and break more than a few. Those that managed to go down with the mower left thick stalks behind called "old pokes" for painfully clear reasons. Those old pokes skulked a few inches above the soil, tripping unwary souls or jamming into an innocent shin. "What good are those nasty weeds anyhow?" Mr. Henry and I asked.

Nearing the cemetery, I had to wonder what the pioneers felt while they trampled over the same soil my family and I trampled lifetimes later. Had they been happy? How many children did they have? Did they work hard like Dad? Although I knew they worked hard, I hoped they didn't end up too tired and disappointed from it.

I hadn't quite made it to the corner where the lilacs met the fence when a late-spring breeze rustled new leaves on the linden trees behind me. That breeze nudged me toward the chain link fence. Once there, I wrapped my fingers around a few links. Then, I considered the ancient Mrs. Davis who'd just trudged into the cemetery. She toted an armful of flowers, no doubt freshly cut from her garden.

Ancient Mrs. Davis, her gait unsteady and slow, trembled like a corn stalk rustling in a southern breeze. Her husband Bill went to WWI when she was six months pregnant with her son Bill Junior. She became a widow even before her son could meet his father. As a young man of 26, Bill Junior followed his father's example, as faithful as a blue-tick hound trotting after him. Junior shipped out to fight in WWII, and as his father, echoed home in a coffin. Silence lived. Junior never knew what hit him. Mrs. Davis was sad that no one carried on the family name.

I spied her red, swollen eyes as she stooped to place flowers on the two graves of her two loved ones—her husband and her son. Wet streaks traced sweeps of moisture below her eyes. Did the heaviness of her losses, the weight of sad and heavy thoughts, press down on her stooped shoulders?

What of her hope? Had it died with her son, after taking ill when her husband died? What if someday my hope died? Would I whither like

Mrs. Davis? Can people live without hope? Well, I guessed I could live without many things, making do with "bailing twine and duct tape," like Dad often muttered. But, I guarantee I'd have a mighty hard time making do without hope.

People other than Mrs. Davis scurried through the cemetery gate to place garlands of green, yellow, and red carnations on tombstones. Mother said some of these visitors were probably there to honor people they'd never met. Their parents placed flowers on the graves of those they loved. Next, these children carried on that tradition in their stead. Maybe some of those strangers were ancestors of the pioneers who founded the Wea Parish! Did their ancestors raise chickens and sheep just like my family did?

I recognized Mr. Jones who'd been inching along the grass with the aid of his cane. Soon, he started quaking like a golden aspen in the breeze. Stopping, he grasped the edge of a tombstone to steady himself. Mr. Jones became lame after taking a nasty fall, breaking his right leg and hip. Both healed all right, but after that he never walked without a limp or his "wooden third leg" that tapped the ground or wedged into the lawn.

Pushing away from the tombstone, he commenced to walk again. In no time flat, he quaked faster than before, as if he meant to catch up on all the trembling he'd foregone while resting. Despite his trouble, Mr. Jones made it to his wife's grave fine. I reckoned he missed her, and not just on Memorial Day Sunday. I'll wager that he missed her every day.

In the late morning sunlight, his frame looked all twisted and gnarled, not straight and proud like his wife's headstone. Hmm . . . what did he remind me of? That's it! "Mr. Jones looks like those thistles clinging to the fence!" I mumbled to no one.

At the other side of the cemetery, a husky parishioner towered over the grave markers, and he casted his shadow in the mounting morning sun. His father was killed in the Korean War. That meant his mother raised him alone, keeping up her farm the best she could. She did well, seeing as how he grew into a strapping lad.

Standing there, did he wish there was a way his dad might return to him, the same way I wished my ducklings might? Of course he did! But people can't come back from the dead, and neither can ducklings. Thistles can, though. I'd seen them.

Dad left the playground to join me on that Memorial Day. After standing silently for some time, he said, "Sean, you know none of our ancestors are resting here, don't you?"

"Yes, Dad. I know. How many times have you told me! They're over in St. Joseph. Heck, they're in St. Joseph, *Missouri*."

"And guess where we're heading as soon as your mother is ready?"

I couldn't think about St. Joseph without my heart quickening like I'd heard footsteps drawing near on a deserted London street puffed with fog, just like Sir Charles had in *The Hound of the Baskervilles*. We were on our way to Mount Olivet Cemetery to visit our ancestors' graves.

St. Joseph was the name of Jesus' foster father as well as that of a town that trudged like a melancholy old man, an "also walked" on the banks of the Missouri River. St. Joseph's ancient homes, heated with natural gas, puffed a mustiness and odor whispering of age and disrepair. It also hinted of potential left fallow. I knew the town hadn't lived up to its promise. Might Dad have reflected the town? That made me feel mean enough to spit!

That proud and ancient river meandered, filling valleys sliced by the glaciers during the last ice age. Massive rivers of ice had carved through a bleak and frozen countryside to leave a path in its wake, one tailor-made for the Missouri River to fill. That path looked haphazard and weirdly comical, like teeth marks a beaver might leave as he gnaws on a tree. (I wondered if the beavers asked the trees if they cared to be part of their lodges.) The aroma from the gnawed edges of the tree and the scent from the beaver's saliva left a whiff of mystery.

St. Joseph hadn't always been a tottering old man. Before the Civil War, it had its day, famous as the starting point for the Pony Express which ran from St. Joseph smack out to the capital of California. Well, that was before telegraphs retired the Pony Express.

Why, St. Joseph was even a riotous, up-and-coming river port with investors wagering the town would prosper. Names like Roubideaux (descendants of French fur traders, beaver pelts a specialty) filled the town and its businesses. Those names whispered tales of intrigue. As the 1800s melted into the 1900s, St. Joseph was larger than Kansas City. But even with that, as if fated by the gods, it ran a poor second to Kansas City, which got the railroads. It never lived out its promise of "what might have been." Did a shadow somehow siphon St. Joseph's life blood and energy, much the way a parasite drains life from its host? In some ways, Dad mimicked that town. Once again the thought of that made me feel mean enough to spit!

Naturally, I connected St. Joseph with Dad. After all, it'd been his childhood home. Most of his relatives were born and raised there. Grandfather (Dr. Thomas Redmond), on the advice of his medical school advisor, moved to St. Joseph in 1907. Grandfather yearned to open a medical practice in "a city west of the Mississippi and east of the Rockies that was primed for growth". Thomas Redmond married Nessie Storey, a nursing student in Chicago. When she finished her training in 1908, he whisked her to St. Joseph where she bore five sons between 1910 and 1917. The last two sons were fraternal twins, which ran in Nessie's family. Dad's dark complexion mirrored Grandmother Storey's, while Jim's light coloring favored Dr. Redmond.

By the time the twins were born, Grandmother suffered from a weakening heart, brought about by damaged heart valves. This she owed to a bout of rheumatic fever in her youth. Dr. Redmond claimed that delivering twins after two days of horrible labor strained her heart further, to the point of causing her death fourteen years later at age 55 in 1931. That's something for which my father never forgave himself.

In 1938, Dr. Redmond, a lonesome widower, married Mildred Darkling. She refused to take her husband's last name, a rare trick in those days! Anyway, when Grandfather died in 1943, his widow and his estate slipped away without a trace, leaving no inheritance for Dad.

Mildred Darkling reappeared in St. Joseph around 1960. She died a few years later. Suspiciously, she left no mention of her assets or a will. Dad was sure she'd cheated him out of his inheritance. The best he could wrest from St. Joseph townsfolk was that she'd left her estate to the cathedral in downtown St. Joseph. When Dad asked the Monsignor for the details of her bequest, the good Father said he'd never heard of Mildred Darkling, much less received a red cent from her!

I was delighted by all of this mystery. Who was Mildred Darkling anyway? Was she a fugitive from the law? Had she knocked off a past husband, gorging herself on his wealth that she squandered on loose living? Did she coax little children into her cottage, only to roast them in her oven? Who knows? Anything's possible. All I know is that people both feared and despised her! Some even wondered if she played a hand in Grandfather's death! Dad was entranced by this mystery too, much like a bloodhound focusing on a treed coon. The hound doesn't back off until his master calls him in, and Dr. Redmond was by then long gone.

Plainly and simply, Dad needed cash, and he knew that cash had to be somewhere in St. Joseph. It just had to be. If only he could solve the puzzle of his father's missing estate. And, darn it, if he couldn't do that, he aimed to land a loan there. Mother fretted about his "obsession", and she begged him to stay away from there. "It's not good for you. Look at yourself, will you? You leave here with high-flying hopes only to return looking sorry enough that even death is afraid to take you. This must end!"

But Dad kept right on going, too near his dream to know his own thoughts clearly. He carried on hyped up like a nervous pup before it wears down.

At the time I didn't realize Dad's frustration. But over the years, I watched it change into melancholy that some called depression. It gripped Dad like an icy wave. But even so, Dad kept tight on radiating pride tempered with self-doubt. He kept insisting that Redmond pride meant never admitting defeat.

"Dad, why do you reckon you've been cheated?" I asked once. (I knew it was a sin to cheat while playing board games and such, but I didn't know how anyone could cheat someone out of an estate.)

"Your Great Aunt Margaret—you remember her, Grandfather Thomas' sister—often openly declared, 'Tommy's my favorite nephew and the son I never had.' When she died, I got most of her leftover money. That is, she willed me most of her estate. I made my down payment on the farm with that money."

"Your aunt didn't cheat you, did she?"

"No, Sean. But leaving that money to me—the youngest and all, Jim was in the hospital by then—riled my brothers something dreadful! I can't help but wonder if they worked with Father's second wife to pay me back, to punish me by hiding Father's estate from me." His thirst for the answers never slackened. I worried for Dad's health.

In time, Dad failed to get the backing he needed, and he was forced to declare wage earner's bankruptcy. That meant he promised to pay back every cent with interest. Even if wage earner's bankruptcy preserved Dad's good name, it ruined his credit. He refused to be absolved of his debt through regular bankruptcy. "To do that would be dishonorable. To do that would mean I had no name left," he sputtered. "Besides, it's the bankruptcy that Mark Twain declared, and he paid back every cent! I reckon that what was good enough for Mr. Mark Twain works fine by me."

I mulled over these puzzles every time I made the trip to Mount Olivet country cemetery holding Grandfather Redmond, Grandmother Redmond, and Uncle Jim. There were many questions for a little boy—and for his dad.

"Born 1917; Died 1960" was etched into Uncle Jim's headstone.

"Hey Dad, Uncle Jim was 43 years old when he died!" I'd been solving subtraction problems and wanted to show off. Would he realize I was a big boy?

"Too young," Dad murmured.

Well, I thought 43 was *mighty* old. But, seeing as how he appeared kind of low at the time, I figured I'd best not mention he was ancient.

"Did Uncle Jim die at work the way Grandfather did? Wouldn't that have been something?" In the corner of my eye, I spied my siblings racing through the cemetery to trounce a stand of wild flowers—daisies and a kind of iris. I imagine they planned to craft a bouquet for the graves.

Dad almost cracked a smile. "He was in a hospital."

"The one where Mother works?"

"No, not that one. But, it was a state hospital where people might stay a long time. Tired folks like your uncle ended up living there." Dad brushed some dirt from Jim's headstone. "We took him there, your other uncles and I did, on account of his lungs and mind needing rest."

"Oh, I remember. The doctors popped one of his lungs because he had tuberculosis in it. But that didn't work out so well. What did they do for his mind?"

"Too much . . . and too little. You see, your uncle was the brightest person I ever knew, or didn't know."

"Aw, come on, Dad. Twins know everything about each other. You two went away to high school in Minnesota—to the high school run by the Christian Brothers. How can you say that you did not know him? I mean, weren't you the same?" Dad took a few steps away from me, and then he turned back.

"You would think so. But . . . your uncle was special . . . different from me. He learned things the first try, better than most folks can after a dozen tries. Why, he could spend a few seconds glancing at a page, and then recite it back to you, grammar corrections and all."

This had me spellbound. I didn't think anyone could be smarter than my dad, and here he was telling me about Uncle Jim.

"Yep, and that's not all. He could hear a tune once and then play it out on the piano, sweetening it with added chords. That's only the beginning of what he could do . . ." Dad sighed. Mother called to us from the car. It was time to get back home. Dad waved. "He felt wonder in just about all he touched. He felt it so much that it wore out his mind."

"Why didn't he rest a spell?—take naps like me."

"If only it could have been that easy for Jim." Dad thought a bit. "Say, do you remember the Inuit story about two men gazing into the night sky?"

I nodded.

"Legend has it they came upon a hole they could climb through to see all of the night sky. The first man crawled up as far as he could. Then, he asked the second man to give him a boost. 'I'll hoist you up as soon as I get firm footing,' he told his companion. Well, when he beheld the night sky, he lost himself in all its wonder and threw himself into the pitch black mystery and the magic of the night, never to return. He'd witnessed an echo of the mind of God!"

"An echo of God's mind? It must have been a horrible racket pounding against that man's head."

"Yes, it hurt a bunch. And you know, I think my brother heard that same echo—that is, until the beauty and noise of it became too much to take. He got tired out and started becoming different people because of it."

"I know what you mean. He starting acting in plays and such, like I do, right?" Dad took my shoulder then stooped down until his eyes were level with mine.

"I don't know if you'll understand this, but he wasn't acting parts of other people. He *became* them. Do you know the way a head of cauliflower is cleaved into its parts, into its flowerettes? That's what his mind did. It split into pieces, each one toting a different person with a different name. The horrifying thing was, they didn't seem to know they were all part of the same person—Uncle Jim."

"Dad—uh—did he become a like a three-headed monster?" Dad pulled me close, "Dear Lord, no. He was as gentle as ever."

"Couldn't the doctors glue his brain back together somehow?"

"They tried, but they didn't understand who he was . . . or that he'd heard an echo of God's mind. They misdiagnosed him. They gave him all sorts of medicines. Sometimes they put electricity through his body."

All I could think of was the electric chair, and that terrified me. I gripped Dad hard.

"Sean, I shouldn't have told you that. The doctors really did mean well." An impatient car horn pierced the air. Dad swiped his right flannel sleeve—or was he dusting off his brother and pain?

"I think I would have liked Uncle Jim."

"Sure you would have."

Afternoon Pool, Evening Picnic

Several times each summer, Mother hollered, "Kids, help me load the station wagon. We're going to the pool!" Party time commenced when we flooded to Wallace Park Pool in Paola, fifteen miles southwest of our farm. Our outings blossomed on Saturdays, seeing as how Dad often had weekends off from the railroad, provided he hadn't signed up on the extra board. Often we capped our swims with an evening picnic, adding tall pleasures to our already considerable adventures. Oh, there were water fights mean enough to drawn a duck and cannon balls powerful enough to pick real fights. Our fiestas stretched lazily from lengthening afternoon shadows into falling evening darkness. Our duet of pool and picnics tickled us all, and Dad was first in line.

Dad carried me on his shoulders, and he toted me around even after I'd grown water-logged and wrinkly. Clinging to him, I wore my pride as surely as folks must have thought he wore me, like a too-eager tree frog that latched onto a man instead of a tree. Often, he held me next to him as he taught me how to swim. "Now, kick and pull your body with your arms straight in front of you. Move your head to one side and breathe," he coached. I'd make it to the side of the pool where I'd gasp and sputter. But I was only pretending. After all, if I learned too quickly, Dad wouldn't need to teach me anymore, and I needed lots of time to lap up his care. (Meanwhile, to soak in the baby pool felt all wrong since I was not a baby—but a big boy!) My swims on return trips to him fared far better.

Dad came alive during those outings. He stood straight up just like a fireweed. His shoulders and back weren't hunched, and his breaths came in long and relaxed draws. Maybe the change lifted his mind, much the way water buoyed his body. Lines in his face eased, and his weary look faded. Dad glistened as he dove into cool waters. All the while, we savored visions of an evening picnic in the park across the way.

Since my siblings knew how to swim, they worked the diving boards and the water slide all afternoon. Sometimes the fun swept them away, and our lifeguard saw fit to banish them from the pool for a whole hour, owing to their illegal high jinks. "Whoever said two kids couldn't leap from the high dive together?" they argued, sans even puny success. Well, "she" said so, and the next time it happened, she'd evict them for good! Never did time move so slowly as when my brothers eyed it waiting for each second to tick toward their time to flood back into the pool.

Watching my brothers and sisters splashing, I wondered how much energy they burned. Who knew how many calories it takes to hold one's breath under water while one counts to sixty? I reached only thirty-five before a powerful urge to surface snatched me. My lungs wanted to explode.

When we weren't splashing, we saved energy for our next underwater bout. I studied the waters, sucking me in the way metal shavings are drawn to a magnet—you know, the powerful kind with red paint on each of two curved hunks of metal. Water drops sparkled in an afternoon sky brilliant with the summer sun. Then, they changed for a moment into liquid prisms. Time slowed, as if everything I eyed moved in super slow motion. If I watched and thought carefully enough, the water drops separated into tiny pear-shapes as they lurched into the air. Weren't those flying drops large and round at the front but long and narrow at the rear, like a tadpole? Maybe the front ends were more eager than the hind ends to hit the pool. Their back sides stretched out lazy tails in flight.

As the drops splashed from the sparkling water, they stretched skyward in a silly path. I fancied guessing where they might land. Usually, I didn't have a clue where they would go or what shape they might take along the way. Weren't all of us kids like those water drops, soaring from the pool on arcs and with shapes and sizes hard to predict? The mystery and wonder of it all felt too grand and wonderful to grasp fully. Somehow, we'd all end up back in the pool with stories to share. In a twinkling, I peered at the pool and kids by squinting between my thumb and index fingers of my right hand. Then, I slowly pinched those two fingers together. Might that somehow swish all of the scenes into one?

Our hunger grew steadily as the sun sank further into the western sky. Near dusk, the aroma of the barbecues being grilled in the park teased at our hunger and reminded us that the afternoon had fled. Our appetites had grown from all that bother and splashing in the pool. We abandoned the pool, seeing as we were more interested in food than water. Besides, by then our fingers looked like prunes stretched over bones! We pushed ourselves to waddle from the pool right before our lifeguard blew her whistle to command, "Everyone out! Pool closes in ten minutes."

You can't imagine how fast we changed from suits into shorts and tee shirts then. On one such evening, Mother's sister Aunt Laura and her husband Jim Ogle stood across the way with their two sons, our cousins Jimmy and Mike. With our grandparents, they had staked out four picnic tables and two grills. Uncle Jim Ogle, Aunt Laura (Mother's only sister), and the boys drove up from Hot Springs, Arkansas for a few days at our grandparents' home. Then, they planned to drive to Kansas City to see Uncle Jim Ogle's folks. While they were in town, we kids could not contain ourselves with all the excitement. They also drove to our farm for an afternoon that stretched into supper. What a wonderfully short time we had to play.

"We must show you everything: our hay barn, the chicken house, the ponds, the pear trees, and the mean gray goose that hissed wickedly, with red eyes and hot breath," I yelped. Of course, our cousins helped us gather the food for our supper. With heaped armloads of sweet corn, we scampered back to our kitchen where Mother, Aunt Laura, and the girls peppered them with a magic that might charge any alchemist enough to writhe with envy. Then, our cousins helped us milk the Jersey cows. We flicked tiny hairs out of the froth, piling up with milky suds that rose inside of our aluminum milk pails.

Cousin Jimmy is two years older than I, and Cousin Mike was born four years after Jimmy, landing me smack in the middle. Naturally, Mike looked to me for ideas, while Jimmy panted to my older brother Mark to lead his fun. I noticed then that boys normally do that, as if he older boy stores a treasure of secrets to share.

We took turns wrestling with one another on the lawn. Often, we brought home emerald stains from all of our horseplay. Mother was not pleased, seeing as how those stains meant more work for her.

Aunt Laura waited with iced, vine-ripened watermelon that brimmed with sweetness. Its crimson flesh was sprinkled in sharp contrast with jet black seeds hidden within for spitting fun. Grandfather had tucked under his arm the tightly wrapped sack holding a half gallon tub of vanilla ice cream from the Main Street Dairy Queen. As I ran to greet him, his lips commenced to move even before he spoke, as if he needed to prime them for action.

Grandfather was at least as partial to vanilla ice cream from the Dairy Queen as he was to all of us. He had assigned himself to the ice cream detail to ensure we had enough to finish off the peach cobblers, which Mom had stashed in the rear of our white Pontiac station wagon. She'd made two cobblers of fresh peaches from the bounty we gathered the past afternoon at a widow's orchard. Mrs. Strosser let us climb a ladder to pull a few peaches off the trees to taste their splendor. Then, she warned us, "Don't climb the ladders for any more fruit! That's risky work, best done by someone who really knows how to handle a ladder in a fruit orchard."

I told her Dad's father had run an apple orchard on top of handling a full-time medical practice, and we held a real talent when it came to handling ladders and fruit trees. Mrs. Strosser wasn't impressed.

Following her into the shed, which smelled too sweet to be real, we saw where she stored the pecks and bushels of fruit arranged in neat rows all along the sides of her storeroom. The fruit rested there, shaded and much cooler than outside. She told Mom, "I pick only what I'm able to sell within the week. Then, I don't risk spoiling fruit. The peaches taste better fresh, anyhow."

Mother had bought a full bushel of those golden peaches, which was enough to make about a dozen huge cobblers with some left for all of us sticky-fingered kids to munch. Aunt Laura and Grandmother had pattied out hamburgers spiced with chopped onions and other secret ingredients before she lined them up on waxed paper. With nine patties per sheet, there were at least three sheets to grill. Sizzling burgers on the grill wafted aromas to melt in the mouth. We topped them with all the fixings: tangy cucumbers garnished with white onions and tomatoes right off of our vines.

For starters, we smeared that red watermelon into our faces, flushed with excitement and exercise. Then, we competed to see who could spew the seeds the farthest. As we shot black watermelon seeds out of its red flesh, our oldest brother Paul helped Uncle Jim tend to the fire. Paul had grown enamored by fire, as fascinated as a moth is by flames. I had watched him gazing into the flames in our trash burner on the farm. They mesmerized him, and I thought he must be in a different world when he tended fire. He often tended the flames, and they cast a spell over him. His left eye began twitching as he stared right into the flames, hooking him. When he entered his trance, I imagined he was in a world unknown to any of us mortals who didn't appreciate fire as fervently.

We plopped the corn wrapped in aluminum foil onto the edges of the fire. Isn't there something special about the flavor of corn on the cob roasted on a barbecue? The ears tasted better that way, each kernel exploding with luscious sweetness. Corn on the cob glistening with butter and a dusting of spices could not have tasted better. Corn wrapped with butter, pickled cucumbers, sizzling hamburgers, and iced cold watermelon could have done in any appetite overflowing from a day of pool pleasures. The peach cobbler ale mode put us over the top.

Even before all of those courses, my cousin Jimmy found a bunch of trouble with the corn. He had seen a cartoon with a horse sitting at a desk. The horse devoured corn on the cob with a speed and rhythm mimicking an expert typist. Jimmy gobbled the kernels from left to right, and then he spitted to sound the word "ding" as he finished his row. Gleefully, he pulled the ear back to the left side to start another line. Each time he shouted "ding" gobs of kernels flew out of his stuffed mouth. His exploits felt funny, but his dad disagreed. After a few lines of that nonsense, Uncle Jim Ogle swatted him upside his head. "Behave! Why are you acting like a little jackass, Jimmy? Sit down over there and cool off!" (Some letdown for Jimmy, who had been yanked out of the limelight.) It's true he had been wasting most of the kernels, but it's also true that he was drunk with laughter, just as we all were.

With the sun setting in the west, twilight in that park took on a life of its own. There were quick games of starlight star bright, with each of us scurrying about to keep from being tagged by the ghost. For those who made it back to base without being tagged, the next round became even more scary and intense because the ones who had been tagged joined the side of the ghosts. With worsened odds of making it back to base again on the next round without being tagged, the dwindling number of survivors made later rounds with racing hearts and pounding breath.

As I recall these outings, I wonder whether Our Maker will ask us one day to explain why we did not grab every one of these pleasures and hold onto them like a snapping turtle grasps its dinner in its beak. On that question, I reckon our family will all score the highest possible, provided the subject is limited to summer afternoons in the Wallace Park Pool and summer evening picnics in the park.

Finally, a bit of peach cobbler dessert dazzled our taste buds. Mother's peach cobbler creation topped off a picnic with homemade flavors not found in supermarkets. We crowned the cobbler with a scoop of vanilla ice-cream, capping our glorious afternoon that stretched into evening drowsiness. After ice cream I often melted. I couldn't stay awake for our drive home after those evening picnics. Had I been drugged? The next thing I knew I awakened on my bed at out farm, about fifteen miles northeast of the park. After all, water sports and picnics during lazy days of summer are tiring shenanigans that call for serious rest.

Flower Gardens, Allspice, and Rocket Ships

I can't say how many times Mother's "quick visit" to her parents' white clapboard home in Osawatomie blossomed into all-day events. Well, I can't say that I blame her much either, for their home invited us to while away most of any day. You see Grandfather John and Grandmother Cloddie Kearney meant flower gardens and allspice, which revved up my imagination! With thoughts soaring, I wondered about hitching a ride on a rocket ship as it blasted into orbit.

I couldn't decide if all of those flowers smelled better than Grandmother's kitchen. One day the kitchen won, while other days the garden eked out a victory. Memories of Mother's childhood home are awash in swirls of colors and scents inside the kitchen and in their garden.

At those "all-day" events, I could *not* understand how Mother and her parents found so much to talk about. They began with the usual subjects: updates of classmates and longtime friends, what Mother's baby sister Laura Lee had done, and the latest news of my siblings, all of them older than me. There were reports of school work and of church activities, of summer socials, and of First Fridays. Then came the more serious stuff—financial and personal. While I kept only half an ear tuned to the doings, I recall fusses about crop prices and failures. Then, I listened with both ears wide open. In my grandparents' living room I first heard that ugly word "bankruptcy". I also heard "wage-earner's bankruptcy". Those were grown-up words—worrisome words—which I didn't like. I much preferred listening to Grandfather rattle off names of every flower and vine in his garden.

Grandfather knew both the "common" and the "Latin" names, which sounded strange enough not to be real. (People had sputtered about how Latin was a "dead language", and that Catholic Masses would be spoken in English. How odd that all of his living wonders had names from something long dead!) Was there some connection between life and death, between a dead language with funny names and Grandfather's living masterpieces?

Grandfather needed a bunch of time to tend to all of his plants—
including their proper names. Time he had, given his lengthy retirement.

First and foremost, Grandfather grew gladioluses. I spied yellow,
orange, chartreuse, purple, white, and pink glads. He set out red ones
next to blue ones, which left my head spinning. One variety was the
color of newly spun comb honey! Glad stalks towered above most of the
other flowers, pouting in reply. Grandfather tended day lilies and tiger
lilies of yellows, oranges, and browns. One variety sported stripes,
reminding me of the snarling large cat in whose honor it was named. It's
true he doted on his delphiniums with their long stalks crowned by
spindly blossoms of blue. But mostly, he favored roses: Queen Elizabeth
pink and Mister Lincoln red, for starters. And he worked on a hybrid of
his own named after Grandmother. One morning I overheard his plans
to grow a new rose that he might name after Aunt Laura Lee. That
seemed right, seeing how she lived far away—probably in Hollywood—
and looked like a star! Her color 8 by 10 photograph—the one with her
off-the-shoulder gown of taffeta—hinted of celebrity. Had she worked in
the movies? Was it Aunt Laura we had adored in "National Velvet"?
My grandparents hid her photo in the back closet next to the shoe rack
where Grandmother tucked her package of Camel cigarettes. (She knew
I'd snooped.) I reckoned they hid Aunt Laura's photograph in order that
my family might not feel poorly by comparison.

Grandfather's roses towered over me on vines higher than my head—
much higher than the gladioluses. As I peered up at them, beams of sunshine twitched through the vines, heavily ladened with morning dew or
sprinkles from a shower.

Curiosity gripped me as I followed Grandfather into the shed where
he worked on grafts. With a razor-sharp knife, he sliced at the roots of a
rose bush, teasing out a wedge. Then, a slice of another root went into
the empty space to form something new! I don't know if my eyes played
tricks on me, but that's what I saw. You'll excuse me, as I was barely
four years old at the time.

Grandfather also grew partial to petunias that he set out in beds lining
his driveway: petunias of salmon and cherry, of fuchsia and pink, of
lavender and grape. I dubbed him the "King of Hibiscus", seeing how he
coaxed 10-inch blossoms from his tropical Kansas paradise. He knew
better than most how to tease blossoms to their full span. (I'll never forget the way he could add two inches to any blossom at will.) Although a
hibiscus scrunches together in a kind of cone at night, in the morning
they have their day! They reminded me of Morning Glories, and he grew
gobs of those, too.

Naturally, Grandfather raised irises, especially the bearded kind with the fuzzy-looking insides. Was that a blue caterpillar I saw crawling in there? Heck no, that was an iris beard! He even crafted a hybrid that he named after Grandmother Kearney. And he shared in his wealth, often letting us grandchildren enter his flowers in the Miami County Fair. More often than not, our entries won blue, red, or even purple ribbons! Those colors couldn't compare with the wondrous hues that nature and Grandfather conspired to create.

Grandfather knew everything about his flowers. He knew what soil was best for which ones. He knew when and how deep to plant them. Like a sailor with his nautical charts, Grandfather scribbled dates and strange sounding names on his papers. Did he learn that in the Missouri-Pacific depot where he worked as the chief clerk? He'd tracked trains and their cars on charts, hadn't he?

Grandfather navigated his garden with calendars and schedules—with graphs and formulas. Were his swirls of soils for his homegrown palette all guided by his timetables? I reckon they reminded him of when to set out bulbs, when to fertilize, and when to water. Back issues of *The Farmer's Almanac* rested in drawers in the tool shed. Graced with success, Grandfather conceded only that "hard work" had crafted his garden . . . *and* his lily pond. I suspected that something else was afoot, something wonderful!

Grandfather dug his pond deep enough to discourage ornery raccoons, opossums, cats, or polecats from fishing out his orange koi (or goldfish) for supper. Come winter, he moved them into the garage and the hallway leading to the back room, sparing them from bitingly cold Kansas winters.

Upon seeing that he didn't use lids on the buckets of koi, I sputtered, "Why don't you cover them with wax paper or something?"

"Now, why in the Sam Hill would I do that?"

"To protect them from varmints! Something might nab them."

"Like raccoons?"

"Yes, sir!"

"Come now. Raccoons in the garage? Your grandmother would never stand for that. Wax paper wouldn't help much, anyhow. Besides, the fish need to breathe, don't they?"

"Well, yes. I mean I thought they breathed water through their gills. But maybe they are really breathing air through their gills, right?"

"Yes, they are. Even when koi are drowsing, they need air. Well, not air, but oxygen in the air. Remember that."

"Yes, sir. And covering them with wax paper might cut off their air, er . . . oxygen . . . Right?"

"Now you've got it."

I smiled and stood on my tiptoes next to Grandfather. Whenever I got things right, I felt like I'd grown, and I wanted to show him as much.

Every spring Grandfather toted the koi back to the lily pond to pick up where they left off the past fall. Stunned koi floated near the bottom of the pool. At first they protested a rude awakening from wintertime slumbers. Soon, they commenced to explore the hollows in the stones that lined the pond. They nibbled on mosses: appetizers for springtime snacks.

Grandmother had claims on the garden, too. But, after her leg amputation following a blood clot in it from her cancer operation, she focused on houseplants. Tending African violets and Boston ferns, she made sure they thrived. Naturally, they did, as had her two daughters.

Occasionally, Mother left me with my grandparents while she ran here and there on errands. This left me all alone to "wonder" through Grandfather's garden and to steep in Grandmother's cooking. (I know, I know . . . It was a tough assignment, but I found the courage, somehow.) Usually, Mother dropped me off after lunch. There sat Grandfather and Grandmother relaxing in the yard or at the kitchen table. They cradled cups of freshly-brewed coffee as they speculated on the weather or what flower bed to tend next. (Dad let me sip coffee once, and I found out its rich smell is far better than is its bitter taste).

Well, after they were through resting, Grandfather usually invited me into the garden with him. Of course, I never passed up such a chance. The funny thing was, every time I walked through Grandfather's blooming garden, I craved peanut butter and honey sandwiches—folded over, one slice per sandwich. I needed a few more years and hundreds of trips to his garden to cure my craving for honey-scented flowers (or, more correctly, for flower-scented honey).

Sometimes, Grandfather went his own way, leaving me to be teased by Grandmother. "Sean, I have something simmering on the stove, and I need your opinion." One August I innocently followed her into the kitchen. I was nearly knocked over by an intoxicating aroma from her "secret" cooking project.

"Sean, what do you think? Is there enough cinnamon and sugar in this batch? Is it spotty with allspice?" she inquired, pulling a stainless steel slotted spoon from her drawer. She waited expectantly while I toted a chair over to stand upon so that I might reach the stove. Then, I hovered as I ever-so-carefully dipped my spoon into her cauldron of mystery. Before I could even swallow, Grandmother offered, "I thought so, too," and then she shooed me off of the chair so that she could doctor up her concoction. Even though she had asked for my advice, I knew the final word on spices belonged to Grandmother Cloddie.

Jonathan apple trees lined two sides of my grandparents' property.

Grandmother delighted in tart green apples, doctored with gobs of white sugar to make applesauce. She fine-tuned her recipe based on the tart-ness of those apples. In her battle, she drew on an arsenal of powders smelling of allspice and of cinnamon stashed around the kitchen. She relied on them liberally. Often, she used a lemon zest! One day she measured a dark colored liquid from a mysterious flask.

"This will spark the batch with some encouragement to taste finer," she whispered over her steaming kettle.

Creeping near enough to catch a whiff of that liquid, I turned up my nose. "Grandmother, that's medicine," I whispered.

"No, it's rum. Shhh, don't tell." She glanced over each shoulder, as if she were a spy who aimed not to be nabbed with forbidden truck and government secrets.

Hmm . . . rum. "Yo-ho-ho, and a bottle of rum. Dead men tell no tales!" I know, pirates! And ships bearing secret treasure chests from ports of call unknown! And . . . I became so lost in my search for sunken treasure that I began to paw at the doors underneath her sink, as if they were the forward windows on a Spanish galleon.

I must have appeared to be a poor risk to keep her secret, seeing how she huffed innocently, "Sean, let your conscience be your guide. But, you really don't need to tell anyone about our little secret, do you? Okay, honey?"

Was she "funning" me? Of course, I didn't ask, for fear she might think I was dimwitted or such. Nodding politely, I agreed to hush up for a spell. Her delicious applesauce surely held our secret well, and no one was the wiser.

Scents of stews and casseroles, of salmon or meat loaves fortified with Saltine crackers, of shepherd's pies, and of pot roasts spiced her kitchen with tempting flavors. I still don't know which made my mouth water more: was it Grandmother's kitchen or Grandfather's beguiling, honey flowers?

The kitchen was home to a pale pink oblong table that folded down from the wooden cabinet. Its carved leaves and rose patterns couldn't equal Grandfather's prized roses. The table, combined with the rose-pat-tern bone china on the top shelf, led me to believe the kitchen was a place of overlap with the garden. My grandparents sat sipping freshly-brewed coffee there from rose-pattern bone china cups as they laid their plans for rose garden lollapaloozas!

With so many plants surrounding their one-story white frame house, I wondered if the temperature there was a smidgen cooler than it was across the street. Knowing his hobby would grow, Grandfather bought the lot south of the house. He crafted it into a showplace, evincing his expertise.

With applesauce season in the summer, springtime was the season for the flowers to awaken. I smiled at the crocuses. Those beds later framed summertime marigolds and snapdragons on the driveway next to the kitchen window. On the south side of the driveway (bordering the extra lot) stood rows of petunias and daffodils. Petunias in full bloom made me drunk on their sweetness, drowsing me to sleep. Dreams followed.

But not all was sweetness. The words "bankruptcy"and "wage-earner's bankruptcy" kept sprouting up when Mother visited in the early afternoon. I felt there were better subjects, and indeed there were! One day just before Mother and I left my grandparents' home, we caught live coverage of a Mercury space mission. The rocket would blast into orbit from that launch pad at Cape Canaveral!

"Just how fast will that rocket fly, Grandfather?" I asked.

"Faster than anything you know, perhaps faster than a speeding bullet."

"Super! Just like superman, huh?"

"What . . . ? Oh, I suppose."

"But how fast is that?" I persisted, seeing how generalities never did me proud.

"If the rocket travels 3,000 miles per hour, that is fast enough to fly to your farm in about thirty seconds. That's half of a minute. Does that answer your question?"

Stunned, I replied, "Yes sir! That covers it!" Wow, who could believe it? The Mercury rocket can reach our farm twenty-five miles away within thirty seconds. That was way far: past the county seat! In those days the highways were not great, although they far outranked our dirt roads. Usually only blacktops, the highways were smooth. When I rode in my grandparents' new Impala on our rutted dirt roads, it felt as smooth as riding in our rickety station wagon over those blacktops. Although nothing to brag about, when Mother gunned our station wagon, it cranked to forty-five mph along longer highway stretches. Most of the time I wanted to roll down the window to let the breeze sweep through my hair. I knew better, though, and I never went further than thoughts of such fun.

At least one time each trip home, I froze. That was when we neared the hairpin turn called "Dead Man's Curve" midway between my grandparents' home and the county seat. That turn left me white-knuckling our dashboard! What if Mother went too fast, spun out, and crashed? Our tires might slide and then pitch us into the ditch. We'd be goners, just like the others! (There had been six deaths from crashes there during the past two years alone.)

"Careful, Mother!" I sputtered.

"I'm always careful. Now sit still."

"All right, but slow down on Dead Man's Curve. I'm in the car, you know!"

"What difference does that make?"

"That curve kills men, but it also kills big boys! In case you haven't noticed, I am one. So watch it!"

"I see . . . Advice well taken."

Mother slowed for "The Curve". She also stopped completely at railroad crossings to wait for slowpoke trains creeping along at less than 5 mph. It wasn't the engineer's fault. If he clattered any faster, a section of loose track might wiggle free to derail his train. Caution was needed most, and that meant mighty slow-going. Even after the trains passed, the list of errands that Mother toted stretched on lazily with ease to slow our trip even more, as did our occasional car trouble. That was a too-frequent hazard of old cars. With all of our delays, driving back to our farm usually gobbled the better part of an afternoon. In fact, we usually ran late picking up the kids from school—even if we left our grandparents' home early in the afternoon.

"Let me get this straight," I mused. "The Mercury rocket travels a distance in thirty seconds that our car takes most of the afternoon to travel—allowing for side trips and problems." Of course, that was less time than we took to back out of my grandparents' driveway. Sometimes, Mother took at least 5 minutes to back out of our grandparents' driveway. There were farewells and last minute messages, which meant a few more waves to cap off the fun. Draped over Grandfather's head rested a white terry cloth towel moistened to guard against sunburn.

Thirty seconds! Each time we backed out of their driveway, I counted to thirty, monitoring our progress by spying the number of day lilies we passed that skirted the south side of the driveway. Usually, we crept by only a dozen or so plants, and I'd memorized the location and color of each one. From my special viewpoint as I peered over the front passenger door to spy the blossoms below, thirty seconds seemed like a powerfully short time.

After we left the driveway and headed through town, I spotted the trestle bridge over the Marias des Cygnes River which ran parallel to the county road. The Missouri-Pacific line used that bridge on the northeast corner of town, and the builders made it high enough to avoid flooding. Even so, the river flooded only about once every 5 years or so. The past spring had been one of those times, and I remember people fussed about how the tracks had been covered and how the town had been cut off for over a week. The only way into and out of town had been with rowboats. When I saw people in rowboats floating around town, I gasped, "Do you think they're escaping from the State Hospital, Mother?"

Mother worked there, and she had told me of a man who had escaped one night. The sheriff tracked him with baying bloodhounds. He was considered dangerous because the sheriff claimed the man killed his brother. But he didn't go to a regular jail. His mind was not right, so he lived in the state hospital in Osawatomie instead. Mother spied my troubled look. "What an imagination! Now, honestly, settle down."

That normally peaceful and slow-moving river with swans floating down it had became a favorite fishing spot or playground for young and old alike. A few times each year the town had smaller floods which were not as serious because the river had not covered the tracks on the trestle bridge. If the water covered the tracks, that meant most of the town had flooded. Otherwise, the damage was not too severe, and only a few folks used rowboats to leave their home for higher ground.

After we passed the trestle bridge, Mother raced the car to about 45 mph. A sturdy bridge of concrete and steel for cars and trucks ran parallel to the trestle bridge. "Sean, strong and patient men finished this bridge in 1930 to give farmers a way to take their carts to market. In fact, this one is called the "Creamery Bridge." My playmates and their fathers rattled wagons filled with milk and cream to market over that bridge."

I pictured all of the farms and mailboxes, the bridges and silos, and the cattle and the goats we'd pass as we wended our way home. I thought about the damaged cement posts lining the county seat bridge with its rusted rebar showing through them, and I remembered the single span wooden bridge over the creek that flowed southwest through our county. It's wooden planked lip on the north end shot cars airborne for a second. Each car plopped down onto the gravel road after a few yards. Such fun!

I pictured the county seat and its 1890 courthouse, except in my world I saw horses clattering their wagons and buggies. Wheels hummed over the cobbled streets. I pictured the local airstrip and the silos. I saw the stone-lined wells with wooden cranks. Then, I dwelt on the row of catfish heads mounted on the fence posts near the turn for our farm. I thought of the tree lazily growing in the abandoned and rusted silo. All of those familiar sights and landmarks flashed.

Then, I drifted to imagine those swans floating gracefully down the Marias des Cygnes River that flowed near our grandparents' home. All of these images flashed as if I spied them from a low-flying airplane that had groaned aloft from our county's airstrip. I saw all of the people scattered on farms and in towns all along the way back to our farm. Then, one more thought pounded:

"A Mercury rocket travels fast enough to pass all of those and more in less time than it takes us to back out of Grandfather's driveway—in less time that it takes us to pass a dozen day lilies as our car creeps and then pauses in their driveway." That idea and the smell of those flowers have remained with me all of these years. It seemed too incredibly fast to be true!

Just in case I hadn't heard correctly the first time, I asked again about the Mercury rocket. "Grandfather, please tell me. Just how fast is that fool rocket anyway?" I pawed at the carpet with my left foot to trace lines nervously in it.

Whenever Grandfather peered up at me with squinted eyes and pursed lips, I knew he'd grown weary of answering my repeated questions. "It's faster than a speeding bullet, which means it can reach the farm in half a minute," he sighed in frustration.

It seemed too fast to be true, although in my guts I knew it to be so. The rocket was unlike anything else I knew. "Most things were pretty slow moving down here on earth," I thought. "That includes cars backing out of driveways, rowboats on water, and swans floating down rivers."

As I finished that thought, I spotted a puff of white fluff wafting in the air next to our car. It was late May, and cottonwood had begun to spread their seed. In the ditch next to the road I spied several small purple flowers."

They are thistles," Mother had told me. "They will form thistledown in June, and that will puff away into the fields and meadows."

"Most things move slowly down here on earth, and that goes for thistledown, too," I thought. Thistledown moves slowly down here on earth as it hunts for a place to call home. It's mighty choosey.

"Thistledown is not like Mercury rockets," I imagined. It makes up in patience and in hope for what rockets have in speed.

Suddenly a thought dawned on me. Maybe Mercury rockets are not as splendid as I imagined. Maybe, just maybe, thistledown was more marvelous than I rerckoned. The sight of those cottony puffs of fluff and the gentle rocking of the car drowsed me to sleep that afternoon as Mother gunned the car to forty-five miles an hour and headed for the farm. All of those thoughts had tuckered me out, and thoughts of drifting thistledown in June lulled me to sleep.

The trip to the farm seemed shorter that afternoon. Sleep has a way of making it so.

Train Ride West

"Now, don't you fret a pinch, Mrs. Redmond," Mr. William Knuckle's words leaked from our kitchen. At 6:30 a.m. on a Thursday in July, the kids were out of school, and Mother and I were the only ones stirring. "Every morning and every night we'll be sure to feed and water your goats, chickens, cows, and sheep."

"That's fine. And you'll milk the cows and goats at dawn and dusk?" Mr. Knuckle nodded. Mother pointed to several dozen empty egg cartons she'd set on the floor next to the kitchen door. "Fill these with our eggs; they'll store all right in our porch refrigerator. Take what you need as partial trade for what we'll owe on your work. How does seventy-five cents a dozen sound?"

Mr. Knuckle glanced toward the ceiling.

"Some of the eggs are double-yolked. I'm offering a fair price."

Mr. Knuckle dropped his eyes back down to look at Mother. He nodded agreement.

"The chickens roost at eight, and you'll need to gather the eggs before you close up their shed for the night."

"Sure. Mrs. Redmond, you're covered."

"And about the garden, I-"

"Right, we'll water your garden every other day—whether it needs it, or not. Point me to the hose and nozzles, and consider it done."

Mark and Paul walked into the room for breakfast. Jean and Julie followed suit.

Before we moved to our farm, Mr. Knuckle had farmed our half section in exchange for a third of the crop. Dad kept that arrangement, seeing as how it made more sense to rent machinery rather than to buy it.

We kids finished our breakfast of oatmeal, scrambled eggs, buttered toast, and fresh milk while Mother pulled a ten-page list (well, maybe two) out of her dress pocket. She proceeded to recite the day's chores.

"Mow the lawn and terrace, fill the cistern, and buy Purina Chows at the feed store. Make sandwiches. Oh, the chickens need calcium since their eggshells have been spongy lately. Buy a twenty-pound bag of crushed oyster shells. Finish packing. Best buy a mineral block, too. Mum cow has been poking around her feed box for it. Questions?" We couldn't afford to raise any. "Good, let's get started."

And so began our day. First we fed, watered, and milked the cows. Paul and Jean commenced mowing, while Mark and I filled the cistern. Ann plopped two briskets into the oven and cranked it up to 400 degrees. Then Dad, Ann, and I hightailed it to the feed store in town. We drove home by way of Donner's Drive-in. Ann insisted on her stead-fast slurp of Dr. Pepper poured over crushed ice and flavored with two hefty squirts of cherry syrup—her "usual". She acted like she owned that drink, her own recipe fizzing iced cherry delights higher than any-one thought possible.

Once home, we trudged into the house to find Mother on the phone with Mrs. Knuckle. "Brenda, I meant to warn you about the black snakes that slithered into our chicken shed last week. They plundered eggs—swallowed them whole." Mother listened for a spell and then said, "Thanks, but I don't need them killed, only moved. Someone will leave a couple of gunnysacks for you to tote them to the ditch." Mother listened intently, replying, "No, Brenda, they're not poisonous. If you're feeling nervous about getting too near them, I'm sure William will help you." Mother motioned for Ann and me to draw closer. Then, she covered the phone's mouthpiece. "Jean and Mark are mowing. Go spell them." (Even though it was July, a time when dusty winds blossomed to suck traces of wetness from the soil, native grasses and weeds took no heed. They pouted in ditches, sprinkled with dust.) Mother focused on Mrs. Knuckle, "Yes, their slithering sight startles me, too. But please don't kill them."

Of course, we all knew that polecats (skunks) and opossums were a different story. We had no choice but to kill any that even dared traipse near our chicken shed. They didn't limit themselves to egg hunts. No, they grew partial to chickens at night—fresh on their roost. Polecats and opossums fancied gnawing breasts of horrified fowl. They ate them alive. A chicken in darkness often won't move even while being eaten. (Were they more frightened of scurrying in darkness than they were of being eaten alive?) Dad and I had chased down an opossum last week, and it had hissed at us to show its razor sharp teeth still dripping with blood. Its victim's body lay warm on the straw-lined floor inside the chicken shed. Acting like a vampire, it went further. Not contented with sucking blood, it gnawed the victim's flesh to kill it. I never understood why the hens didn't make a ruckus and run away. Did they aim to pro-tect their eggs?

One by one we crossed off chores on Mother's list until at last we came to "sandwiches", and make them we did: ten dozen. We'd need at least that many to see us through Kansas, Colorado, New Mexico, Arizona, and into California.

Firing up our assembly line, Ann took command. She sliced briskets with a fervor that made any electric meat slicer appear sluggish by comparison. Mother and I slapped sandwiches together. We plopped slices of brisket between two slices of bread. Then, we wrapped each sandwich in waxed paper that Julie had cut into measured squares. By twilight we were finished—with the sandwiches that is. There were plenty of last minute packing details, and distractions left us half dazed.

Paul searched our wooden toy box closeted in the storage room under our stairs. He had designs on my white play dough to fashion a map to record our route. He rubbed his hands together over the prospect of a U.S. map of clay. Ann sent us kids to fetch sturdy shoes for hiking Southern California hills. Through the mayhem I sputtered, "Do you reckon we'll spot Lucille Ball? I'm toting my autograph book, just in case."

The first wave (we'd take two cars to the station)—Dad, Janice, Mary, Mark and Jean—started down the driveway just before evening chores. Dad and his crew planned to grab a few books from the Kansas City Public Library for reading on the train. They promised to hold a spot in Union Station for us (near the escalator at our train's gate).

The second wave—Mother, Ann, Julie, Paul and I—finished fussing over sandwiches and packing by about 7 o'clock. Mr. Knuckle tended the cows and chickens. Then, we locked our farmhouse doors and bolted.

At 10 o'clock on a hill overlooking the train station, I spotted a huge knife slicing a gigantic loaf of "freshly" baked golden-brown bread. Wispy lines wavered over it to show it was still warm—a loaf of Manor Bread. It reminded me that I'd grown powerful hungry from the day's chores. Might that colossal knife also slice through the night air to help cut the smell of diesel fumes? Years later, developers built the Westin Crown Center Hotel there. In fact, its atrium fountain is framed by the bedrock on which the sign stood.

Pulling up to Union Station was like pulling alongside another planet, or at least to the space station where I fancied Dorothy and the Scarecrow flew to do battle with the witch. Even though it flew miles high overhead, that spinning world became my "Red River Valley" which meant home. I'd grown partial to the song bearing that name. Activity hummed, bloating the evening air as taxis whisked passengers curbside. Pulsating amber and white lights framed and highlighted signs with eerie shadows. The oversized station clock—a metal all-day sucker with all of its raspberry swirls missing—stood near the front door. It told passengers how soon conductors might shrill, "Alll abbooarrddd."

We had two hours to wait for our Chicago train to arrive for our westward voyage. Taking my hand to lead me into the station, Mother said, "People aren't riding trains as much as they did when I was your age. More and more people are riding airplanes, and the railroads have shut down a few routes. This place isn't as busy as it use to be."

Although I didn't know what to do as I stepped into the great hall, I felt dazed by what swelled in front of me. A sea of fabric swayed. Swirls of gray and brown, tints of white and red, and shades of orange and pink blurred. When Paul showed me his new box of crayons the past fall, I pointed to a crayon. "What color is that?"

"Pink, a girl's color. It's not for boys."

Studying the crowd, I spotted two girls and one woman in pink. Paul was right—no men in pink. The woman wore a half-finished fuchsia blouse, one on which she'd forgotten to fasten some buttons. She'd smeared layers of blood-red lipstick over her lips until they crusted. Crimson blotches sweltered on her overly rouged cheeks. She spoke loudly, and in between sentences she puffed on a cigarette hard—and I mean hard. Shaking her head, Mother sighed. Did she disapprove of that woman's smoking, her makeup, her dress, or all of the above?

Some people wore smooth fabrics, while others wore nappy and itchy-looking ones. We passed a man who wore a "shiny" suit. Tugging at Mother's hand, I whispered, "What's sewn into his suit?"

"Silk. Tiny worms weave it."

"Magical worms? Where do they live? Anywhere near Lawrence of Arabia? Did those worms see Marco Polo in The Orient? Did the worms smell like spices?" I gasped.

"No, they live in cocoons on black mulberry trees."

She had to be funning me, seeing as how we had a patch of mulberry trees. I'd spent my share of time in them, enough time to stain my fingers purple-blue from berries. Heck, I hadn't seen any such worms spinning fancy threads. Maybe they crafted silk only around rich people, not around those who couldn't afford it. After all, it had to take eons to make enough silk for such a suit, and that meant it must be costly.

"Do you think he's a silent movie star?" We were long past him, and he said nothing.

"Who, that man? I doubt it. We *are* in Missouri, you know."

I'd lost my head for a spell, which my sisters had done for weeks. Fussing with the supper dishes, they'd suddenly pat each other on the back. On cue, one cocked her head to the side, muttering, "California?"

The other sighed, "Yes," swishing her hand across her forehead. "Yes, take me there. Take me home. Please, dear Lord, sweep me away. Bathe me in rose-scented milk."

"Overacting," I mumbled to myself.

Mark, on the other hand, figured himself fit to correct them. "When you're reciting your lines on stage or when you're being photographed, you must throw your head back. Your chin shows up better that way. Do it, and movie directors will take notice."

"Like, you would know?" Mary asked, her hands planted on her hips.

"That's what Liz Taylor did, and she's a big star! So yes, I know. What the hell would you know?" Mark had been squirming and rattling on and on about California and Hollywood for all of my life. He'd set his heart on being in "pictures" before anyone knew enough to calm him down.

A magnificent clock dangled from the great hall's 60-foot ceiling. Its numbers had to be as large as I was, and I was a big boy. Dazzling! Diesel fumes oozed right on through the hubbub, through the endless tide of people and clothing. Were those waves unstoppable? Were they roaring shapes, sizes, and numbers? Aiming to keep track of people, I fixed on a half dozen or so as they scuffled toward a gate, gift shop, rest room, or restaurant. But the waves of people ebbed and grew, and then they ebbed once again. They formed an inland sea, one that breathed and twitched. Excited dreams sounded of distant places, misting tales of far-off voyages. Might such a blur of people hold dreams too numerous to list? Even if each person cradled only one dream, I couldn't keep track of them, seeing as how those folks kept right on moving.

Gate 10 lay just ahead, and that meant only three more gates before we reached the entrance to the ride of my life. What a ride it would be! "Allll abbbooooaarrrd!" meant my family would spend two weeks prowling the routes used during the heyday of train travel. The Atchison, Topeka, and Santa Fe Railroad (AT&SF) owned and operated the track. Working for them, Dad earned free passes on any AT&SF route for all of us.

Dad and I had made a trip the prior week to the Santa Fe freight offices in Argentine, Kansas to renew his rail pass and to schedule our trip. In the front office men wore starched white shirts. They handled train scheduling and routing. Ceiling fans twirled, and typewriters clattered. I mistook a man typing near a window for Grandfather. But then I remembered he'd retired from his post as head clerk for the Missouri Pacific Railroad a few years before I was born.

Leaving the office, I felt my mind churning. We were bound for The Grand Canyon. Then, we'd board a night train to California where a bunch of stars lived, not to mention Knott's Berry Farm, Disneyland, and San Diego with its mammoth zoo! And San Clemente! There we'd rent cabins and spend a few days swimming and fishing from the San Clemente pier. Would I hear waves crashing on the beach during high tide? I wondered if I'd be able to taste the salty air as day drifted into night, the sea mists tiptoeing over sandy shores.

Hundreds of people swam or floated to make that "sea" inside of Union Station. Would it end someday? I asked Mother, "Do numbers hold strength?"

Keeping up her pace, Mother shot me a startled look of, "What are you asking?"

"Could this crowd live forever?" I asked.

Mother smiled. "This is just a bunch of people. Everyone will eventually die, and new people will be born to take their places."

Do crowds ever die? If they keep replacing members (by filling the spot of an old man, say, with a boy), then they might live forever in a way. If someone died recently, maybe I took his place. Who will replace me one day?

While I was nursing that thought, Mother, Ann, Janice, Julie, and I reached Gate 13. Mark and Paul were waiting for us. "What took so long?" Mark chirped. Dad and the rest of them had hightailed it to a gift shop.

In front of me stood smoothly varnished benches. Each one invited travelers to sit for a spell. A motionless man, as if slouched under some kind of a weight, sat there alone. The bench dwarfed him, as if it was too long, stretching far enough to hold most of our family. How could someone be alone in a place brimming with people? He needed company.

"The girls and I are going to check on the luggage," Mother said. "Sean, don't go anywhere. In fact, why don't you sit right here so your brothers can keep an eye on you. Paul and Mark, don't let him out of your sight."

That old man's solitary nature nipped at me. It tugged at me like a gigantic hand, one misty but also sturdy enough to reel me in on a line. In an instant, I stood in front of him.

"Hello, Mister. I'm Sean. Are you waiting for the Santa Fe Chief?" I began, hoisting myself up next to him.

He didn't answer at first. Was my chirping only an echo that interfered with his thoughts? Finally, my words registered, and his eyes trained down to mine.

"Oh—no. Not me. I'm headed to Lincoln on the Union Pacific line. The name's Jansen—John Jansen.

Mark and Paul squirmed up next to me.

"What's in Lincoln? Friends?" I asked.

"Only a couple. I live south of Kansas City now."

"Then what's in Lincoln?"

Paul elbowed me. "Sean," he said.

"No, it's okay. My father's there. I mean, he was there. He died on Tuesday."

"We're taking a two-week trip," I announced. Paul and Mark nodded. "How long's your trip?"

"I'll bury him on Saturday, and then I'll head back to Kansas City Sunday afternoon."

"What's the rush? Why not rest in Lincoln for a spell?" Mr. Jansen's face was drawn with weary lines. Those lines made him look almost too old to have a living father. In fact, he looked old enough that I guessed he must be nearly Grandfather's age. I was wrong.

"There's nothing to keep me there. I'm his only relative. Besides, I must work on Monday, and I can't stay away from my wife and kids any more than a few days."

"How many kids?"

"Two girls."

"Why can't they come along?"

"Too young."

"Oh, well. I'd have liked to meet them. How old are they?"

He paused a second, then said, "Nine and twelve."

I scrunched my eyes.

"I know—but they're my babies. How about you? How many are in your family?"

"Well, there're eight of us kids and two parents and two grandparents, a dozen cousins, and other relatives. You know the drill, uncles and aunts. My family is a big glob of people, I reckon."

"Stay," Mark ordered as if I were a dog. Paul and he were off to the bathroom.

"Where's your mother? Your dad had a wife didn't he?"

Mr. Jansen's face went gray, his shoulders drooped, and he became sadly silent. Then he slowly turned to look into my eyes. "Gone," he whispered.

"Gone?"

His head dropped. "She died in childbirth, my birth."

"Was your dad mighty sad about it?"

"Sad yes, but mostly mad. He never stopped blaming me for her death."

"Never?"

"Never. And that left him mean."

"As mean as a someone who'd snatch a fly from a blind spider?"

"Yep. Dads aren't supposed to be mean, you know. When I was your age, I cried myself to sleep time and time again. I cried for my mother I never knew. You're lucky you have one."

I felt sorry for him—even if he cried as a boy. Then, I had to ask, "Who fed you and washed your clothes if you didn't have a Mother? Who looked after you when you got sick? Who listened to your questions?"

"I did. Did the best I could." He sniffed, showing a tired smile. I hoped he wouldn't commence crying.

Imagine, his father blaming him for something he didn't do. That was too much.

"It wasn't your fault, you know."

The man blinked rapidly as he grasped my right hand and patted it. "I know, I know," he whispered. "But thank you for saying so. I needed to hear that right about now."

We sat for a spell in the hum of the crowd. It began to sound like a mass of hungry locusts as they honed in on a row of sweet corn. They jostled for position.

"Never grow old. If you do, trouble'll come."

"Yes, sir."

"Age of mind spells trouble. Makes the mind go bad."

"You mean like milk left too long in the icebox? Like milk gone bad, thrown out?"

"Sorta like that. It's no good. Hmm, I wanted Dad to love me."

"He didn't?"

"Oh, he might have. But sometimes he didn't even want me around."

I thought how anytime I wasn't around Dad, he was working to earn money on the road, especially on the extra board. Sometimes he drove to St. Joe, but Mother tried to help break him of that. We all knew St. Joe wasn't good for him.

"It's poison."

I started, "What?"

"Yes, it's poison. Just look at me. Bitterness ages a body."

"Enough to kill?"

Mr. Jansen slowly nodded. "Remember that, will you?"

"I sure will."

"Bitterness takes root for good. It kills hope, and it ages a body."

I nodded once again.

Mother bounded up to us. "Where are your brothers?"

They hadn't returned from the restroom yet, but in a twinkling they were back and flooding onto the bench like a couple of Rhode Island Red roosters fixing to roost.

"What did I tell you?" Mother asked them.

"It was only a minute," Mark fussed.

Mother pinched her lips together in a "we'll-talk-about-this-later" manner, and then she focused on Mr. Jansen. "I hope Sean hasn't pestered you much."

"Not at all, ma'am. I rather enjoyed our little chat."

A voice over the loud speaker announced the arrival of Mr. Jansen's train. He rose, tipped his hat to me, and strode away.

With his soft, departing footsteps came the hard, arriving sounds of the station and of my sisters, shrilling in unison, "We're going to California." Dad brought up the rear of their gift-shop foray.

"We're headed to California!" Mark echoed. "We're really going!"

Indeed we were, and what adventures lay in store?

West with the Night

Dad's eager arms jolted me to my feet. We headed to an escalator leading down to the trains. As high as an ensilage silo and a quarter as wide, that escalator riled me. Warily, I planted my feet onto the step that formed just in front of me.

As we neared the bottom of the escalator, Dad reminded me to jump off of the step before it ended in the grate. "One, two, three, jump," he said, timing our exit.

Then, faster than you might say Jack Robinson, the view swept me away. Each track held a breathing, belching train fixing to head out to places far away and stranger yet. Couldn't I ride every train there? Mother told me, "Fewer people are riding trains. Some will be put out of service. They will be mothballed." All I could think about was that funny smell–giddy and perfumed–of mothballs slumbering in Mother's upstairs closet. That would need to be one giant mothball to cover anything as large as a train, I guarantee! In spite of this strange scent, I wondered if I might ride some of those trains before they burped farewell.

The trains fumed and chugged, screeching in the evening air. My heart leapt. Did the engines bid "welcome" with hissing noises and pouting bodies? Signaling at every car we passed, I yelped, "I want to ride that train! No, that one. How about that one?" I puzzled how anything powerful and inviting might one day be no more. In that moment, their metal skins shimmered under lamp lights, twinkling in Union Station of Kansas City, Missouri. The trains waited, ready to whisk guests to ports of call unknown.

Their grumbling nighttime sounds let on how they suspected a hasty retirement. They didn't wish to hear that prospect. Didn't they whisper, "Where's the thanks? Where are the people we helped? Why don't they plead on our behalf, delaying the time we are put away for good?"

In our voyages, how many dreams have such cars borne on their steel wheels? How many miles have they gobbled along dusty prairies and sweltering deserts? How many beginnings and endings did they help to frame?

It all felt sad. Do machines (like people) also fade, replaced by gadgets? I wanted to ride every train before it was too late—before they all left for good.

Bolting from Dad and Paul, I hopped onto every car we passed. Of course, I inspected the metal side, rivets, and steps on each car. Dad or Paul kept peeling me off of each car, reminding me, "Not this one. Keep moving."

After boarding "our" car, I spotted an ancient looking man who snored heavily with ease. Dare I waken him to hear his stories? Maybe after he prayed that someone listen to him, he tuckered out and drifted to sleep. Would he be disappointed come morning when sunbeams glinted to awaken him? No one heard his memories.

Dad saw me staring. "Such old men ache to share echoes of life," he said. "They were once proud, feeling all the promises in store. Maybe few people know that he once stood strong as the head of his family. He mattered."

What happened? Who will take his place, and when? Who decides such things?

"Well," I huffed, "if time moves only forward, it's not fair. Why can't time run backwards, or not move at all?"

"Time may be harsh. But maybe we don't see it fully," Dad said sitting down in the seat in front of Julie and me. "If there isn't more to time than movement forward without end, then time is menacing."

I asked myself what happened? Does anyone care? When will everything change?

As 1 a.m. slipped into history, three Santa Fe engines groaned and bumped cars to attention, rippling a wave of gentle stretching throughout the train. Grudgingly, car wheels ground and clanked against steel rails, reminding me of a stirring hound that stretches and presses his front paws into the soil before he rises slowly onto his front legs. The Santa Fe Chief oozed out of the Union Station yard at a galloping speed of 5 mph. That wasn't even as fast as I can run, I fumed, folding my arms over my chest. But at least we're moving, I guessed.

Our car rocked gently as we crossed each switch in the yards, reminding me of how our cows swayed when they chewed their cud during milking. I felt drowsy until the train's whistle snapped my eyes open. Diesel fumes wafted through the air, and the clackety-clack of the wheels on the track managed to keep me awake for a spell.

Although lead weights tugged on my eyelids, I bravely resolved not to miss even one scene flashing before me. I had to see everything as we headed west across Kansas: west over an ancient route, west with the night. We glided over the old Santa Fe line. Peering out of my window into the night, I spied faint lights in sleeping towns. Lights shone from barnyard poles, and I glimpsed a shadowy outline of homes. Who lived there, and would I ever meet them?

All of that motion and a bruising day of work ripened my hunger. Reaching into my sack lunch, I pulled out a red delicious apple that I buffed against my shirt sleeve. As my teeth pierced its skin, the car's overhead lights dimmed. In the semi-dark, I nibbled in time with the swaying car.

As we pulled into Topeka, Julie and I decided to check out the lounge two cars back. Should a bon voyage party break out there, we naturally needed to be part of it. We had our rights. Risking harm, we set out to reach that lounge. You see, couplings—giant clawed hands—connected the cars. Only flimsy metal plates covered the couplings and shielded us from the clankety-clank of wheels below them. We had to walk across those plates, but it felt like we had to jump. What if the car lurched, twisting and collapsing those plates with us on top them? We'd fall in between the cars to be sliced by wheels into bloody pieces. When we opened the car's door it taunted us, "It co-o-uld collapse. It mi-i-ght collapse. Care to give it a try? Heh, heh, heh." Since Dad advised me to jump to dodge being gobbled by the escalator, maybe he'd advise doing the same to be safe from couplings. So Julie and I jumped for our lives, our hearts pounding louder than the train on tracks. We made it. Staying balanced was tough, but we did it.

That fool lounge was hardly worth our efforts, though, "off-limits" to kids. We scurried to an open table and melted into the cloth seat covers to keep a low profile. Grown-ups sat hunched around tables, or they leaned against the wall, their arms dangling while they puffed on weeds or swilled drinks. A few customers sipped their drinks, which I guessed stretched the time they lasted, and that reminded me of how Ann swirled her cherry-flavored colas, rattling the ice with a straw. She savored every drop.

The air smelled of trash burner and Chubby Grave's breath. He was a red-faced clown whom our priests shivered with joy to mock. "That's one genuine alcoholic," Father Shudders would hiss. "For shame," gasped another. They laughed giddily.

Since Julie and I figured one drink was as good as another, we opened our fizzies and pixie sticks. We poured their powders into cone-shaped cups filled with water from our car. Although we spilled a pinch as we jumped, we still had plenty for "mixed drinks". We sparked any alchemist's wonder while we worked. Alas, our designs fizzled. "There's a hole clean through our cups," I gasped, and in a twinkling a sticky pink mess spread across our table.

"You kids clear out of here, now! Look at this mess." The porter did not take kindly to our trespass. "I'm gonna tell your parents. I swear I will. Shoo, you hear me?" His ranting sounded like a senile old man intent on rustling chickens out of a garden. (We'd warn the other kids not to bother with that fool lounge.)

Surviving the trip back to our car, we opened the door to see passengers fussing about their water cups. Grumbled curses took to the air after each victim had swayed to the water fountain to fill a cup. "Well, I'll be go to hell!" a man about Mr. Jansen's age said. A young woman yelped as ice water funneled down her blouse. A boy about my age hurled his half-filled cup into the trash. "Piece of crap!"

"Isn't he charming?" Paul snickered. "Look at all of those fools. Why can't they learn?" A glint in his eyes and a sharpened #2 Ticonderoga pencil in his right hand explained everything.

Lead sleepiness invaded my eyelids once again, but I fought on and was even winning for a spell. The train sped by poles lining the track as the land unwound like a frayed and lumpy carpet. Tracks stretched flat and straight in front of us to bridge the darkened Kansas prairie. Did those tracks connect us with folks who snored in distant states?

Despite my best intentions, the scene became foggy, and sleep drifted into me. At half past five o'clock, I was roused to attention by, "Dodge City, Dodge City in five minutes!"

Dad had warned, "Don't leave the train. These stops are brief, and I don't want the train leaving without you." But . . . Dodge City was waiting for me. How could I resist touching the place where Marshal Matt Dillon had lived—where Boot Hill rested? What if something remained from long ago? I struggled to resist, really I did, but I *had* to plant my feet on Dodge City. Clamoring down the steps, I used both hands to slap the concrete lining the tracks. Then, I leaped back onto the train.

I did it: touched the ground where famous outlaws had marauded . . . where gun fights had sounded! I brushed my feet on the same ground as had brave sheriffs, their deputies, and their posses. Did I feel how it was to live back then? I hoped so. People dreamed of cattle drives and roundups, of train robberies, and of plowing the prairie's sod. Thinking about all this, I felt satisfied. My risky voyage was worth it. Besides, no one in my family had seen me. That felt delicious. I had swished my hands and feet on Dodge City.

Later that morning, I awakened from a nap to find that an elderly woman had boarded the train. She sat by herself. Her eyes drifted from person to person, her lower lip drooping. She gripped a brown paper bag that I reckoned held all the food she'd eat that day. After about twenty minutes, she pulled two slices of Wonder Bread out of her bag, and she wrestled a turnip from a plastic wrapper. Cutting three hefty turnip slices, she laid a foundation for her sandwich. Freeing two dill pickles from their wax paper, she splayed them down the middle, laying their planks over the turnips. She topped all of it with two slathers of salad dressing and another slice of bread. Had she been crafting a stone wall, those globs of salad dressing might have been a fine mortar. The woman squeezed her concoction together, imprinting the bread with her fingertips. That oozed salad dressing over the edges of the sandwich. She did not miss a morsel, slurping up the fugitive dressing. She smiled with each bite.

Her satisfaction reminded me of my hunger. An apple goes only so far, and her sandwich looked mighty tasty. Somehow, we'd managed to haul all ten dozen roast beef sandwiches to the train station without thinking to load them from the car onto the train. In all the confusion to unload our luggage, we must have thought one or the other of us had them. Mary had swung a half dozen sandwiches under her arm when she left the car, but they were gonners before we left Kansas City. My siblings pouted and whined in hunger. I hushed up. Sounding off wouldn't make our sandwiches magically appear. Eating in the dining car was too costly for a brood our size, so we went hungry until we reached Flagstaff that night.

About thirty minutes after the sandwich lady finished her lunch, she commenced to groan. "Was the salad dressing spoiled?" I whispered. Maybe the turnips were to blame. I surely wasn't pinning any blame on her pickles. They held too much taste to be ornery.

All day our train rocked through Colorado and New Mexico. At two o'clock we pulled into Albuquerque for a thirty-minute break. "You kids may use your own money to buy one souvenir apiece," Dad announced. Ann fussed about what she would buy with the change she earned for doing chores at our grandparents' home and with the dollar bill she pocketed from a blue-ribbon flower entry in the county fair. She chose a cinnamon candy stick pointed like a rocket. Julie set her designs on an Indian doll complete with a tan and brown leather dress and moccasins, red beads, and braided ebony hair. I pulled out my birthday money as well as coins settled in the toe of my Christmas stocking to purchase a coloring book. It was choked-full of drawings: famous lawmen like Wyatt Earp and Bat Masterson. Before I could exhale even once, our thirty minutes of adventure had ended, and the conductor hollered, "A-llll A-boar-r-r-d!"

At once I began adding life to my coloring book's black and white drawings. "Should some of these drawings be gray?" Maybe the outlaw snatched what the government had stolen from him in the first place. Maybe the outlaws were getting even with dirty politicians. Dad had told me once about a sorry politician who was so dishonest and stinky that he reminded him of the time skunks had littered under our barn. I had heard how rich men in Washington stole land from Indians and then sold it as their own. "If no one can say who owns what's taken, then is it really stealing? Who is the rightful owner?" I pulled out a gray crayon, and I began to rub away at the afternoon which passed about as fast as a too-tired snail.

The Santa Fe Chief finally reached the Arizona border at 6 o'clock. No sooner did it cross the state line when I saw a thick black string in the distance. I decided it had to be my first sighting of a forty-mule team toting Borax. Giggling, I remembered a kindly-faced actor with raven hair in a Borax ad for Death Valley Days. Was he called Ronald?

While I passed the afternoon coloring, I also tallied abandoned passenger cars on side rails. I declared, "I want to ride that car—no that one." I felt sad for the ones left behind. But after counting 100 cars, I had to stop wishing to ride them all. There were too many. I had to choose. But how?

Should I pick the most brightly painted ones or those with fancy black metal gratings? I saw a car with wooden trim stretched clean around it, as if it was done up in a wooden Christmas bow. I'd need to ride that one. And then there was a swell-looking sleeping car with "Pullman" stamped on its side. I had to consider riding that car, too. Would there be enough time?

By 10 o'clock we pulled into Flagstaff, Arizona which was as welcome as an ice cube on a parched tongue. Compared to Flagstaff's heat, Kansas felt cool and inviting. Even so, I was glad we chose Flagstaff as a stop for food and a place to sleep on our way to live in a fairy tale. Ordering sandwiches from a café, we crept back to our rooms where we plopped down for the night. Mother strung pillows and blankets across the floor to stretch two rooms enough to hold all ten of us. Mary switched on the television, and I heard Shirley Booth as Hazel cooing us to sleep.

The next thing I knew, light beams teased at my eyes. We took a spur line to the north rim. As our train lumbered nearer the end of the line, my heart pummeled my chest. I would see what I'd imagined only about a thousand times: the edge of the world!

A mist fell upon the Grand Canyon's observation deck that overlooked a gorge that stretched forever. An angry brown ribbon wound its way along its bottom. "That's the Colorado River," the park ranger told us. "It's taken about a billion years to cut the Grand Canyon from the plateau you're standing on. It stretches a mile, rim to rim, and bottoms out 2,500 feet below us."

How can it be? I thought. That river looks powerful weak to be the Colorado River.

"The river might not look like much from up here," the ranger continued, "but down there, it's crashing fast and high on account of our wet winter and spring."

The Colorado wore the earthen hues of grown, gray, and beige. Its hitchhikers swirled and trudged on their course. That left gaps, and I could see where they were missing. Enough of them went missing to leave a crater and a canyon that seemed sliced as easily as knife cuts through creamy butter.

Many faces peered into the canyon: young and old ones; male and female; white and bronze, and black and yellow. A man with a wooden leg limped by me. A married couple bickered over money. A woman older than dirt—nearly forty—hunched alone, her eyes fixed downward.

Did she register what she saw? Was she married? I wondered. If so, where was her husband? I imagined she'd been married without children for nearly twenty years. Would she divorce her husband? But why? I looked for bruises on her face, and no she hadn't been beaten like Mother's friend Lilia Crocker had. I was glad for that.

Did these people share my questions? Did they want to know where these gobs of sand, silt, and rock were headed? Did they consider the hitchhikers' mysterious voyages, what deltas they formed, and if they'd craft alluvial fans? Did they wonder, like I did, where every morsel of earth began its voyage? I felt almost faint from the near uncertainty of the answers. Did these people also wonder how all of that weight in the plateau moved? But why hadn't its grandeur meant it would stay put: fixed in time, and secure against wind and rain?

Will these folks be swept along by time, wind, and rain, too? Will I? Dad said that we're all subject to nature. Did those folks tote dreams as uncertain as the Colorado River's silts and sands? Did I? It seemed to me then that dreams and their mysterious outcomes might be important to consider. Heck, if a body's to be puzzled by a mystery, I thought, why not choose a fine one?

"The ranger says a storm is brewing on the other rim," said an elderly women holding a cup in her trembling right hand. "No gauging its strength, he said. Told us to brace ourselves for it."

Growing storm clouds bathed us in a half-light. Had the ornery winds declared, "It's time to frolic!" The winds decided to swirl grit, sand, and seeds around us. Would those seeds journey in a timeless dance to parts unknown, just as their ancestors had for millions of years?

Later that afternoon Mother announced, "It's time to go on a little hike in the canyon." She sure didn't have to tell me again. Running toward the trailhead, I spotted flashy stones along the way. They glinted in the after-storm sunlight: stones with fiery veins of mica and blood; amber and verdant greens; stones of black, salmon, and aquamarine. What an assortment of souvenirs just begging to join my rock collection! I thought.

Dad said, "You kids may walk down the trail as far as where mules are rented." I reckoned that was pretty far because the people and their mules looked like a stream of fire ants. How blooming large the canyon must be, I thought. As we tromped down the trail, I knew why those folks were riding mules. It was hard to breathe, and the air was hot and dusty, even that soon after a storm. Dust puffed into my mouth and up my nose, striating there in charming colors of green, brown and darkness. Dust gritted my teeth to make them feel the way toothpaste does before I swish it out of my mouth.

Walking back to the gift shop, I thought about how lucky I was to be part of life's mystery. Maybe I was the luckiest boy in the world. I was also feeling fine that I had enough money to buy black licorice at the gift shop. Chomping on that licorice powered my wondering.

While our spur line train clanked toward Flagstaff that evening, I strained to glimpse the last darkened edges of The Grand Canyon's rim. I knew that I'd visit again one day. And I knew just as well that it'd look mighty impressive the second time around, too. I mumbled to myself, "Maybe some things don't change much . . . or they do so darn slowly."

*N*ight *Train to Los Angeles and Points Beyond*

We boarded a night train to whisk us away to a place where Dad said citrus orchards perfumed morning breezes and where bushels of movie stars roamed the streets in Joan Crawford elegance. "All the way . . . on Santa Fe!" (All the way west to Los Angeles). There the Pacific Ocean splashes sandy beaches. Its thrashing waves tease shores with coolness. Waves also lap delicately at the beaches, the way a mother dog grooms her pups. We were headed to California where I longed to stretch out on the sand, and where I'd grow a quarter inch simply for the bother. Surfers—paddling marauders—clutched a kind of freedom I hadn't known in Kansas. I latched onto the ocean's mysteries the way metal shavings suck onto a large magnet, its curved metal portion painted crimson.

I awoke at five in the morning (How could I have slept?) to the conductor announcing, "Pomona, Pomona in 10 minutes!" The train slowed to crawl through San Bernadino, Pomona, and smaller towns. Without looking out the window, I knew where we were. I could smell it. A breeze flirted in orange and lemon groves, just as a bee might in a nectar-filled peony. Aromas leaked into our car and into my nose.

When I did peer out of the window, I saw otherworldly trees whispering in the pre-dawn blackness. Streetlights beamed an eerie, albeit dignified glow, robbing my breath. I squirmed to dash off of that train in order to explore that other world.

Dad stirred. Stretching, he wondered, "Shall we walk to the engine?"

Was he kidding?!

"I think Shorty Stokes is the engineer. I was his fireman for nearly a year."

We reached the dining car as a waiter unlocked its doors. Dad plopped down and ordered a glass of orange juice. "Don't tell the other kids," he whispered. "This is a reward for keeping me company." He offered me a sip. "Besides, no one really tastes California without a nip of ambrosia."

"Ambrosia?" I puzzled.

"A heavenly drink. Ages ago some men fancied it a drink for the gods: Greek ones, that is. Imagine it. Drink in what those orange trees crafted."

Being a light sleeper has its advantages, I thought. A young couple stepped into the dining car. Dad smiled at them and mouthed, "Newlyweds?"

The woman laughed. "How could you tell?"

Dad grinned harder. Then he leaned into me. "Did you know I met your mother on the Swope Park train?"

"Not really. What happened?"

"When I was on a leave from my assignment in New Caledonia, I spotted your mother sitting next to Grandmother Kearney. Lola asked, 'What's that new pool?' Knowing all about the 'new' Swope Park Pool, I told her so. The next moment, we traded names and addresses. I wrote to her every other day while I was overseas."

"How long was that?"

"Nearly a year. I was discharged on Thanksgiving Day 1945. Since your grandfather Redmond was gone, and since your uncle Bill was wrapping up his stint in the South Pacific, I hopped on a train to ride back east to Washington. A bus ran from Union Station in Washington to The Catholic University of America where Lola studied for her RN degree. She'd nearly finished it, and I brought a ring. The following day when we visited Mt.Vernon, I proposed to her under a light snowfall, soft and feathery. She said 'yes' at once."

"Were you running a fever—romantic fever?"

"No, you and your romantic fever. It wasn't a fever—romantic or rheumatic. It was something much finer. Remember, your grandmother Nessie Storey-Redmond came down with rheumatic fever, not me." His eyes misted.

The sun had not yet risen when we pulled into Pomona. "Let's step outside," Dad said.

Snatching Dad's hand, I felt the scene was eerie. Even before I hit the sidewalk, an enormous bouquet of rare flowers wrapped itself around me. A fluid scent of citrus from the groves just beyond the tracks hinted at tales of adventure and wonder. Each grove harbored a sulking work of literature chaffing at the bit to be written. Must one only notice it waiting there to be crafted into words, as Thornton Wilder said? There was nothing like this in Kansas. If "trees" might flutter such treasures, imagine what humans might do? Could we also steep morning air with sweet bouquets or create luscious fruit: ambrosia for the gods? Maybe . . . guess what? I knew I was the luckiest boy alive as I stood there with Dad on the concrete lining the tracks.

Once back inside the train, I asked, "How do trees grow fruit that sweet? I mean, what makes that flavor? Is it trapped in their wood? You know, maybe that wood tastes sweet, too? If someone burned an orange tree, would its smoke be perfumed?"

"Sean-"

"Maybe burning orange trees smell better than oranges taste. After all, coffee smells a lot better than it tastes, right? Or does that luscious flavor start in the tree's roots? Or, what about this . . ." I glanced up to see Dad smiling. "Dad?"

"Your imagination . . . The trees form a kind of sugar."

"Sap, I know. Like the maple trees in Vermont."

"Yes, something like that. Sap flows in the trees, almost like the way blood flows in your body, only much more slowly. Finally, sugar collects in the fruit so that its seeds will be fed. They need help to grow into a seedling and beyond. Does that make sense?"

"Well, I reckon so. This sugar is like egg whites that feed developing chicks." I understood this, but I still liked my wood idea better. The trees must smell of oranges. After all, I'd read that California winery casks soaked up odors from wine they held. I also read that wine takes on the flavor of the cask that holds it. So, I thought there must be a two-way foot path inside trees. Why couldn't the wood and sap share each other's flavor and aroma? I might be right. I promised myself that one day I'd burn an orange tree to find out if its smoke is perfumed like an orange. Oh, it would have to be a diseased tree I put out of its pain. My word, why would anyone consider hurting a healthy tree?

Dad continued toward the engine, and I walked a step behind him. As always, I studied his gait. I read what he felt. This morning Dad's arms swung freely at his sides, and his shoulders rose and fell loosely. His walk held a bounce, the closest thing to dancing I'd seen from him in quite a spell.

Reaching the engine, I saw Shorty who, sure enough, wasn't short at all. In fact, he was a tower: at least a head taller than Dad. Shorty was studying the controls in front of him. The engine reeked of diesel, and all the knobs and levers were coated with a greasy film.

"When did you start making the long haul?" Dad asked Shorty.

Shorty's head jerked up. "Well hey, if it isn't Tom!"

"Good to see you," Dad said.

"I'm out of Flagstaff now. Been running this route a couple a months. You still switching?"

"Yeah," Dad answered. I took Dad's hand.

"And who might you be, young man?" Shorty asked, wiping a hand on his overalls before offering it to me. How many kids did an engineer greet that way? I reckoned not many were asked anything at all.

"Sean Redmond, sir."

"Ready to man the controls, are you?"

Why wasn't Dad answering? I waited. I rattled Dad's hand. "Dad," I whispered.

"He's talking to you, Sean."

"Me? Oh, Yes! Thank you!" A body would've been as slow as winter molasses to pass up such a chance.

Dad boosted me up to Shorty's squishy, upholstered stool. Gadgets and gauges with curious arrows, dappled with mysterious messages, eyed me from that space. A panel of green lights glowed on the left like a rocket ship. When Shorty needed a rest, had the Scarecrow offered to help, secretly rigging his controls to guide the spinning space station where Dorothy and the Tin Woodsman battled the witch? The Scarecrow might do that when Shorty wasn't looking, gobbling a roll in the diner car . . ..

"Grip back on the throttle slowly," Shorty said. At least a half a dozen metal rods (levers) perched on the counter to my right. "The long one." Shorty tapped the one I needed.

Easing down on it with one hand, I felt the lever hadn't budged. When I used two hands, it wiggled, cracking about a half inch. Could a small boy—excuse me, a big one—feel more powerful than this?

"Easy now, not too fast," Shorty said.

Not too fast? I wondered if the throttle was even working because the train didn't speed up at all. At least, it didn't feel like its speed changed.

"A locomotive this large takes considerable time to gather speed," Dad said.

After catching each other up on work and family for a few minutes, Dad yawned, "I'll be heading back to my seat now. Sean, you coming?"

Might I remain in the engine? Nah, Dad had only been funning me.

"Good seeing you," Shorty said. "My best to your wife."

We passed through hushed sleeping cars while the train slipped through dozing Los Angeles suburbs. Slumbering hills surrounded us, their sidewalks deserted. Were the ants and other critters under the sidewalks taking advantage of the drowsiness, which felt like a drug of too much ice cream and homemade peach cobbler? My ideas swelled, like a mountain stream at spring thaw. What possibilities gripped Southern California? For instance, if the citrus trees could exude aromas, what kind of life was possible for people? Who knows what might come of their gifts? Might Los Angeles breathe and spring like a blue-tick hound chasing its ghost coon in slumbering Ozark hills?

I stopped alongside an open window at the door where the conductor opens the train and lays out the step stool. We were next to the last sleeping car's exit.

"What's got you?" Dad asked.

"Oh . . . I was thinking about how much life will pop out of those darkened lanes when morning comes. I suppose the fragrance of the citrus trees and the whispering branches teased me to think of that."

Dad must have felt lightheaded, too. Gazing at me, he slouched toward that open window on the exit door of the car. I stepped atop a metal-grated stool propped against the wall. Standing on tiptoes, I braced myself against the door latch for balance. As I peered over the metal window sill, I whiffed the salt air that wafted through the window.

The citrus trees whispered more loudly than before—their tales of adventure clad in secrets, mysterious and delicious. Yes, I was the luckiest boy in the world—or maybe the universe.

Dad covered his mouth with his right hand and collapsed forward, as if he might faint. He's dizzy, swaying from these strong fragrances, I thought. Then he fluttered his right hand, and wafted it toward his chest. Was a spell creeping over him? He clasped his hand over his mouth and gasped, "Oh, My God!"

"Dad. What?" He was scaring me.

"Can you feel it?"

"Feel what?"

"Lord, even the cottages are alive."

A glow oozed from underneath the door sills of cottages, their inhabitants only beginning to stir. That glow leaked between every picket or paling on every fence. It misted from every garden pebble and cactus.

Gasping for breath Dad again swished his hand in circles. He uttered, "Oh, My God! Even the fences are alive! Can you feel it?"

I couldn't answer except to slip my right hand into Dad's left. A warmth buzzed me. Steadying myself against his left arm, I stared into his glistening eyes. "I love you, Daddy. Uh—Dad."

Now I'd done it. Did he suspect I was still a little boy? Only a little boy would have called him Daddy. Well, I had lost my balance. Yes, that was it. I lost my balance, and in my surprise, out popped "Daddy".

A passing conductor scowled at us with gimlet eyes.

"My dad isn't feeling well. He needs fresh air."

Dad didn't face the conductor's stare. I didn't blame him. That would've been a poor show.

"You feeling better, Dad?" I asked for the conductor's benefit.

Dad shrugged.

The conductor growled, "All right," and then he grumbled, "but get that darn stool out of the way," before he hobbled off, his left leg stiff.

Shortly before eight o'clock, our train powered into the Los Angeles Union Station. Its white stucco walls, arched doorways, palm trees, and mosaics begged me to linger. But the southbound train to Anaheim was keen to whisk me to Disneyland, and it wasn't about to wait. Did it know we had nearly no time to see and do everything?

I always thought Grandfather's luxury Impala with its upholstered seats and smooth ride was mighty "fine", but that was before I rode Disneyland's monorail. That was better than fine. It was slick—slick with a capital S. It was space-age machinery, something that the Jetsons might ride, and it was all wrapped with a silver bow.

We used "D tickets" for the monorail. When we exited it in Frontierland, the conductor was supposed to stamp each person's right hand. Then, we could reboard as often as we pleased. He stamped everyone's right hand, except for mine. Maybe we wouldn't reboard the Monorail. If so, I'd be safe. If we did, what would happen to me? Well we did reboard. When the conductor asked to see my Mickey Mouse-stamped "paw" I presented my left hand. Maybe he'd assume I had a stamp on my right hand. No such luck.

"Your other hand," he mumbled.

I hesitated. What will happen? Will I be thrown off the monorail? Will I face charges for trying to reboard without a stamp?

"Stick out your other paw," Dad said.

Trembling, I did what he asked. Of course, there was no stamp. I half-expected to hear, "Arrest this boy!" (my brothers might have cheered that) but instead Dad said, "In the rush to stamp the eight kids' hands, the other conductor must have missed one."

The man smiled. "Mr. Disney is honored you're here as his special guest. I'm sure he won't mind if I let you back on this once."

Thank goodness, I wasn't going to serve any jail time. I'd seen a makeshift jail with its black metal bars in Frontierland, and I wanted nothing to do with that bother. I wondered if that man was nice to me because he knew I fancied adventure stories, maybe the way Walt Disney had when he was my age.

"Next stop, the Swiss Family Robinson Tree House." That place set my mind to whirling. What if we were marooned on a tropical island? We'd need to build an Irish Family Redmond Tree House! I'd invent clever contraptions, like coconut bombs with homemade fuses. That would make my family safe. Mother would allow herself to go barefoot, and Dad might grow a beard. Oh yes, one big plus is how the land would refuse to grow turnips.

I couldn't get enough of this attraction, or of the Mississippi Paddle boat: a real S-t-e-a-m S-h-i-p (not really). Was that Mark Twain I spotted riding on the upper rails, edging his way toward the bridge? He needed to pilot the ship, and so did I. He must have been like me as a boy, sitting on a railing and crafting *Adventures of Huckleberry Finn*. Oh, I knew better, that he didn't write it until he was all *grown-up*. Whenever he did, I'd be there alongside of him. What fun we'd have swapping outrageous yarns, I guarantee.

And then there was the Matterhorn Toboggan ride that Khrushchev had not been allowed to ride in 1959 when he came calling. As Premier of the USSR, his guards claimed they couldn't protect him from bad men hiding in caves inside the Matterhorn. Unlike Khruschev, I was allowed to ride it, and I knew how lucky I must be. On the other hand, a wooden man standing slack-jawed, imitating a Swiss mountaineer, teased me. He pointed to a ruler and said, "You must be at least this tall to ride." Undeterred, I poofed my curls, stood on tiptoes, and passed the test. I could have taught Khrushchev a thing or two, except he had no curls, was all grown-up, and was barred on other accounts.

That toboggan zipped up the mountain and through caves strewn with treacherous boulders. Did I spot a dreary witch who might snatch me from my family, toting me off to her cabin in the woods where she . . .? Sometimes the toboggan barely clung to the mountain. I imagined it might let go, whisking off of the Matterhorn. Would it plunge into the icy water below? Of course that didn't happen, but it might have.

The day at Disneyland ended with me behind the wheel of a pointed sportscar—a red and white racer. Being not much of a driver yet, I let my car skid against the middle metal rod, a trainer rail for us beginners. Riding with me, Dad advised "Keep a balance. Work on that."

Mark and Paul floored their fool cars, zooming them to full throttle— a whopping ten miles per her hour! Their glazed eyes told me how jazzed they were.

As darkness grew, we flooded into a seafood restaurant for supper. "Put on bibs," advised a waiter. I'm not a baby, I thought. And I'm *not* wearing a bib. But when I saw Dad and Mother wearing their bibs, I figured it was tolerable. Soon our table was loaded with steaming platters of deep-fried cod and strange looking potatoes. I had never seen slivers of tators, greased and fried. The waiter called them cottage fries, and I wondered if they were alive too, just like the cottages that Dad had spied that morning with their lights glimmering underneath the door sills. The "fresh" seafood hooked me, what with its meaty and sweet flavors. The waiter showed me a dark colored bottle with a spicy smelling liquid inside. He called it malt vinegar, and he advised me to sprinkle it on top of the fish. That memory lingered long afterwards, long past the time when the cod's steam fizzled out from over our plates.

We spent the next day at Knott's Berry Farm where I witnessed a real gun fight in an Old West ghost town. This was even more amazing than Dodge City. I had seen no gunplay there; no one had claimed real ghosts were afoot. One gunslinger dropped from a roof after taking a shot through the heart. "Oh my!" slipped out of my mouth before I understood the whole fight was a show. The man splatted onto a pile of mattresses. He popped up and sauntered toward a shade tree.

We wandered through that ghost town which was dotted with statues of old-timers who sat on wind battered benches. One stooped next to a mining pan as he slurped a beer outside of a saloon. Three others hunched over poker hands. Cargo laden mule trains threaded through a patch of desert-looking land outside of town. As I wtched the mules trudging along, their scuffed-up dirt got me to craving cistern water from home. Would I see the kindly, raven-haired announcer who advertised Borax? (I think he was called Ronald.) He didn't show that day. I'd wanted to ask him the name of the fancy white shirts he peddled.

I guessed it all seemed too grand and foreign to be real. Dad assured me that the West really was wild once, complete with miners and mule trains, saloons and bloody duels. My mind whirled as I invented adventure scenes of my own. Of course, I took on the fastest gun in the west and, of course, I won him over to the good side without firing a shot. My twitching right eye did it. I might have done Tonto and the Lone Ranger proud.

Alas, that afternoon we left our Mecca for a new wonderland: San Clemente. The Santa Fe line ran right next to the cabins we'd rented, and our cabins were only a few hundred yards from the ocean. The trouble was, we had to climb a steep hill to reach them. As we crawled up it, I counted every bush and palm tree we passed. Would they never end? Finally, we reached the cabin office. The manager Mr. Peer took one look at our brood, wheezed, and offered, "Let me help you with your luggage the rest of the way."

"Why does Mr. Peer breathe oddly?" I worried to Mother.

Mother whispered, "He may have emphysema. He's thin, and he breathes in shallow huffs."

"Should I talk to him about the dangers of smoking?"

"I think he already knows. Don't you?"

Mr. Peer bought Mary a double-scoop blueberry ice cream cone every afternoon that we stayed there. He was partial to her, even though he was nearly as old as Grandfather Kearney. Mother smiled warily and thanked him kindly, not letting Mary out of her sight.

San Clemente was known for the fishing off of its pier. Walking along that pier, I watched a boy as he reeled in a twitching see-through blob. I couldn't believe it: my first jellyfish.

A man stood at a sink that hung out over the railing. He was cleaning a sand shark. "Tiburon!" he advised. ("Spanish for shark," Mom said.) Dad asked how it tasted.

"Fine," the fisherman answered. "Something like chicken. Sharks got a bad rap, you know." He wrapped a fillet in newspaper, and he handed it to Dad. "See what you think."

Yuck! I thought. Who'd want to eat a shark? It might have eaten a man for lunch! But *that man* was fixing to eat *that shark* for lunch. Just who was the predator, anyhow?

The man chummed the shark's guts into the ocean. No sooner had they splatted into the water when fish swarmed to eat it. Maybe there's a certain dignity about that. At least not much is wasted that way, I thought. Customers at last night's fish restaurant sure could learn something from that man, what with all the food they wasted.

That night I experienced firsthand what I'd been imagining for weeks: the sound of waves striking the shore and the smell of the ocean. This was nothing like the Kansas that I knew. (Well, maybe it was like the Kansas that had slept at the bottom of an inland sea.) After foaming onto the sand, the water misted cool salt air onto my face. Its residue tingled my skin, crinkling a film on my face. As a wave crept up the beach, it acted like it was plain tuckered out. Somehow, it kept right on coming, forming white skins that bubbled and waited for several seconds before popping. Had that tide come to visit for a spell?

The next morning, I awakened to the gas furnace grumbling and spitting out warm air next to my bed. But, folks spouted about how California was a sunny paradise, not a wintry one. Dad reminded me that even though we were by the ocean, we were in the desert. We could expect to be hot by day and cold by night. The desert was like that. I also learned that the Pacific currents ran north to south, toting crisp breezes with it. Anyone near California's seashore feels them, especially at night.

As I lay on my side to watch the furnace's flames, I thought about the ocean. What makes it mysterious? Maybe it's the way it flashes from a serene body of blue glass into a stormy mess, roiling with attitude and cashing waves. Maybe it's the allure of tides. I hoped to see how far they shrank away during low tide, but that would have meant rising at three or four in the morning. Mother said, "No." For some reason, she worried about a boy traipsing around the surf at three a.m. Who knew? More importantly, I wanted to see how large the tides swelled at high tide. And one evening we did just that.

I crafted small sand walls to see how long they would last in the rising tide. Within a few minutes, a wave plowed them down. Moving a few feet farther up the beach, I molded another wall. Paul also got into the act, only he built a two-foot high sandcastle with six-inch thick walls. It took punishment from the crashing waves, and it stood its ground. "I think this castle'll last," Paul boasted. But it didn't. Come morning Paul's stronghold had splatted and worn to a ridge of sand.

Those waves held mystery beneath their surface as well: powerful mystery. Their undertow felt like an invisible hand yanking at all parts of us. No squirming can shake it loose. One caught hold of Mark, terrifying both of us, but Janice swam to save him. After that scare, Dad warned that no one younger than Paul was to wade in above the waist. But within an hour, the current grabbed Jean also, and it sucked her into water over her neck. It gripped her there, toying with her. That time Ann swooped Jean up, pulling her to the shore. Short of breath, Jean was otherwise unharmed.

The ocean wasn't the only impressive element. In only a few hours on the beach, the combined effects of salt water, wind, and blazing sun turned us as pink as salmon. By nightfall we took the shade of red lobsters, our skin straining for relief before popping. When blisters started on my back, I knew I'd be sleeping on my belly or side for the next few nights. Even so, I thought that was a small price to pay. We were vacationing at the beach, after all. I fancied living in San Clemente, and I'd have suffered many sunburns to do that.

As our week there drew to a close, I faltered. Southern California was not like Kansas, a home I'd grown to love. Kansas had lain at the bottom of a shallow, inland sea. But it didn't look a thing like California, which was a land where The Wizard's balloon might have lighted, a land aglow with color and alive with salty aromas. It was a magical place, swirling with a foment of surf and luscious, sweet flavors. No, it wasn't anything like Kansas. Maybe California was an interesting foreign land, but I missed my land with its prairies and wind that swirled dust, seeds, and nearly everything else. I missed my pastures and cows, my chickens and garden. I even missed my mean gray goose. I'd grown homesick for our gravel roads and barbed wire fences, and for old pokes pouting in dust-strewn ditches. I even missed the smell of chores—the cows and chickens included. Well, maybe not the chicken shed when it needed cleaning.

I could *never* miss the smell our car held after it incubated dozens of roast beef sandwiches for two weeks. When we reached Kansas City, we found our car had been towed for being parked too long in a 24 hour parking zone that wasn't marked clearly. It was embarrassing that Dad had to "post bail" to release our car, as if it had been dubbed an outlaw. The official stamped some funny-looking papers after Dad paid, and I wondered if the image was Mickey Mouse. We all felt embarrassed when no one wanted to edge near our car, seeing as how it reeked: whew, some stench! Although those sandwiches were a large idea, they turned out to be an even bigger mistake.

Our adventure officially ended when we pawed up our driveway. The first thing out of our car, I sniffed for familiar farm air. Where was it? Why, it smelled different from what I remembered. Had the farm flown on its own adventures while we were away? Had our farm nudged up against some kind of monster to change its scent? Or had I only grown accustomed to California's salty sea air. Had I forgotten our own?

What had changed? I did, and I changed a bit on every journey thereafter. Maybe home shifted the day I first left Kansas, and maybe I realized that when I returned to see and to smell it again—as if I had just been born.

Had the chicken shed rearranged itself somehow? Even the fouled straw, reeking of manure that the Knuckle boys raked out of it, smelled different. But that didn't matter. I'm home, I thought, and that idea tingled my spine. I felt happy. Heck fire, I even felt all right when I remembered the messy chores waiting. I wouldn't mind doing them at all. Well, I *might* mind them—a pinch.

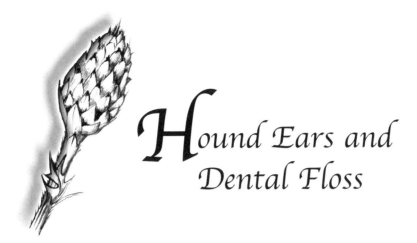

Hound Ears and Dental Floss

We thought we might lose him as he whimpered up to me, his tail hanging low and his eyes fixed on mine pleading, "Help me! Help me, please!" Our hound PJ had cut paws and legs, glinting of rich, crimson liquid. It wetted his head, muzzle, and ears. That frightened me. I knew at once that the gobs of blood oozed from his velvety ears, cut up and broken.

His ears, although soft and warm, were far more comforting than any manmade blanket or treasure. My brother Leo once boasted, "Why, once he's gone, I'll craft fine purses out of his big ol' ears." That horrible image shot through me, and I sprinted for Mother. Since the rest of the kids were in town at a ball game, and Dad was on the railroad extra board, Mother and I were it!

"PJ's hurt! His ears are all torn up!" I gasped, finding her fixing dinner.

"What? How?"

"I don't know for sure. All I know is he needs help. He's lost a gob of blood," I warned. "He needs help now!"

Without hesitating, Mother turned off all of the burners. She grabbed a bottle of hydrogen peroxide from the cabinet, a large sewing needle from the utility room, and a spool of dental floss from the bathroom. "Tote those rags from the box over there to line his basket, Sean." Mother also retrieved a bunch of terry cloth from the kitchen drawer next to the sink. "We'll need these to wrap his ears to stop the bleeding."

We rushed out to PJ who was lying down low. Mother threw her hands to her face, "Oh PJ, what did you do?" If I had any doubts about his condition, I knew for sure it was serious once I saw Mother's worry.

We gingerly lifted PJ to his basket, which I'd already lined with soft rags. Mother cooed, "It's all right. We'll take care of you now. It's all right. That's a good boy, a very good boy." Her low, soft voice calmed him. That was what PJ needed to hear just about then. That was what I needed to hear, too. Her tone helped to shrink my towering worry. PJ's tail swished with low, rhythmic sweeps next to his body, and his grateful eyes and crouching body told me he trusted us.

PJ was half beagle and half who-knows-what, but his loyalty and kindness surely made up for any shortcomings in his breeding. Why, once when I came down with the flu, PJ stayed plastered to his guard post next to my bed all night. I knew I'd be all right every time I glanced up with fevered eyes to see my best buddy whining and watching over me. Mother let him sleep with me that night—not in his doghouse next to the cistern as usual.

And then there was the time he saved my life! PJ and I were sliding on our pond's ice when I slipped and fell. All went dark. Dad declared, "PJ zipped up to me on the stoop of our back door. He was whining and a fussin', barking to whip up a storm! Even a know-nothing Republican would've known enough to follow him."

The next thing I knew I lay in my warm bed with a hot water bottle pressed to my neck, and PJ's chin rested near my hand. I shudder to think what might have happened on that subzero day without him.

On the awful night he staggered up to me, soaked in blood, I quaked with worry. Did this mean his kind and gentle spirit might seep away? Could Mother and I help PJ before time—and blood—ran out?

Mother said most of the trouble lay at the ends of his ears, far from major blood vessels. Would all of his blood run out of him anyway? Mother prepared to "operate". First, she rubbed hydrogen peroxide on the needle to clean it. Then, she threaded it with dental floss. "Here, hold this while I clean PJ's ears." Our loyal half-breed hound lay still, trembling only slightly when Mom rubbed against the deep part of his wounds around the ends of his ears and at the spot where they connected to the rest of him. He must've been very brave to hold steady! The biting hydrogen peroxide smelled like it would surely burn the hide off of a rhino's behind, much less a dog's. Anything mixed with that much blood, salty and metallic, meant trouble. I knew PJ's loss of blood was serious because of what I smelled when we killed chickens. That smell meant death!

I declare, even as brave as PJ was, I expected him to yelp at least once. But he didn't, peering up at us. He only whimpered like a child who had lost his best friend. Maybe the needle stung just a bit—no more than the way prickly spines of thistles smart when a body brushes against them hard. I hoped that the needle didn't hurt him anymore than that. Mean old thistles are more than enough for a body to take, but who could handle this! I'll bet PJ knew that we were helping him with all of those pricks to his ears. Oh, he was powerful brave!

Mother cooed at PJ while she stitched, "Now PJ, what kind of trouble did you get yourself into tonight? Huh?"

Maybe he fought a coon. But if he did, where was the body? PJ would've surely won, and he'd have trotted it back to our farm. His saliva-coated prize would dangle from his mouth. Maybe he got tangled in some barbed wire that pouted in the ditch near our northeast pasture. Or maybe…a forgotten ankylosaur crawled out of a hole, and PJ fought him to the death to protect us!

Blood has a way of stretching matters clean out of proportion. A half cup or so appears to be a half gallon when it pours out of a wounded hound, and that made me want to cry, but I dared not! Men and even little boys can never, ever cry. Our priest said so. Well, instead of crying, I stiffened to be brave like PJ. So, I shoved out my chin and bit my lower lip to look like someone who could muddle through that ghastly night.

"It's serious, Sean, I know," Mother warned. With that I wilted, slinking behind her so she couldn't see my face. She mustn't see me cry, and I didn't know if I could hold back much longer.

My arms glided to hold onto PJ—to comfort both of us. With Mother's warning I worked to speak, but only a muffled hiss came out, and then a raspy sound.

"What, Sean? Please don't talk now. I'm fixing to tie some sutures."

Mother didn't need to ask me to hush. I couldn't have spoken, even if I'd tried again. As I clinged to PJ, I felt his body trembling with each prick of Mother's needle. Otherwise, he was still, not yelping even once. Turning my face, I felt my lower lip trembling in tune with PJ's body, as if I echoed him. Really, I was doing the best I could to halt any moisture in my eyes. "Mother must not see me cry. 'Sides, who knows what terror that would weave into PJ's heart."

The thought of losing my best friend had my stomach in knots. Dad would have scrunched up his eyebrows, disappointed, and have lectured me on how death is part of life. He'd have stuck out his chin and chided me for forgetting that both life and death are parts of one grand mystery. Had he dared say that, I might have barked at him to hush, flushed with embarrassment for speaking that way to Dad. Children had no business ever talking that way, and I knew it, but I would have smarted off just about then! I had no use for all that jabbering and truck about life and death being one—not that evening. All I wanted to do was to ease PJ's pain and to calm him. Whether or not life and death are one mystery is a topic way beyond me, and I didn't know for sure. What I did know was that PJ needed help. That much I knew for certain!

As Mother's handiwork progressed, PJ began to tremble less and less.

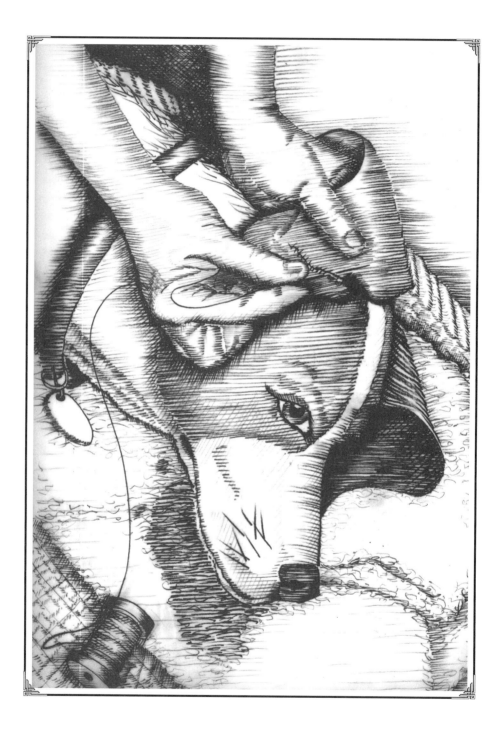

That led me to stop biting my lower lip, which also didn't quiver quite as much. Already plans of our glorious jaunts revved up in my mind: voyages on moonless nights through the magical hills folded around our valley. Heck, if PJ and I were lucky enough, we might even tree a coon! Watch out coons!

Mother's emergency surgery lasted for only twenty minutes, but it seemed like hours. Did Mother think so, too? Oh my gosh, soon I could see all of PJ's ears, and not just gobs of velvety blood! As the sutures began to squelch the streams and then trickles of blood, the beads of sweat left Mother's forehead, which was no longer all scrunched into wrinkles. It commenced to smooth out. Her eyes weren't as narrow as they had been, and her breathing came in longer draws. I tried to relax with her. Still, were we too late? Would PJ live without all of his blood?

Less than an hour after PJ first dragged himself to me, Mother finished the last suture. She dabbed away the drying blood to sigh, "I've done all I can, and now nature and healing must take its course."

"Wow, so much blood!" I worried. Only a few splotches had made it onto Mother's apron, but it looked as if a dark jug filled with blood had splashed all over *my* shirt and trousers. Peering down sheepishly, I heard Mother calmly reassuring me, "Amway concentrated detergent will take that out in a spiffy, Sean. Don't worry a pinch."

Of course, I wasn't worried about stains. It was PJ that had me scared. Would his velvety ears heal up, growing sticky and crusty as his scabs held and dried? If we were lucky, in about three or four days Mother could snip out those dental floss stitches. In the meantime, she fashioned a cone of cardboard for PJ to wear about his neck. That cone would persuade our loyal hound not to dig at his sutures. Any such digging might reopen his wounds, and then what might happen?

"Well, it's a strong sign that PJ came for help. He might not be hurt as badly as I reckoned," Mother said.

"How so, Mother?" Wow, I could speak again. No more raspy voice—not even a muffled hiss!

"Well, as I recall, when hounds are hurt powerful bad, they don't limp back home for help."

"What do they do then?'

"They crawl out into the dark, out into the hills folded around a valley. They find a lonely, brittle spot to plop down onto and to break. They find a spot to crawl into or onto to die." Mother's words sent first a shudder of dread down my spine—one of fright—and then one of warmth: a ray of fine feelings. For PJ had indeed crept home for help, not to the rocky hills where he might crouch down to up and die. I began to feel better, I declare.

We covered our snoring half-breed hound with his tattered yellow blanket, a hand-me-down from "yours truly". It was my favorite blanket when I was a little boy, but I was a big boy now—a whopping four years old—and had no need of it any more.

We lugged PJ—basket and all—to the cloak room just east of our kitchen. Mother said he might need lots of water since he'd lost so much blood. "But Mother, will he be able to drink anything with that fool cone around his neck? I mean, if he can't scratch at his ears, how can he drink?"

"We'll leave his bowl filled to the brim. His tongue is long enough to reach."

Comforted, I fetched him a bowl of fresh cistern water. Then, I left him so he could sleep, and I tried to sleep myself.

Well sir, sleep was out of the question! I checked on PJ four times through the night, and I sighted a shadowy figure in a nightgown walking up the stairway two of those times. Mother was on the prowl, too. Each time I found a snoring hound with wounds slowly crusting over. I knew that was fine because Mother said that meant his sutures were holding. Leaking blood would've meant trouble. The dental floss and terry cloth had done the trick.

By morning, I found PJ whining to lick at his cut paws. "Mother, Mother, PJ is still alive!" I called up the stairs. Soon my two older brothers, Paul and Mark, leaked out of the boy's room, "What's all the hollering about, Sean? Sit down and shut up, if you know what's good for you!" Without blinking or uttering a word, I kept right on tending to PJ. (I reckoned I'd better follow their advice, seeing as it came from kids at least twice my size and age.)

Knowing there's something a hound finds very comforting about licking his paws, I took off PJ's cardboard cone and let him lick. There! That was his reward for being a fine patient! He left his ears alone as if he knew that scratching there might hurt him. After cleaning up his paws, PJ kissed my face. And although he trembled and tottered at first, he soon stood with firmness: a mighty solid stance, not a weak one that I'd expected after he lost all that blood. He appeared to be smiling, proud that he stood strong and sure. I smiled back, and PJ beamed. Then he attacked his water bowl. I imagined he was lapping up new life in all that fresh water.

Our evening of hound ears and dental floss had been some kind of crusty success! As I stood guard, PJ kept gulping that life-giving water. All the while I knew he would be just fine. And who knows? Maybe Dad was mostly right, too. I'd think about it when I felt up to it.

Trouble Came Calling

Each and every time Mrs. Crocker shuffled up our sidewalk, I rushed to see what new bruises she wore. The really dark ones reminded me of diamond-shaped signs on ski slopes that I'd seen in magazines. Only, instead of being solid black in the shape of diamonds, her bruises were light in the center and dark around the edges, something like the outline for a bulls'-eye target. On poor days she wound up wearing two black eyes—double black diamonds marking "expert" ski runs. I couldn't keep track of her shades of black and blue!

Mrs. Crocker aimed to cloak her injuries with face powder, maybe the way newly fallen snow cloaks torn up fields. But heck, even on fine days (when she was only lightly bruised), her layered makeup hardly hid her lonely runs of pain. Did she reckon she could disguise her wintry marriage? It lay bleak and barren.

Owing to my young age, Mrs. Crocker allowed me a certain liberty, permitting me one question. "What happened this time, Mrs. Crocker?" (I wanted to catch her with a different story, but she never faltered. Not once did she offer a slightly different shade of explanation.)

"This? Oh, nothing, really. I simply fell down the stairs, shuh 'nuff!"

"Well," I stammered, stomping my right foot on the sidewalk to send puffs of dust airborne, "Mrs. Crocker, you'd save a powerful piece of time if you jumped down those fool stairs. Chances are, you wouldn't be falling down them, leastways not every time."

Mrs. Crocker smiled politely through pain. Then, she dismissed me.

Our little talks seem downright silly now. How could she think she hid the truth? Even a small boy like me knew what happened. We all did.

And I heard everything. How? By keeping a low profile and slipping in and out of the rooms where Mother and Mrs. Crocker talked. Most of the time they didn't even bother to shroud their talks around me. And why? Well, no one thought a boy my age knew what they were talking about, leastwise understood it. Oh sure, once in awhile Mrs. Crocker and Mother lowered their voices when I crept by them. Most of the time, Mrs. Crocker pawed one hand at the other one, sadly lowered her head, and loudly wrung out her pain.

"Lola, I don't know what hurts worse, childbirth or marriage," she choked out one stormy afternoon. Lilia Crocker had borne six children in ten years of hell with Jeb Crocker.

"Jeb drinks when he feels the pinch of money problems. But he beats me only when he's drunk."

Mother's words echo still, "You must leave him, Lilia. You must, before it's too late!"

"Oh, he's always sorry later. And he never hits me when he's sober." Did that somehow made up for the beatings?

I sensed Mrs. Crocker felt safe confiding in Mother. Do adults need to talk about their troubles to ease their pain? *I* knew talking about pain helped me, so I mumbled lines from several stories to myself. In my stories characters swapped dark secrets. Sharing made me feel snug, even it if was sharing with imaginary friends.

As the Crocker family grew, so to did Mr. Crocker's financial woes. More often than not, he slurped down enough liquor to make him stupid. He pounded rage on Lilia. By Labor Day after my fourth year, their prospects screeched trouble with a capital "T".

"But I have no where to go, Lola. What can I do?" she said desperately the last time Mother advised Lilia to leave her husband.

"Stay with us for a spell," Mother offered, "or, don't your folks live in town?"

"Well, yes, but I have six children. They can't help all of us for long. I . . . I . . . don't know what to do." Mrs Crocker glanced furtively around the room. Was it her beatings that made her wary, like a stray dog afraid to trust a new friend for fear he might turn on her? Did she fuss that her mister would crash through our door, tie her up, drag her back home, and beat her senseless for telling Mother nasty secrets? I reckoned her troubles were sparked, then seared, by the shame of it all—poverty, drunkenness, her helplessness—just as surely as fire laps at kindling once it's ignited by a spark from a flint stone. Each time I heard Mrs. Crocker's sorry story, I hung my head and moped. Walking outside, I'd dig into my pants' right pocket and finger my lucky Peace Silver Dollar, always there, a gift from my aunt's father Mr. Guffey.

"Don't spend this. It will be valuable one day," Mr. Guffey huffed the morning I pointed to the right hand clasping the coin behind his back. "It's a special kind of money, rare and old. Powerful, patient men toiled in deep, cold caves to find it." He plunked it onto my upturned palm. Yes, it was cool, owing to the depths from where it came. "The longer you keep it, the more precious it grows," he coached. Did he mean that it might sire a dime or a quarter?

Kind Lady Liberty, an immigrant woman named Teresa, came to this country from Italy when she was a five-year old girl. She smiled to calm me in the morning sunlight. Her husband, Tony de Francisci, sculpted her profile when she was all grown-up. She wore a spiked headdress, similar to the Statue of Liberty! Well, I imagined that Teresa must have ached to be Lady Liberty when she was small, which is natural for any little girl who spots the Statue of Liberty when her ship glides into the New York harbor. What little girl wouldn't have wanted to be Miss Liberty? Maybe Teresa felt sad if not chosen to play Lady Liberty in patriotic school plays. Maybe the honor to be on the front of a Peace Dollar made up for that.

On the flip side of the coin stood the majestic eagle perched on a crag. He peered keenly into the dawning of a new day with sunbeams streaming into view. Was that eagle storing up all the fine and cozy feelings that brought? He grasped an olive branch with his talons, and the word "PEACE" was printed beneath him. I thought that was swell, seeing as how that eagle stood for peace and not for war or armed might. Glinting in the morning sun, the Peace Dollar certainly had its work cut out for it.

Once I imagined Lady Liberty coming to life, but not as a skimpy little fairy. No, she was a full-sized adult who cocooned Lilia Crocker in her flowing cloak, cushioning her from Mr. Crocker's blows. Oh, he kept swinging at Lilia anyway. But after a spell, he plain tuckered out and gave up. That settled his rage on that day.

The Crockers lived on a no-name dirt road about one-half mile south of our farmhouse. I saw a storm gathering along that road one late afternoon just before Labor Day. It was the Crocker family. Their car raced up our driveway, clouds of dust mushrooming over it. Then, it skidded to a stop. My, that car spewed debris farther than a frightened polecat can spray!

The Crocker clan bounded from their 1953 Studebaker and scrambled up our walk. Lilia Crocker towed her youngest child, while Lilia's oldest daughter Dianne hurried her little sister Danielle. Then came Lilia's three sons: Rickie, Harlie, and Jimmy. Clearly, things had grown worse. Lilia's face was riddled with bruises, and she'd dusted the raised patches with face powder. Dianne stood hunched, her face puffy and her left eye nearly swollen shut.

"When would this all end? How could it all end?" I wondered aloud.

Once inside, Mrs. Crocker rolled details of the attack, like an unstoppable tidal surge. Jeb Crocker was busy beating Lilia when Dianne, who until then usually cowered nearby, crossed the line and tried to help her mother. Jeb's anger, fed by the shame of his daughter standing up to him, erupted even stronger. Blows rained down on Dianne's face. (Was Mr. Crocker shocked to see a stranger's hands—his hands—pummeling his daughter?) With this, the rescuer became the rescuee, and Lilia twirled about to free Dianne from Jeb's fists. Both women began to struggle savagely. He hurled filthy curses, which didn't stop until he fell, cracking his head on the corner of a coffee table. Blood splattered all over the couch. Out cold! The other five of Lilia's other children swished in to help. A wave of gasps pulsed through their living room.

"He'll come after us. I swear, if he takes another swing at me, I'll pump his guts full of lead," Dianne said, the danger and fear reigning as twins in her eyes. She pulled a small caliber handgun (a relic from the Great War in which Mr. Crocker had served as a drill sergeant) from her purse. How sad if Mr. Crocker survived a war only to be killed by his daughter with his own gun!

Dianne wasn't kidding. Had Mr. Crocker stormed into the room, she would have capped him, pounding slug after slug into his guts . . . if she could have. We all knew her rusted old gun wasn't even loaded, and it couldn't fire if it was. But Dianne clung to that gun, her comfort in a world gone mad.

"I'll handle him. I'll handle everything," Mother soothed, passing warm wash cloths to our shaken neighbors. "You stay here tonight. Give him a chance to sober up." Scanning everyone in the room, she purred, "Things will look better, come morning."

Since Dad was working out of town, Mother phoned her parents in Osawatomie after our hasty supper.

"Call the sheriff, now!" Grandfather Kearney advised.

"Dad, you know what'll happen if I do," Mother sighed. She hoped to keep the news quiet, not adding to the shame. As it was, shame was huge news in Louisburg. Most townsfolk called it news, but Mother called it gossip—what "trailer trash" huffed to waste time. She'd have none of that. Had Mother called the sheriff, she might just as well have rolled through town with a public address system: "Attention, Jeb Crocker turned up drunk again, and he's been beating on his mousy wife! But she showed him what for, and now he's sputtering on the floor in his own blood!" (It wasn't that the sheriff couldn't keep a secret; it was only that he'd never done so.)

After phoning Grandfather, Mother readied everyone for bed. Lilia stayed in Mother's room, the three boys slept in the "boys" room, and the two younger Crockers bedded down with Janice and Ann. Dianne slept on a cot on the other side of a locked door in our second floor bathroom. She insisted on the lock. That way, if she caught wind of him at her door, she'd have time to "pump him full of lead!"

The night wore on, dragging every squeak and shadow front and center to conjure it into a bloodthirsty and sinister Mr. Crocker, hell-bent on revenge. I scared myself by thinking, What if Mr. Crocker's dead? Would he haunt us as a demon ghost? And what if he's alive? Would he be any less dastardly as a demon madman?

Tossing in my bed, I dreamt feverishly of all kinds of intruders skulking. They lay in wait, itching to pounce. Suddenly, I caught sight of Mr. Crocker's face, his eyes closed in sleep—death, or feigned unconsciousness. It didn't matter which, seeing as how his eyes fluttered open. I jolted awake to see eerie, bloodshot eyes piercing me! "He sees me, just as I see him," I fretted. Sweat drenched my tangled forelocks. " He lives! He lives in a drunken stupor, and he'll come looking for his family. There'll be hell to pay!" I gasped.

I was right. Standing in the yard with my sister Mary, I watched her activate our solar-powered clothes dryer. She hung clothes on cords strung between two metal poles. I was watching the garments flutter in the early morning breeze when I caught a flicker of light on the south road. Sure enough, there was a shotgun-toting figure marching along the top of the hill about a quarter mile south of us. Faint puffs of dust shrouded his feet as he trudged toward our farm.

Out went the alarm. "He's coming! He's coming, and he's toting a shotgun!" my sister and I bellowed all through our house.

Mr. Crocker eased himself over the barbed wire fence lining the road, and then he scampered down the hill toward the creek.

He could have been hunting rabbits, I guessed. I felt embarrassed that I might have sung a false alarm. Just to be sure, I darted to the walnut tree. I shimmied up with, my heart racing. A chill shot down my spine when I saw the "demon madman" racing up the pasture east of our house. (Racoons tracked by baying bloodhounds take to the creek to hide their scent, and Mr. Crocker had done the same.) Did he aim to trap Lilia before she could flee?

I scrambled down that walnut tree fast enough for its bark to furrow my legs. "He's coming, right up our barnyard!" we hollerd. "He's coming, and he's nearly at our gate! He's coming!" And there he was: Mr. Crocker himself in person, sprinting toward our house with his shotgun in tow.

"I'll handle all of this. You kids stay out of sight," Mother ordered, tense and low. "Quick. Upstairs! Hide under a bed, in a closet! Lilia you go to my bedroom. Lock the door!" Most of us did as we were told. "Everything will be all right," Mother murmured, probably more to herself than anyone in particular. "I'll send him home . . . alone."

My siblings and most of the Crockers darted to safety under beds and in closets, while Dianne locked herself and her rusty gun in the upstairs bathroom. I crept downstairs to watch over Mother, vowing to protect her. Clutching a brass letter opener, I was more than ready to plunge my weapon where it would hurt most. It glinted menacingly. Hovering in the morning shadows of our utility room off to the west side of our kitchen, I was ready to heave that letter opener into his guts to save us all! My heart pounded almost as loudly as Mr. Crocker's banging on our kitchen door.

"Mrs. Redmond, open up. I know they're in there!" Mr. Crocker's heavy voice snarled with a slur. He'd been drinking again. "Open up, or I'll kick 'er in! You know I will!"

Glancing furtively around the room, Mother brushed off her dress, and she smoothed its creases while she strode to the door. "Boom! Bang! Clank!" sounded as Mr. Crocker rammed the butt of his shotgun against the metal door frame. Tossing her head back and taking in a solid breath, Mother muttered, "Stop," as she creaked open the locked inside door. Just as she wouldn't have opened a wild tiger's cage, she certainly wouldn't unlock the screen door for a crazed man.

"Now, Jeb," she purred, "you head right back home. Yes, Lilia is here. She and the kids plan to rest here with me for a few days. You need some time alone, too. Head home where you won't be disturbed."

"You're harborin' my whole damn family, and I won't have it!" he barked. Even through the dried blood and the mean bruise on his forehead, I spied a throbbing vein. "I want all of them, especially that little bitch Dianne!"

My fingers clasped the reassuring metal of my letter opener. Glancing down to ensure its loyalty, I saw crimson streaks trickling down my right hand. I had clutched that opener so firmly that it had become part of me. Now, I was becoming part of it. "Get ready," I told myself. "Steady now. Not yet, not yet."

"Jeb, let me help you with that wound. I'll get my dressings."

"Never mind that. Tell me, where's that little whore? I'm gonna teach her- "

"Dianne didn't do that to you. You tripped and fell. You did it yourself. You slipped, that's all. You know it, and I don't need to tell you so. It was just an accident."

"The hell it was! Open this door, or I'll break it down! I'm the head of my family, and I'm not leaving without them! You want to see me lose it? Do you? Open up, now!" Mr. Crocker's yellowed teeth ground out the words in curses. Danger loomed in his eyes.

"Jeb, you aren't able to care for your family right now. Head home to rest. Give yourself a chance to heal. Your lump looks serious. I'm a nurse. Let me help you. Drinks and head injuries don't mix. I'll come outside to dress your wound. Let me help you, really."

Her concern settled him a bit. "No, I'm all right, Mrs. Redmond" (Such formalities like "Mrs." at a time like this? He'd learned to greet women this way when he'd been raised by a single mother, long since abandoned by her alcoholic husband, the prior Mr. Crocker. I'd overheard Lilia tell Mother all about it.) "I want to take my family home. Please, let me pass. I have a right to run my family. After all, I'm the man of the house-"

"No, you aren't welcome here today, Jeb. You know you aren't coming in," Mother's jaw clenched, her resolve clear. "Like I said, go home! We'll talk again tomorrow."

"Open the door and step aside, Mrs. Redmond. You are not a party to this!" he hissed with a wisp of respect in his formal address. Then, he pounded on the door frame again.

"I'm telling you, don't come in. Lilia and your family are my guests. In case you don't know it, Lilia and I are best friends. She's staying here. That's all."

"Mrs. Redmond, open this door . . . NOW! Don't you dare make me shoot my way in!"

Did I spot shakiness in his voice? Were his hands trembling? Yes, slowly at first, his hands twitched with growing force! Sweat beads moistened his brow. His eyes softened and glistened. His frame—weakened by years of heavy drinking—stooped more . . . fragilely.

It looked as if his enraged eyes began to plead for help, like a man with a raging fever who craves icy relief. Maybe he wasn't really demanding that Mother surrender his family. Maybe he was begging for help. I knew he must've been desperate because a man is raised never to ask another man—much less a woman—for help. And here he was asking Mother for help. That meant dishonor, and a man without honor was no man at all. Shame lived.

Mr. Crocker was wrestling with two mighty forces which conspired to rip apart his soul: betrayal and shame. He had to know Lilia feared him.

She probably didn't love him anymore. Did that give her cause to go around blabbing his business to the world? Maybe their marriage needed love, long since stunted by kicks and blows.

Could he feel anything but shame when he thought about how he couldn't support his family? That led to beating his wife and then his daughter. Maybe as he beat them, was he watching a stranger in horror? He had to return to himself and to the shame of what he'd done. All of that incited more attacks. Shame reigned.

Maybe all that stressed Mr. Crocker to the very bursting point: so much so, that his guts aimed to explode. Don't pent-up forces in the Earth—from grinding tectonic plates—rub against each other until something "gives"?

I sensed the change. His bombast and hardness gave way. Shifting his weight from foot to foot, he teetered on the verge of collapse. Did he mimic layers of unstable snow sliding apart at their interfaces. His attitude melted, the way layers of snow are warmed and softened by sunbeams on a mountain pass seconds before they collapse in an avalanche. I imagined Mr. Crocker was about to fall apart, and my fear blossomed into another feeling. I wanted to reach out to him, to tell him things would be all right.

His fingers only casually toyed with his gun. Was he about to cry? If he did, God help us! If Mr. Crocker knew shame before he cried, his life wouldn't be worth a tinker's damn afterwards. You see, crying was an unpardonable sin for any man. Did I dare run out of my hiding place to offer him a tissue?

"Jeb, you should know that the sheriff is coming. Things will go poorly if he catches you here. That would be trespassing, and I'll press charges. That won't impress your parole officer." Mother tugged once at her pressed dress, adding authority to her statement. Mr. Crocker was on probation for provoking a disturbance at the county seat last fall. "Now get off my farm,"she ordered with a gentle but certain voice, not unlike a whispered command.

In the distance, puffs of dust and a low rumble like a miniature earthquake signaled a car racing along our south road. "There he is," she bluffed. "Leave while you can."

Jeb Crocker turned and ran, but as fast as he was, I was faster. I caught him at the end of our driveway. I wanted to tell him, "Never give up." I wanted to show him that I cared, that I understood him a pinch. But, what could I do?

I fished my silver dollar from my pocket. "Don't you spend it!" I remembered. "It is valuable." Reflexively, I shouted, "Mr. Crocker, please wait!" He paused a second, his eyes scurrying up to meet mine, and in a heartbeat I tossed him the silver dollar. "Good luck to you. All the luck in the world."

That scene unfurled as if in slow motion, a faint melody in the background. I imagined sparks and colors swirling from his torso. They swished over me, too. In that precise moment he caught the dollar, I saw a flicker of hope rise in his eyes, reflecting the silver dollar in his hand. In that instant, I knew we were friends, even though anger and shame isolated us from one another. Then, in an instant Jeb Crocker was gone, leaving the way he came: through the pasture and down the valley toward the creek.

Trudging back to the kitchen, I spied Mother calming Lilia Crocker just the way she'd calmed PJ when he tore up his ears: "There, there, honey. It's all right. It's all right now."

Yanking the screen door open, I officiously announced, "He's gone. He won't be coming back, you know."

Mrs. Crocker didn't look at all relieved.

"I mean, never! He's gone for good!" I stomped my foot for good measure.

Abused by his father, Mr. Crocker beat his family. Shame, uncontrollable and unquenchable, thrived. I wondered if the victim sometimes becomes the victimizer. I thought maybe so, but then I was a child who hadn't been beaten by Mr. Crocker. I'm sure his family saw it differently.

Maybe Mr. Crocker aimed to love too completely, or was he in love with love itself? With its absence, his marriage shriveled. Did he fail? The question haunted him, and maybe that led him to drink . . .

So, he left town—for good—and was never heard of again. And while most folks would call it abandonment, I knew better. That last morning at our farm his eyes oozed unspeakable mourning. In that way he was likely the greatest victim of all.

His family carried on and even prospered without him. Lilia divorced her husband and remarried within the year. She was much happier for it, thank you very much. A well-to-do and doting stepfather showered her kids with gifts, and he introduced them to "the right people" to get started in life.

Mother had triumphed, intervening just in time. Yet, I felt badly for Mr. Crocker. "He's all alone," I mused, as I watched him run off. And I'm proud to say, I cried that day. I cried for Mr. Crocker, whom few understood, and who would live on simply doing the best he could. That's how I chose to remember him.

To this day though, I wonder whether that fool dollar lived up to its name. Did Mr. Crocker find the peace he craved? Did he find the love he needed to spark meaning into his shattered life?

I'd like to fancy that he might have found peace and love. I sure did when I warmed it up in my sweaty palms. I declare, that was one mighty fine Peace Dollar!

Waiting for the Bombs to Fall

Spidery shadows cast by barren walnut branches streamed through my bedroom window. They swelled and ebbed to outline a host of pale forms, skulking and darting. From my hiding place, I spied the crescent October moon, its silver moonbeams casting solace over our forlorn prairie. That night I needed comfort, that night in October 1962.

Listening, I stretched the covers over my head. Scratching in the bushes meant invaders hid there—waiting . . . waiting to pounce. Were they fixing to swarm our farm like a bunch of hungry locusts? They'd gobble our fescue field, and then they'd burp, "delicious". Not satisfied, they'd gorge on our cows, sheep, and every last spud we'd hidden in our shed. How dare they let us to starve! Well, they dared, and I tried to act like I didn't know better.

There it was! The full-throated shriek of a little boy seized around the neck and being choked to death. Or . . . was it . . . a screech owl's hoot?

A hideous warning whistle lapped the darkened Kansas prairie. This was no test of the emergency broadcast system. This was the real thing, warning against a missile attack at ground zero: our farm. Well, Kansas City was ground zero, but our farm might as well have been it. I could feel the rumble of monstrous concrete plates grinding apart to free smoke-breathing dragons from Air Force silos over Kansas and Nebraska. Their killing salvos would erupt from ovals of death that rode on fiery missiles.

"This is only a test of the Emergency Broadcast System," droned the hall radio. "We repeat, this is only a test. In the event of an actual emergency, you will be instructed where to tune for official information. We repeat, this is only a test . . ."

Maybe if I played dead like an o'possum, the Communists wouldn't find me. Maybe they'd unleash their bombs somewhere else. But what if they did drop their bombs somewhere else, like Omaha? But as they aimed their missiles at the last second before launch, what if someone bumped the controls, sending them off course? The might blast my family and everything else to bits. How long could we last? Do thoughts last long after incineration? Do they hang like morning vapors under sunlight for a spell before flames sear them into shadows?

Earlier that evening we prayed two decades of the rosary—one more than usual. President Kennedy had revved us up. He'd stared into our living room, and he'd asked us to pray. "There are nuclear missiles in Cuba." His unblinking face said this was deathly serious. "An attack by Cuba on the United States will be seen as an attack by the Soviet Union. Such an attack will be answered by a full 'retaliatory response.'" He did not blink. Heck, I didn't know what a retaliatory response was, but it had to be horrid. A fiery tingle shooting down my spine had told me so.

"Pray for the United States," he said.

Mother's ashen face might have messed up her vision because she fumbled with the television's power knob. Motioning for us kids to come sit around the dining room table, we obeyed—everyone except for Mary, that is. She swayed in her easy chair, her right hand dappled over her left arm as if she comforted herself. At first she looked like she had enough steam to rise, but then she fizzled. After Mother shot her a killer look, Mary moved—*fast*.

With as much care as you might handle shards of glass, Mother peered at each of us kids. Clearing her throat, she asked, "Do you understand?" Most of us nodded in double-time. My sister Julie sobbed.

"Oh, Julie, don't be afraid. It'll be all right," I assured her. This was how a brave, nearly grown-up boy handled scary times. But I'll confess, I was a mite frightened about those Cuban bombs. Deep down, I might have been scared enough for my teeth to be a-rattlin' like a hog eating charcoal.

"Now kids, things look bad. Quite bad." She patted the children sitting on either side of her. "Let's pray for our nation and for the world." We folded our hands. "We must not forget the people in the Soviet Union and Cuba either."

"No way. Not the Russians," one of my brothers barked.

"The people in the Soviet Union and Cuba, too," Mother repeated. "We need to pray very hard. Pray the rosary." She waited for us to nod yes. We held our breath instead. "All right?"

"Holy Mary, Mother of God, pray for us sinners, now and at the hour of our death. Amen. Holy Mary, Mother of God, pray for us sinners, now and at the hour of our death. Amen. Holy Mary, Mother of God, pray for us sinners, now and at the hour of our death . . ."

Having learned to tell time, I flinched over my thoughts about "the hour of our death". We might all die when our kitchen clock chimed the hour, right? But once the hour had chimed, we'd be all right until the next hour had passed. Likewise, the Communists could attack only on the hour—attack Kansas City, that is. But, maybe then it wouldn't be the hour of our death after all. Maybe it would be the hour of getting hurt instead. After all, Kansas City was a world away: thirty miles. And we were in the country, tucked away at the end of a dirt road. And maybe a different person—a steady one—would launch the bomb, and it would hit its target. It wouldn't wobble off course. And besides, it was dark outside.

During the second decade of the rosary, I crept to the kitchen. (Rough times called for stealth.) Hmm, how could we dodge the bombs to stay safe from the Communists? Finding a nubbed #2 pencil, I began to gnaw, sharpening the pencil and my plans.

I needed a war map. Sans paper, I drew a large oval—Kansas City—on the white table top instead. The newscasters thought Communists would strike there because it has industry and defense plants. Folks spoke about Kansas City's limestone caves chock-full of secrets that the Communists were itching to steal. Did hideous, fire-breathing dragons loom in those caves? Were they ready to deliver lethal cargos if they were bothered? Were those dragons aching to fly around like parched peas in a hot skillet? Were they restless enough to roam around the darkened prairies, like a bug on a hot night?

Below Kansas City, I drew a small circle for Stanley. I dotted in its bank building and crown: a chiming clock. That clock must be tolling eight o'clock, I thought. Maybe the Communists would tote it back to Moscow to show it off as their trophy. I couldn't imagine much else they'd want to steal from Stanley.

People needed an escape route to the south. What road? Ahh, that's it, US Highway 169. Being the military strategist that I was, I knew the enemy would want to guard US 169. Everyone needed to move fast to escape. "Thump, thump," I drummed my pencil and focused mightily. Next I drew Aubry as a small circle on the left side of the highway. I added its Sinclair gas station. Would the invaders be tickled by the orange balls inside a glass panel atop the gas pumps? Those balls spun while we filled our tank, and I reckoned they might be dizzy from the gas fumes. Wouldn't the Communists' little boys for sure fight to play on the plastic green brontosaur grinning in front of the station? That funny dinosaur looked as foolish as a jackass eating briars. But aside from the grinning dinosaur, there wasn't much else they'd aim to snatch from Aubry.

Below Aubry came Wea with its wood and metal steeple reflecting moonlight into the evening sky. Seeing as how I couldn't decide how the

Communists could haul away a steeple, I guessed they'd leave it be. Anyway, Father Shudders reported, "The Communists don't have much call for churches."

Next came a bunch of farms, fields, and pastures with the usual barns, sheds, and houses. Maybe the Russians needed to grow food for brave people who lived in the frigid North. Well, if that was true, I giggled, they'd be in for a surprise! Did they know what a powerful deal of hard labor farming is? Did they care to know about our rocky soil?

Would they want our rusty grain silo, its tin siding cracked and dangling in pieces? It slumbered in our east pasture. Long ago the past owner abandoned it. And so it stood as a monument to who-knows-what. A birch tree took to growing inside of it, like a gigantic potted plant. Apart from that, it seemed suited only for grown-up talks. That silo became their pitcher of water to prime their talking pumps. But no levelheaded Communists would be much interested in boring grown-up talks.

And how about our gray goose? She hissed hot breath, and she stabbed her beak menacingly at passersby. Was her only talent strutting around the barnyard to strike terror? Too tough to eat, she was too annoying to live. Surely, invaders with any sense would either kill or ignore her. There could be no in-between.

My map complete, I ceased doodling on the table. I'd almost convinced myself our farm was safe, even if the Communists did attack. But, I couldn't be sure. Could anyone?

I began wondering if another little boy, a Russian, listened anxiously to a radio for reports. Did he let his chin drop like a widder-woman's pig? Was that farm boy in a cold land, frozen silent, on a still piece of Russia? Was he worried about bombs from the United States that might fall on him? Was he scared skinny? I could make out his worried face, aglow in flickering light from dying fireplace embers. Did he live at the dead end of a dirt road? Maybe he outlined "the facts" on a paper tablet resting on his desk in a darkened corner of his room. Did the sound of only the wind keep him company? Or, were his uncles sitting around a table, cheering, "Death to the United States!" Standing to smash their cognac glasses in the fire place, they might chant, "Long live the Mother Land!"

I began daydreaming about a red-haired lady who'd wiggled herself out of many jams. I dreamed of her husband who took to thumping his fingers up his coat sleeve as he bellowed, "Lucy! What did you do this time?"

She seemed unlucky, enough so that it might have been money in her pocket had she never been born. But even when she looked trapped, she found a way to escape troubles. I spotted her that night in October as she bristled on the balcony of her New York apartment. Puffing Lucky Strikes, she peered over the skyline. Her face looked drawn and tense. When she heard, "This is an official news update," on her radio inside her apartment, she rubbed out her cigarette and glided inside to turn up the volume.

There I was, sitting on her couch with my shirt tail all balled up in one fist, the other hand fiddling with my hair. She took one look at me and said in her gravely voice, "Now, kid, don't you fret. We'll make it through all right. Things aren't as bad as you think they are."

I clutched my shirt tighter.

"Now, now, be brave, and you'll be all right," she purred. Then, she sat down on the couch, and she turned to the window. "Don't you worry, kid. It isn't that bad. I should know."

"Ma'am?" I asked.

"Yes?"

"May I stay and wait with you for a spell?" The woman broke her gaze from the city view which had transfixed her. Mechanically, she turned to face me.

"Sure, kid. But why?"

"Well, you know, just like everyone else, I'm waiting."

"Waiting?"

"Waiting for the bombs to fall."

Smiling, she patted my hand and drew me near. "All right, kid, if you say so." Then, she laughed , and "poof" she drifted away.

"Mom, Sean scribbled all over the kitchen table again!" Janice gleefully tattled. Her victory was short-lived. Mother didn't have the heart or steam to scold me. She mumbled, "Sean, time for bed."

Mother stuck with me while I washed my face, put on my pajamas, and brushed my teeth. Climbing into bed, I reassured her. "Everything will be all right. Besides, even if the Communists do attack, which they won't, they probably won't bother with our farm." I nodded to agree with myself. "Besides, we'll be safe if we're brave."

Giving me one of her serious, "and-what-makes-you-so-sure?" looks,

Mother frowned. I sputtered, "It's true," as I burrowed underneath my blankets.

"What convinced you?"

"Oh, I know it. You see, I've got it on good authority."

Mother blinked to keep from laughing. "Good night, Sean."

I knew we'd be all right. A funny redhead had told me so.

Dusty Tales

Dust clouds on Kansas farms ebb and flow in swirls to form oddly shaped bodies. While we didn't need much to remind us, a boarder on our farm did just that. He arrived in a cloud of dust during a dry spell, and he scared us with it, hovering like an all-day fog. "Sean, meet Mr. Zettle, Mr. Carl Zettle," Mother said, springing from our white Pontiac station wagon. Inching toward our car, I spied a gray-haired man who edged himself onto our driveway. Once out, Mr. Zettle stood hunched enough to make me figure he'd been living for some time under Jupiter's crushing gravity. He peered at the ground.

"Hello, I'm Sean Redmond," I said hoping he couldn't tell I was afraid of him.

"Pleased to meet you," Mr. Zettle mumbled, sheepishly offering his hand as he looked up slightly. His brown eyes toted no light, and that sight raced my heart. As I touched his clammy hand, he flinched as if singed. "How old are you, boy?" he queried, looking up about ten degrees more.

"I'm four, thank you very much."

Mr. Zettle squinted like he'd just stared into direct sunlight. And he kept right on squinting as he commenced to wet his lips. He fidgeted like a gun-shy dog that whines and nudges up to a hunter's camp. I stared, wondering who is this man?

He was Mother's favorite patient at Osawatomie State Hospital. She spoke of him often, this man who voluntarily settled there. He had not been committed, meaning he was free to come and go with a note from his doctor. I wondered if he tried to row away when the last flood hit the past Memorial Day. Maybe he thought he would be trapped there, and maybe he tried to leave before the waters rose over the pasture and up the hill where the hospital lay.

One morning over breakfast Mother said she had invited one of "them" to live with us.

"Live with us?" I blinked.

"Yes, live with us," Mother said. "He needed my help so I said, 'Carl, why don't you come and live on my farm for a spell? Maybe you'd feel better there. But don't expect a free ride. You'll earn your keep making fence and such, and by helping me corral my kids.' " (She's asking an insane man to move in with us? She didn't exactly say he was from the locked ward, which is where the murderer lived, the one she mentioned once, but-) "Yet, knowing how much he loves time alone to read, I said, 'The rest of the time will be yours to spend as you like.' I also said that he was welcome to bring his books."

That settled it, and within a few days I was gawking at a man whose face looked lost, enough so that I wasn't afraid of him anymore. Mr. Zettle pulled a bag of clothes off of the back seat of the car, and he flung it over his left shoulder. Then he scooped up a stack of books: some of them fancy with leather covers, and others with dust covers he had fashioned from brown paper sacks. He rested them on his right hip.

"I have a little room for you just off of the kitchen," Mother said. "It's our utility room, but I'll make sure you have a corner to yourself." Then, pointing to his books she said, "I'll ask Tom to rig up a shelf for those. He'll be glad to know there'll be a man around when he's away." And so Mr. Zettle grew out of his hunch, stretching to become nearly a giant. He followed Mother into our house.

What a lonesome man! Why, I need to do something. But what? That's it: I'll become his friend. Yes, that's what I'll do, I thought.

One morning as I was pouring over a leather-bound book Mr. Zettle had left on the kitchen table, he approached me. "I could read to you if you wish." He grew partial to reading in bed in the utility room. I hovered nearby on a wooden rocker stained dark.

Did I want him to? "Oh yes, please." And that was that. Mr. Zettle began reading *The Three Musketeers*. From then on we were friends of a peculiar nature. He read to me from a variety of books: some leather bound like *Great Expectations*, and others with dust jackets he crafted from brown paper sacks. Across each jacket he'd scrawl the title with crayons and a pencil. His printing was wiggly—from old age or illness, I wasn't sure—but I could make it out all right. Sometimes he went on to decorate his dust jackets. There were tales of adventure, like *Treasure Island*, done up all proper in red letters with jewels; tales of mystery and of romance, like *Wuthering Heights*, with brown and yellow flowers on them; and the book he was most partial to—mystery and ghost stories— a collection by Edgar Allen Poe. We gasped over *The Pit and the Pendulum*, *The Tell-Tale Heart* and *The Fall of the House of Usher*. Those were decorated all Halloween-like, in black, white, and orange. The later covers stoked my imagination enough to scare me a pinch.

Mr. Zettle's reading segued into telling stories. He offered tales of

adventure and danger, of storms and shipwrecks. He swished us to foreign countries and battles where we spotted ghouls and demons.
Whatever the story, I was hooked.

But our friendship wasn't always easy. Some days I'd ask for a story
and he'd light right up, but then other days I'd ask, and he'd be surly and
downright nasty. But like a moth drawn to a flame, I'd suffer any of his
moods for a decent tale. It wasn't too long before Mr. Zettle and I settled
into our respective roles. We often carried on something like this: I'd
stumble into his room where he lay on his bed. Luxuriating in his novels,
he stretched out his legs, his feet lounging over the end of the bed. His
toes poked through his mouth-nibbled socks. I'd flop my chest onto his
bed, and I'd prop my chin on my palms as I fixed my eyes on him.

One evening I was firmly at this when Mr. Zettle cautioned, "I really
couldn't care less about anything you might want." I suppose he was
brushing me away like a pesky fly, but I wouldn't be brushed. Besides,
my brothers and sisters were waiting for me just outside of his room.
They'd shoved me in here "to ask" for a story. "Why me?" There I was,
the baby of the bunch, up against Mr. Zettle who was older than dust!

"Because you're cute," Paul said.

"And besides," Mary reminded me, "He's grown partial to you."

Yes, he did like me, even when he scolded, "Sean, you're a real hellion: curious and pushy, and not afraid to show it."

So there I was, as cute as a speckled pup under a red wagon, leaning
on his bed, and rocking from side to side. After a pregnant pause Mr.
Zettle let his book drift to his chest. "What is it now?"

"Oh, nothing," I began. "But, whatcha' readin'?"

"You know, the same old tired dribble." Mr. Zettle went back to his
reading.

After another yawning pause I asked, "Well? What's it called?"

"*The Hound of the Baskerville*s."

"Scary?"

"Not really. You recall, it's the one by A.C. Doyle." He had to be
warming up to me because otherwise he wouldn't have offered that last
morsel.

I said, "Oh, I remember. I reckon it's frightening and *electrifying*." Mr.
Zettle averted his eyes from his book to peer at me. A line creased his
forehead.

"How so?"

No answer.

"How so?" he demanded.

A-ha! I had him. "Well—I'll wager anything written by A.C. Doyle
must be electrifying. After all, he's named after electrical current, isn't
he? A.C.?"

Mr. Zettle shoved his book to his thighs.

"You must think you're cute. I'm sad to inform you othewise." He slowly raised his book while casting me an evil eye.

I wasn't beaten, not by a country mile. Fidgeting, I stood there waiting. I shifted my weight from foot to foot, tugged at my shirttail, and twirled my forelocks until finally, like an old laying hen warming her eggs, Mr. Zettle shouldered his way deep into his bed. Then he eased back to sit nearly upright, his eyes softening a mite. Come on, come on, I thought. I rapped a foot against his bedpost.

"May I help you?" Mr. Zettle asked.

"Thank you kindly. If you don't mind, and if you aren't busy, I was wonderin' if you could, if you would, well, er . . . that is-"

"What is it, boy? Out with it!" I jumped. Was I nervous enough to heave on the old man? "Could you spare a few moments from your reading? I . . . um . . ." Mr. Zettle's faded back to his book. Hurry, before it's too late, I thought. Then I blurted, "Will you tell me a ghost story? Please?"

With this, a smidgen of a smile crossed Mr. Zettle's lips. He stared through me for a couple of beats. Then, he answered, "Well, all right— but just this once."

Here I threw all caution to the wind. "May my brothers and sisters hear the story, too?" By now my siblings were mighty proud of themselves for sending me in to battle, especially since it sounded like I was winning. I spied them, flashing each other a thumbs-up sign, or some such nonsense.

"Chores first," was all he said, loud enough to be heard in the kitchen. Our talk had ended.

My how fast we kids clipped through chores whenever a ghost story waited. (I wonder if Mother had planned this when she invited Mr. Zettle into our home.) Well sir, after finishing our chores, changing into our pajamas, brushing our teeth, and speeding through the rosary, we filed into Mr. Zettle's tiny room to stand in semicircle about a semi-god. He sat straight up in bed, illuminated by candlelight. He harbored a dislike of electric lights owing to their "unnatural, harsh glow." Instead, he favored lighting that undulated to gentle, evening breezes, leaking through his "bedroom" window.

In his room, shadows panted and lurked in corners, swayed on walls, and quivered across the ceiling. They lived! Sitting there, I longed for his fiendish tales. Shadows floated on evening breezes, growing longer and longer still. Each one dared us not to be thrilled. Panting shadows flickered near his bed, as if they showed up to animate an already too-scary tale. Their presence tingled, albeit spooked me, and I worried about an "accident", even before Mr. Zettle uttered a word.

Mr. Zettle cleared his throat, a signal for horseplay to cease. Then, he began in a low voice, "There once lived a Spanish explorer named Ponce de Leon who roamed the New World. There he discovered hundreds of Indian tribes and millions of bison. But this wasn't enough for him. Dear Lord, no. He strove to live forever so that he might explore, discovering new lands and making friends. He searched desperately for the Fountain of Youth." Mr. Zettle raised his voice, "He craved youth even more than gold and silver, more than home and family, more than a captain's wench. Wandering the Great Plains, he looked for that fountain until he died—and then even after that."

We braced ourselves for what was coming up: waves of terror like a tsunami pounding barren shores.

"Yes, Ponce de Leon spent his life in his quest. Failing, he cursed his fate on his deathbed. 'What else might I have done? May I never rest until I soak in my Fountain of Youth.'"

I felt powerful sorry for Ponce, seeing as how even as a child I could imagine the feeling that must ooze from a soul after one tries and tries, yet falls short of his goal. I thought of the quiet dignity of our farming friends who, like Ponce, kept on doing their best even when it looked like they might fail. I thought of Dad.

Mr. Zettle leaned forward, peering at us. "His body dried out, crumbling to dust. You know 'dust to dust' from the Bible? His powdery remains should have gone on their way to mix with prairie dust—but they didn't! No, the prairie wind had other plans. It scooped up Ponce de Leon, and it toted him all over the Great Plains." Our storyteller hunched his shoulders, and then he squinted to whisper, "And that wasn't all the old winds did."

A shiver shot through us kids.

"It moaned as if it too agonized over never finding the Fountain of Youth." Mr. Zettle stopped. This was the time when our eyes begged him to continue. "Presently, the wind moaned to Ponce, 'I'm tired of all this howling on your behalf, so I'm stopping. I've a plan though, just in case we don't find your fountain. If I run across a naughty child who doesn't do his chores, I'll drop your dust where he is. There, you'll suck the youth out of him so that by the time you're through with him, he'll be dust, and you'll be the young man.'" Our jaws hung low as our fright soared high. Mr. Zettle slid his finger along his headboard, collecting a dribble of dust. He made like he was going to blow it at me—No, please no!—then casually, he wiped it on his pants.

"Now, Ponce was mighty pleased—that is until the wind said, 'You'll use up that child's life within two weeks. After that you'll return to dust. Then you must drink from the Fountain of Youth or suck on another naughty child. But don't worry Ponce, because I know of a family not so far from here that has eight children.' One, two, three, four, five, six, seven, eight," Mr. Zettle counted off each of us. His voice quivered, and his words sped up. "The wind shrieked in fiendish delight, 'Ooooo-eh-eh-eeeeeh!'"

Mr. Zettle's wicked looking eyes sent me back a step. Some of the girls dug their fingers into the hands of the one standing nearest.

"First the wind finds a child and knocks on his gate. Then it waits outside the door. Then, it throws itself against the door until Ponce's dust grains swish through, hovering until he decides which child he'll . . . Then? He slurps life from the hellion until all that's left of him is a startled, orphaned gasp." With that, Mr. Zettle exhaled and stopped. I was only starting. Shifting all over the place, I searched that utility room—now a dungeon of doom—for signs of that cursed dust. Could it be stalking one of us?

"I wonder who's next?" Mr. Zettle gloated. He leaned forward, our signal that the story was over, but he stopped halfway up and listened. "What was that?" he asked. We stopped breathing. "Can't you hear it? Ooooo-eh-eh-eeeeeh? Oh no—he's right at the gate," Mr. Zettle whispered. "Now he's just outside the door." He started twitching. "He's forcing his way under the doorsill and, oh no, there, look, I see demon vapors swirling forward, shaping into a hand, moving toward—YOU!"

I couldn't make out my screams from those of my siblings. "He has me, he has me!" Mark and Mary together bawled, spewing salvia. One droplet hit Mr. Zettle's spectacles resting on his bed table.

Mark bit Jean's hand—but hard. "He's got me, he's got me, too!" Mary howled. This sent her tearing from the room with Julie clinging to her pockets like a pilot fish on a shark. I dove under Mr. Zettle's bedcovers where I begged, "Save me from that wicked dust!"

Janice backed out of the room as she mumbed something about unfinished homework. Ann blocked one nostril and then the other to force air through her clogged nasal passages brought on by a "sudden" attack of hay fever.

"Likely story," she said. "That didn't get to me, not in the least."

"Are you obedient?" Mr. Zettle asked with the attitude of a science teacher on public television. "Do you help your mother clean the house?" Our heads bobbed like they were on untrue springs. "If you don't, be assured you're fair game for Ponce de Leon's ghost. And if he hunts you, well, good luck!" And he blew out a candle. That old goat sent us to our beds—and nightmares—with battered consciences and a duty to inspect every nook and cranny for the least sign of Ponce de Leon's telltale dust. We were on guard for his tall tale's dust!

Mr. Zettle lived with us for about six months, after which time I remember suspecting he'd be leaving us soon. I reckon he was planning his exit at supper one evening. His eyes darted from here to there as if he expected a ghost to swirl into the room. He was spooked, that much was sure. I supposed that with sufficient cause he'd bolt from the kitchen and keep on running to parts unknown. He'd hardly touched his food before he asked to be excused from the table. There was no candle's glow seeping under his door that night, telling us there would be no story.

That night I couldn't sleep for fussing about him. When it was nearly morning, I couldn't hold my concern any longer. Creeping out of bed and to his door, I saw it was ajar. A shadowy figure slinked toward the kitchen door. Ponce de Leon? No, I knew it was Mr. Zettle. He had his bag of clothes slung over his shoulder, and he toted an armful of books. Easing the door open, he peered back into the darkened room.

"Aren't you going to say good-bye?" I whispered. He didn't answer, gliding through the doorway. It stayed open a crack. Following him out to the sidewalk, I repeated, "Aren't you going to say good-bye?"

At that he whispered, "Sean, I can't—say good-bye. All I know is— it's time to go."

"What's wrong? Is it something we hellions did? We'll be better."

"That's right, you need to do that, but this has nothing to do with any of you. I need help . . . medicine . . . the hospital."

"But-"

"My mind's on fire. You—wouldn't . . . you wouldn't . . . understand. Every second counts." His right hand trembled.

I hadn't asked him what was wrong before, and I wouldn't dream of asking him. Anyone who is that powerful ashamed or spooked doesn't need someone like me to mound torment on his already considerable pile.

"Why are you toting your books? Can't you send for them or at least let us carry them to you?"

"They probably won't let me keep them anyhow. I thought it might do me good to . . . to . . . carry them one last time."

"But why, Mr. Zettle? What's wrong with staying here? Don't you like us?"

"I like you—all—just fine. No more questions."

"So, you're sneaking away to avoid our nosey questions?" I had to make sure I understood, and my face reddened as I saw he was right.

"Yes, yes, a—thousand times—yes," he said. "Let me go."

"But what about our stories?"

"You and your damn stories! Kid, there's always a story. Just look around." Mr. Zettle paused to breathe. Then he stammered, "There's a story in the barnyard, in the breeze, in the trees. There's a story in the pasture and in the birds' songs. Listen for them, hear them the best way you know how. Story, indeed! Just use your eyes, your ears, your nose. Sniff the story in the wind. Taste the story on your lips: feel the story as you face into the wind. The story's always there. Take the time to sense it."

"How about a special story for me right now—to remember you?"

"Hell no!" Mr. Zettle turned to walk away, and then he looked back. "Maybe. Yes, since you're a hopeless case. Yes." He stepped toward me. "Here, hang onto this. It's my favorite. Read it in good health!" He'd handed me his prized edition: *The Hound of the Baskervilles*. "Remember me every time you hear blue-tick hounds howling in the darkness, as they frolic over hills and into valleys, as they stalk coons."

"Oh, yes. Always."

"Remember me every time you hear a hound baying at a harvest moon, every time you hear the rush of a monstrous beast, his coat gleaming and his hideous jaws dripping with luminescent foam. Think of me as he flies full-throttle toward you on a darkened path. Remember me every time you wonder what 'goes bump in the night', every time you dodge the sinister teeth of a mad dog lunging toward your face, every time you sweep dust from the floor." My eyes traced his and rested on that book which held me transfixed, his book that I held sheepishly in my hands that early morning, its leather-bound volume with a thickness of tales to bind me with wonder.

And then, Mr. Zettle left. He drifted noiselessly down our driveway as he crept along the south road that leads to the blacktop three miles to the south. The morning's light was nearly upon us, letting me see his form bobbing in the distance. As he slid into the dawn, I lost sight of him a few times, and then I spotted him again. That happened two more times before the early morning swallowed up my final, blurred image of him.

He made it back to the hospital all right, but he died within the month. Again, I didn't ask why. I wanted to remember him as a lonely man who loved to read, one who sometimes shared that love of reading with me. He was a master storyteller, far better than anyone else I ever knew. Was it wrong to hope that I might measure up to him someday?

When I remember Mr. Zettle's stories, I think about my favorite amusement park ride. I close my eyes and hold my breath when I ride a wooden roller coaster clattering over its tracks. Such a runaway death trap "thrills us to death"! Are we really managing restlessness about what cannot be seen, about the mysteries shrouded in the fog of daily chores or in the jet-black eeriness of a moonless night?

Mr. Zettle's tales worked my mind the way a harrow works the land because they hit home—my home—with dusty teeth of fright! He delighted in telling stories that tilled my mind like a farmer who tills the musty soils on a windswept, spring day. All of Mr. Zettle's stories fed on themselves, tingling my spine, far better than could any roller coaster ride! And they helped me meet fear dead on. As Grandfather Kearney quipped, " . . . to craft sense out of life, to manage in this helter-skelter world."

When I think of Mr. Zettle, I remember my rides on his wispy words, rides that left me panting in delight, haunting me still. I remember him and all of his fiendish tales when I look toward the rolling hills on still prairies, when I imagine all the adventure in the still of the night. He showed me that stories abound, and that I needed only to listen to notice them: to feel them. I might learn to see and to hear stories dancing on evening breezes, resting on the darkness before dawn on a windswept prairie. I needed only to sniff out stories on the night air whenever I heard baying hounds hunting in the valley. If I tasted the thick night air, I'd know heavenly promises held for blue-tick hounds tracking ghostly prey.

4-H Run

"Kids! I called you more than 20 minutes ago" Mother hollered up the stairs, "Get up! Now! Sean, you too! It's a quarter past seven, and we need to leave by nine."

What was the fuss? It was Saturday morning for heaven's sake. No self-respecting kid would heave himself out of bed at a quarter past seven on a Saturday. Well, not unless there was a darn good reason.

Had I forgotten when "Under Dog", "Mighty Mouse", and Wile Coyote were on tap? Had a carload of kids swept onto our farm for play? Would a carnival come calling, daring us to resist? Since we kids *always* took Saturdays off, I wondered what Mother was fixing to do with us.

"Paul, Julie, Jean, Janice, Mary, Ann, Mark, and Sean! What did I just say?"

Well I'll be hornswaggled, I thought. Has she been snooting the vanilla extract (and I mean the real stuff)? I aimed to find out. Creeping down to the kitchen, I felt dumb from sleep. As I rubbed the night from my eyes, I spotted Jean who charged in all rabid-looking with toothpaste foaming over her lips. As I edged away from her, she began to spin in circles with a certain lost look on her face. She kept right on turning, even when Janice tromped into the kitchen to grumble, "Where's that darn essay book?" Janice stood on tiptoes as she scanned the top of the Fridgidaire.

Then, Mary bounded up.

"Move," she ordered, as she yanked open the refrigerator door, splatting Janice.

"Hey,"snapped Janice.

"I told you to move, didn't I?"

Next Paul and Mark dragged themselves into the kitchen. As they passed me on their way to the utility room, I opened my mouth with the idea of saying good morning. After they flashed a "say-one-word-and-you're-dead" look at me, I clamped my jaws shut real fast. The boys riffled through the utility room before they resurfaced in the kitchen.

"Where's my leaf book, Sean?" Paul barked.

"Yeah," Janice chimed in. "And where's my notebook?"

Then it hit me. This was that time of the month for the kids' monthly 4-H inspection at Mrs.Cunningham's house. "Say Jean, did you finish your hemming?" I asked.

Still foaming and spinning, Jean commenced to squeal and to hop about, flapping her arms. Did that mean, "No, it's not done, and there's no way it's gonna be done inside of an hour"?

Oh, there had been a time when Jean finished a hem and a dress to boot. And what a special dress it was, fashioned for Julie who was six. It called for several yards of blue broadcloth and tiers of white ruffles. Jean followed her pattern directions to the letter, and by the end Julie had her dress. It appeared hot—downright "haute couture". Everyone said so, and Jean was sure to garner a blue ribbon for it. That is, until Julie decided to take a run down the slide in Wallace Park across from the 4-H building.

Julie's ride started smoothly enough, but then a ruffle latched onto a metal edge of the slide near the top. It refused to let go. Undaunted, Julie swished right on down that slide, the ruffle holding on at the top until it trailed uphill behind her like a cottony umbilical cord. The funny thing is, Julie was still fully clothed when she hit the bottom of the slide.

Seeing trouble, Mother hastened over to the slide, persuaded Julie's ruffle to let loose, and began to wrap yards of it around her. Soon Julie looked like a miniature Kitty Carlisle from "To Tell the Truth". (We all suspected Kitty—the "Curtain Lady"—rustled her dresses from low-hanging curtain rods for her shows, what with all of that fabric dangling and folded around her.)

Mother fought back her laughter—at first. But just as she finished packing up Julie like so much tobacco in a Cuban cigar, she let lose a jagged guffaw. Why, she commenced to laugh louder and longer until tears spilled down her cheeks. The rest of us—excepting Jean and Julie, who stood stunned—joined Mother. But in short order, Jean and Julie broke down, too. We dubbed Julie's tattered, wayward dress "the queen of curtain ladies", our uniform acclamation crowing the affair.

"Mom, where's the sewing basket?" Jean called. Fortunately, she'd distracted herself from all of her hopping and flopping about the kitchen long enough to spit out her toothpaste.

"Sean?" Janice hollered. "Sean! Are you listening? I asked where did you put my notebook." She stomped her bandaged foot, the one involved in an "incident" a few nights earlier. It seems she'd been as restless as a bug on a hot night, and she traipsed downstairs for a drink of water. Well, the floor fan in the dining room decided to nip at her right big toe. "He's got me, he's got me," pierced our slumber.

Of course, this raised the house to alarm, sending every single one of us tripping over ourselves and down the stairs. We suspected we'd find Janice in a pool of blood.

Someone flipped on the lights. There Janice sat, smack in the corner of the dining room. Gripping her right big toe, she rocked herself in the corner and whistled hard times. The fan blade had peeled back only a small flap of her skin, but you'd have thought it bit off her whole foot.

Seeing the extent of her injuries, Janice ripened into shades of red. Mother decided that Janice would live, no surgery needed (and maybe only a band-aid). The rest of us decided that she needed only a sound chiding.

With the emergency over, we edged our way back to bed while Janice muttered that she didn't give a tinker's damn about the electric bill, not anymore. No sir, she would turn on the lights, no matter what. (She'd taken Dad's order to switch *off* the lights when she left a room a step further. She wouldn't switch *on* the lights when she entered a room either.)

"Where the heck is it? Sean. Where's my essay book? Did you swipe it, again?" Janice had only half accused me since she knew that I wasn't the culprit—this time. True, a year earlier I'd borrowed her fool notebook to practice printing my name, and true, I'd messed up a half a sheet of paper. But as far as Janice was concerned, a half sheet of paper was a half sheet too much, and she wasn't about to let me forget it.

"No, I didn't swipe it," I answered. "Did you try your drawer?" The three older girls each had a special velvet-lined drawer in the dining room dresser for their treasures and what have you. I'd seen Janice fling her notebook into her drawer a few nights earlier.

Janice huffed and headed for the dining room.

"There you are," Mary clucked at a flask of darkish fluid she'd pulled from the refrigerator. She'd started chilling it the night before. "You stay put now, and let me swirl you all together. Just take your time to let your flavors stew." Grandmother might say Mary "had a hen on" which meant Mary had a cooking project brewing. She carried six hard-boiled eggs to the table, along with her jar of "special" ingredients—vinegar, spices, olive oil, and God knows what. Climbing up across from her, I cradled my chin to watch her concoct deviled eggs.

Mary held a kind of smugness on her face. Was she pleased with herself for commencing her cooking project the night before it was due instead of waiting until the next morning? I wondered what had made her do such a thing. Had someone cast a spell over her?

Maybe she didn't want a repeat performance of her last cooking project. That ended with dear Mrs. Cunningham grimacing and then spitting something nasty looking into the sink. It seems Mary had read the recipe wrong, adding horseradish instead of Miracle Whip.

"I'll take my time with the next recipe. Really I will," she promised Mrs. Cunningham and anyone else who'd listen. "As God is my witness, I'll never be rushed again!"

Yes indeed, soon we'd be piling into our station wagon with our sprinkling of "in-progress" projects in hand, and we'd dash to see Mrs. Cunningham, a kindly woman on the far side of her middle years. She surrendered her spare time for our Miami County Sunflower 4-H club. She monitored the kids' progress on projects. She read essays, inspected hemlines, sampled recipes, and reviewed nature scrapbooks (leaf collections a specialty). Every project held challenges that needed finessing before Mrs. Cunningham could stamp it "satisfactory". This helped the kids earn project points for their 4-H awards.

The boys still hadn't found their leaf collection books when Paul tromped back into the kitchen and commenced closing in on me. "You made off with our books! Where the hell are they, boy?"

"Why, would I touch your fool books? Besides, didn't you all put them on our desk last night?"

As if my words were rudders, the boys veered away from me and made for the stairs. I was still making "payments" for leafing through their nature notebooks the previous fall. That meant I was suspected. I couldn't understand why they hadn't taken kindly to my need to catch up on whatever topic they studied. After all, *they* got to attend school, didn't they? I had to stay home, seeing as how my age was held against me.

Mother started out the door, her car keys in hand. "Let's not keep Mrs. Cunningham waiting," she said.

Once again her words set off a free-for-all rivaling what happens when hens and roosters are turned loose into a field of flying grasshoppers. A cloud of dust and chicken feathers, misted with squawking, spews every which way. Finally in the car, we scrambled from the farm with Janice scribbling madly in her essay book, using words and penmanship only Mother could care to decode. Jean was threading a needle to finish her hemming—far simpler on stable ground than while bouncing around at breakneck speed. Ann speed-read the last three-quarters of her book while she smeared her clutch of sentences onto a page—which she called her book report. The boys madly pasted and slapped leaves into collection books.

Well, once we got there, Mrs. Cunningham lavished praises on their projects when she found the chance. The trouble was, she didn't spot many chances.

It wasn't so much that my siblings worked on "ill-conceived" projects. Most were well-planned and looked downright fun. And it wasn't that they rebelled, not even bothering to try. In fact, they might even have liked 4-H a pinch more than they despised the loss of freedom that came with it.

No, I reckon the problem rested squarely in the recipe. Swirl seven excitable children with two parts of hellion and one giant dollop of procrastination, and what do you get? Whatever it is, it won't be 4-H assignments finished before the "eleventh hour." Why? Because each of my brothers and sisters had promoted stalling to an art form. And I felt satisfied. Why? Because I was sure lucky to be in the midst of that high comedy—keystone cop mayhem, embattled hemlines and all.

I suppose Mrs. Cunningham pulled through 4-H reviews by reminding herself how her own youthful intentions proved more loyal than her deeds. I also suppose she enjoyed giggling under her breath when she tasted the girls' recipes with their ingredients haphazardly heaped into them. Maybe she couldn't help but laugh when she read nonsensical chicken-scratched essays, or when she brushed her fingers against still-wet paste. I suppose she also muffled gasps of disbelief when she squinted at hems done up in stitches that only a madman might have conceived. Maybe that made it all worth her while.

Despite their worst efforts, Mrs. Cunningham rewarded most of the perpetrators with a "satisfactory" stamp. With that the kids would spin round about, smiling nervously. Their stamp meant they'd be eligible for district competition and real prize money, maybe two whole dollars. That meant loads of spending money for the Paola carnival in August, our final fling before school days. But could the kids hope for Mrs. Cunningham's same leeway at the district meets? Once I heard about one of our club members rising to state competition, promising yet higher prize money.

I wondered how she chose which projects to recommend to district competition. Did she sift through disastrous projects with hopes of advancing the "least shoddy" ones? Maybe, but not always. Come to think of it, even Mary—or was it Jean?—once brought home a red ribbon for a no-bake cookie recipe. I know, because I rode my bike to a friend's house for the recipe. A certain German Shepherd there insisted that my britches allow more airflow. His tugs to tell me so registered firmly all up and down my pant legs and seat.

Mrs. Cunningham must have seen hope in some of the least obvious places, finding meaning in messes: uneven hemlines, spelling errors, and all. She must have seen something in everyone, and that kept her going. Maybe it was the rare, hard won victory that convinced Mrs. Cunningham to volunteer as our 4-H leader year after year for more than ten years. Yes, I say "our" leader, because soon enough I joined in on the Saturday morning 4-H runs.

And for all of her caring I say, God bless you, Mrs. Cunningham, wherever you are.

$\mathcal{F}$resh Milk and Fodder

Twice daily we bargained with our Jerseys: at dawn and at dusk we swapped pails of feed, buckets of water, and piles of fodder for their milk. They bellowed up the hill toward our milk barn. Prime milkers that they were, our cows suffered swollen udders, the milk squirting from their tits with each step. They needed to be milked and they were hungry. I'll wager they felt sorry for us dimwits, who both fed them and eased their udders to boot. And I reckon they might have trotted toward our milk barn on that account alone, even if we ever "forgot" to feed them. Maybe they knew we fancied them as pets, figuring they'd milk that for all it was worth.

As Dad fed the cows a blend of cracked corn and milo, he petted them. "That's a good girl. What a fine girl, Mum," he'd purr, and then he'd move to Suzie. Their menu of pasture nibblings, cracked grain, and alfalfa gave them all they needed to make milk.

After cleansing their tits with sudsy water, Dad sat down to milk. If a cow was hell-bent on kicking at milk buckets, out came the "kickers", a length of metal chain joining two curved steel plates, both of which fit over the cow's hind legs. If a "kickered cow" lifted a hind leg, the other leg acted as a brake.

Unlike Ethel and Lucy who pumped a cow's tail to try milking, Dad used a more recognized method. He snuggled a tit between his thumb and index finger. Mark gripped it between his thumb and his four other fingers. I reckoned that such a grip was reserved for little boys.

The first milk squirts sounded sharp, piercing against the metal pail. Later ones grew muffled by the pooled milk. The two-part rhythm (swish-swish, swish-swish) of milk jetting into its pail threw me into a trance, and I could only gaze to the side of the barn. My right eye was squinted, and my lips tightened. The cows subtly swayed with each squirt, all the while mulling, swallowing, and then regurgitating wads of fodder—their cud. While they "chewed their cud" to process grasses, I liked to think they did it to soothe tensions, maybe the way some gum chewers do.

I felt milking all around me. Might the swish-swish be the "lub-dub, lub-dub" of a beating heart? Could a body blend aromas of grains and alfalfa to create milk? Did the sweet smell of alfalfa twitch at milk glands in cows to craft rubbery milk molecules, ones lighter than most others? Dad called that cream, and he marveled at how it rose to the top to form a skin. But what fed those flowers of alfalfa? Did something need to die to help them grow? Do grasses take on the ways of whatever died in order to live? If a body is partial to grasses, does that mean his spirit may live on inside the grasses? Dad had lectured me on the virtues of such ideas when we read parts of Walt Whitman's "Song of Myself". Maybe Mr. Whitman was right.

Soon a creamy elixir foamed to the pail's rim: a staple for calves and kids alike. Once in the refrigerator, the cream rose. At least once a month Dad had to exclaim, "Will you look at how that cream forms a skin?" Mother took it even further. "Our rich milk forms a rubbery topping. Not a hard rubber, but a squishy one."

Cats meowed their way into the barn to rub against Dad and the boys. "Feed me, feed me," they said. At first the milkers ignored them. But as their meows grew pushier, milk squirted their way. Before long four or five tiny motors in their mouths cranked up to a steady rumble. The cats flapped their jaws even when they didn't slurp milk. But then, after a spell they shrilled, "More!" and they kept shrilling. Seeing as how they hunted mice, Dad put up with this until he finished milking. Then, each cat commenced to lick its paws. Finally, they groomed each other, making sure to track down every atom of goodness.

Once the cows meandered back to pasture, the barn became our lab, beckoning us like an invisible hand that wafts over unsuspecting faces. The barn drew us into its shaded hiding places. Sunbeams streamed in between weathered planks, and a mist of dust swirled all around us.

Our barn had seen better days. "Those boards in the walls and in the ceiling have stood for fifty years," explained Mark. Each board had begun to shrivel with age and with brittleness. I'd heard Dad talking about how some folks also grew brittle, only he called it osteoporosis. Then Dad winced, rubbing his hands crinkled with rheumatoid arthritis. His thumbs were gnarled, and they'd begun to bend away from his hand as if they were broken. That had to hurt.

"Does anyone know if a barn feels pain when it shrivels, the way people do?" I asked my siblings.

Before the last word left my mouth, I heard sweltering laughter. "What a moron!"

"Who reckons a barn feels pain?" Mark chortled.

Clouds of dust and bits of hay tried to follow us as we swished farther into the barn. The late summer's newly minted alfalfa bales rested fragrantly under and atop the hay loft. That meant we must inspect each bale. Clambering up a wooden ladder cobbled from planks long past their prime, I saw how each board was spiked to upright beams.

In the loft rested the hay bales. Sturdy twine had bound alfalfa into what looked like "Shredded Wheat" biscuits. The twine grumbled when we tried to free the hay. Paul cut the twine with his jackknife, and we tossed the hay overboard. Its sweet juices—watermelon and lemonade on the Fourth of July rolled into one—kerplopped into a pile. Did you know that a respectable pile takes at least half a dozen bales? Coughs and sneezes reminded me that hay teemed with dust.

I swished my arms while the half-century-old lumber creaked and groaned under me. That reminded me I was free to glide through space, provided the fool loft didn't decide to act up and collapse or some such nonsense.

Swaying in slow motion I called out, "Look! I'm a clump of tall grasses, floating on a sea of wind!"

"Sit down and shut up, you freak!" someone said. A wad of earth screamed past an ear. "Try growing in that, you numbskull!" someone else said.

"All right, then. I'm a castaway marooned on a miniature, alien planet. The gravity is much weaker than on earth. I'm floating!"

The kids must have taken better to that, since nothing shot by my face.

When it was time to jump into the haystack I held my breath. Once I landed on my side, I began to breathe again. Smelling the sweetness of honey, I tasted dryness swirling about my head. Then, I saw it: a rusted pitchfork, its four prongs peering wickedly at me from the corner. Would it slink into our hay pile? I quivered. Did it wait secretly for a victim to impale himself on its prongs of death? Nah, by facing my fears, they'll flee, I told myself. Then, I jumped again. Still, that phantom fork had me good and riled.

Oh sure, I fancied most of my excitement. Pedro the ram became a marauder hell-bent on robbing me, leaving me for dead. And why not? One time that mean old ram butted Grandmother Kearney off of her feet, reared up, and planted his front hooves on her stomach. He'd snorted wickedly over her. Didn't he aim to finish the job he'd started with Grandmother? I knew that he craved mashing kids with a volley of mighty blows, his horns battering us to pieces.

Likewise, other unspeakable tales flitted into me. A kicker dangling from a length of chain became a torture device in a dungeon, dark and silent. The prisoner was bound, the kickers wedged onto his legs. With the certain cranking of a wooden wheel, the prisoner was pulled to pieces, the kickers digging into his legs until bone met up with metal.

Hanging metal buckets stored poisons for games of chemical warfare. They held potions so potent that sometimes the maker fell victim himself. And so it went: ordinary objects became extraordinary. Each one looked and felt like a lethal weapon.

"My turn with the kickers," Mark said yanking them from me before he shoved me into the hay. (I "let" him have those fool kickers since he was almost twice my size. Besides, I knew he'd tire of them soon. Sure enough, he did.) Do wonderful discoveries fancy wearing out kids quickly, thereby making room for other toys? (Maybe each toy grew bashful, wishing we'd move on to another one.) Did that make playtime fun, or was it only our squabbling over each toy that did the trick?

Soon we focused on King of the Hill, a game required for any self-respecting kids frolicing in haystacks. The oldest and largest child usually crowned himself king. And after that? Avalanche. The king stands on the loft to hurl bales at his subjects. The bales were meant to "graze" the target—like knives do in make-believe knife throwing—but sometimes an excited king scored a direct hit. Bam! A bale punched out Julie. Would she come to? Would she be all right?

"I'm going inside, noooow!" she wailed as she ran for the house.

The game over, everyone but I rocketed toward the house to slake their thirst. A glass of milk usually did the trick.

Welcoming the quiet, I plopped down on a hay bale. *Naturally*, it lay opposite the pitchfork. Like the other kids, I was thirsty. My thirst couldn't be calmed by chilled milk. Tilting my head to the left, I gazed at the rafters. Sunbeams streamed between chinks in the planks, and hosts of alien worlds—dust particles—swirled in my barn galaxy. The aliens played, ran, and wondered about other worlds—as did I. My adventures calmed me. Imagining that I sat in front of a roaring fire one wintry day, I kicked off my shoes, and then I rubbed each foot with the other. What rhythmic happiness, one toasty from the inside out.

And the haystack! All of those grasses had swayed and frolicked on our pasture that last spring. First, they'd been only tender sprouts. Then, they flourished. In their prime, we mowed them down to make hay.

Mowing the grasses felt sad, and I felt sorry for them. Nevertheless, feeding hay to our Jersey cows thrilled me, and I reckoned they didn't mind it much either. Then, a warm thought came to life. Although our madcap adventures in our dusty milk barn didn't amount to much, maybe there were far more enchanting voyages in store on Earth and on other worlds! Could I feel it in my bones? Why, I might soar on mysterious voyages to ports of call unknown, my feelings toasty with real caring. Maybe I'd do that after I left my body behind, the way a snake sheds its dead skin, the way the moon casts off its waning shadow.

Dad often spoke of how the body doesn't amount to much, even though most folks thought otherwise. Uncle Art spouted, "When I die, prop me up on the prairie and let the coyotes get me. Yep—leave my shell for the varmints and the soil."

I thought Uncle Art might be on to something. What if we did what he asked? What if we left his body to tease at prairie soil, persuading new grasses to grow? I reckoned his body might return a favor to the grasses. After all, they once helped him grow. And then . . . I thought about my ducklings.

"What's snatched your imagination today?" Dad asked, drawing up to me with a milk stool.

"Oh, it's one of those times. Some powerful questions are nibbling at me."

"Name one."

"Well . . . I've been thinking about the ducklings I drowned." I sat up. "Dad, is death forever? I mean, when something dies, does it disappear for good?

"What do you think?"

Squirming at the chance to tell Dad what I'd been thinking, I began, "Do you remember burning the weeds in the south pasture last autumn?

Dad nodded and waited.

"Do you know what happened to those old pokes and weeds?"

"What?" Dad moved a little closer.

"The pasture sprouted new plants from where they were. It happened in the spring."

"Uh-huh?"

"Do you suppose the dead weeds had a part in helping new plants grow?"

"Yes, burning the weeds breaks them down. They enrich the soil with minerals."

"Enrich? Hmmm. Is that sort of like Mother cooking meals for us so that we get what we need? Is that like fertilizing us?"

Dad clapped my knee, "Well, sort of. You're getting the idea."

"Although they weren't weeds, I'm hoping my ducklings-"

"Will help something grow, too?" Dad asked.

I put my head down, ashamed. I nodded.

"What did you do with your dead friends?"

"I buried them in the garden. I wanted to wrap them in a bread bag first, but Mother said not to. She said that would slow things down."

"Do you remember exactly where you buried them?"

(Now it was my turn.) "What do you think?" I asked Dad.

"Of course you remember. Did anything grow there?"

"Dad!"

He let me steep in my newfound assurance.

"Um, Dad?"

"Sean."

"Do you suppose this works for humans too?"

"Do you have someone in mind?" He gave me one of his suspicious looks.

"Uncle Art said to prop his dead body on the prairie for the varmints to nibble. Can we do that?" Then he said what was left of him could help the soil.

Dad sighed. "Uncle Art drinks a bunch, says foolish things. We can't leave bodies on the prairie. You know that, right?"

But what if we could? My imagination shifted into full gear. What if corpses were hung all over the place like scarecrows? Wow! Then creepiness took over, and I shivered with it.

"But supposing we did as he asked? His body would help the soil, wouldn't it?"

"Yes Sean, Uncle Arthur would become human fertilizer. What does that tell you?"

"That plants and humans could form a kind of circle of life."

"Paint the entire picture with words, please."

I traced a circle with my toe and with loose alfalfa. "I know cows eat grasses in the prairie, and the grasses help them make milk. Milk feeds children and helps them grow. Then they die. If their bodies are left on the prairie, they mix with the soil to feed the new grasses, so they can grow. The bodies will enrich the soil, as you said. Cows eat the grass and make milk that feeds children and-"

"Fine, that's called a cycle. I declare, someday soon you'll be a big boy."

"Soon? I'm nearly grown now, in case you haven't noticed. Anyhow, I can't see the whole picture. Sometimes, when I turn my head to one side, squint my right eye, and twitch my cheek, I catch a glimpse of it. Like your brother."

"Uncle Jim? Where did he come all of a sudden?" Dad asked.

"There's something about him I can't look at straight, like the glaring sun."

"I know. But you're young, and-"

"You said that the last time I asked about him. How much older do I need to be?"

"Older than you are today."

"Until I'm six? Don't tell me as old as dirt, say seven?"

Dad shifted as if he readied himself to stand. He changed his mind. "I can tell you . . . a piece of what happened."

I stopped breathing. Aliens swirled nearby.

"I tried to protect him—but I failed." Dad massaged his temples, and then he cupped his fingers over his eyes. He breathed deeply. Three breaths later, he dropped his hands and slowly turned his face to mine. "Jim suffered a bunch on account of folks who knew better at the Christian Brothers' High School in Minnesota. We studied there as freshmen."

"Did the other kids yell, 'Sit down and shut up'? at him. That hurts."

"Well, that hurts gobs, but this was even worse."

"Is there anything much worse than not being able to talk when you need to?"

"Let's just say wicked things happened to him," Dad said. "Oh, I tried to stop it," Dad rubbed his temple, "but I failed. Instead of helping Jim, I was expelled, kicked out of school. The Prefect said I didn't have an 'obedient spirit.' He commanded that I leave Jim at the Christian Brothers High School. A few months later, the Prefect sent Jim home— what was left of him."

"Was it because Uncle Jim . . . ," I lowered my voice, "cried?"

"There was no doubt he was mighty sad. But no, it wasn't because of that. His mind commenced to splinter."

"I remember."

"You do?" Dad cocked his head.

"We talked about it shortly after my ducklings, um . . . died."

"I don't-."

"Well, we did, and I do. Did his mind mend when he came home?"

"It was already too late. The wickedness at the school burnt like a range fire, a wildfire that scorched Jim as if he were in a tall grass prairie. Once burned, he changed."

"When we burned pastures, the plants came back fine. Why didn't Uncle Jim come back?"

"He was too mistreated to recover. That tall grass in his prairie was too disturbed. And he was much too sweet and tender." Dad brushed some hay off of his shoe.

"Ornery thistles sure aren't done in by fire. They spring right back up, no matter what. How can they do that? And why couldn't Uncle Jim do the same?"

"Umm . . . no one knows why one plant lives while another one dies. No one knows either why some are taken while others, um, live . . . ," Dad gulped. He tried to talk, but his voice wouldn't come out solid. His nose sounded stuffed up.

Was Dad fixing to cry? Or was it all the dust? Just in case crying was fixing to sound, I studied a piece of alfalfa hard, as if I'd never seen one before.

157

"But when people are taken, there's more room for other people. Right, Dad?"

"What? Well . . . maybe."

"There's a reason they make room. I know what it is. I sure do."

"Why are kids cut down by cruel people?"

"Because those kids are fixing to rev up and strike out on voyages to ports of call unknown." I started to march where I sat.

Staring at sunlight shifting between barn boards, I caught sight of a wisp of thistledown wafting by.

"Like thistles and thistledown," I said.

Dad didn't answer . . . couldn't answer.

Could thoughts and dreams held by thistledown replace sad songs of plants that died? I'd better keep these thoughts to myself. The kids would never let me hear the end of it. And our priest? He'd say, "Have you fallen and hit your head on a rock? You better have, for you're being disrespectful." And he would be the first one to throw me to the ground so that I did hit it really hard. I didn't think priests placed much stock in 'weeds' or in how they hurt people—slicing them down for no reason.

Dad recovered. "The poet William Wordsworth might have been thinking of thistles when he wrote, 'The meanest flower that blows can give thoughts that often lie too deep for tears.' I reckon purple flowers on a common thistle are what he had in mind. But those thistles aren't common at all. They're special. And Mr. Wordsworth reminded us not to grieve for that which has gone away, but to remember that which remains: the human heart, and the tenderness by which we live."

Dad sat in his thoughts for a long time. When he started to fidget, I knew this time was about done. I had to ask one more question before he left. "Dad, if an idea feels dear and warm, should we hide it inside?" I'd hoped he'd say a boy might speak of the idea only with his dad.

"You be the judge of that. Think twice about showing thoughts if someone else is liable to hurl rocks at them. Beautiful ideas need protection from fires, scythes, and wickedness. They need protection while they grow."

The next thing I knew, we were startled to hear, "Sean, time to come into the house!" It was Mark. Had he made amends with Julie after punching her with that hay bale? Oh, she hadn't been injured much, only frightened. He'd knocked the wind out of her. When you're small and can't breathe, it's scary! (Is that true at any age?)

Dad declared, "Mark is trying to apologize. I suppose we play many different roles in life," he mused. Right about then I wanted to play the role of a thirsty and weary child, smacking my lips for a snack and nap.

As Dad and I ambled toward our farmhouse, I said, "Well, I could go for a tall glass of milk right about now." Dad yawned, and I hurried my steps to keep up with his lengthening strides.

"Come on in, Sean! Mother says it is naptime!" Mark shouted.

I hear his voice echoing through all of the years that framed many other acts in an unending cycle of birth, of death, and of rebirth: this magical and mysterious story we call life. The world brims with mysteries, all rich fodder for reflection. That day I knew Dad was right because what he said felt right. I knew that we're all challenged to find our way, to seek answers to the questions we ask. I reckon that to do less is a kind of sin. To do less is not to live truly. Maybe I've kept such thoughts hidden too long.

I've often thought about what Dad and I shared that morning. I've seen how energy moves from one form to another, from one body to the next. I sense the wisdom of plants, and I've glimpsed the cycles of life. We're all related in time and in space. Each life touches others, as well as the lives of future generations in times unknown.

I've seen all of this as I gazed into the sunbeams streaming through the rafters, and I have smiled. It felt fine, sensing how life swirls into dusty barns in between weathered planks, silent and peaceful. Life twitches in musty barns crinkled with age.

A Puff in Time Saves Nine

Brach's hard candy glinted at me from a bowl sitting in the late after-noon sun at my grandparents' home. It begged me to snatch up one or two pieces. Grandfather Kearney had bought a pound of it from a neighbor's children when they came calling. (They sold sweets for one fund-raiser or another.)

Grandmother lectured, "Now, John, you know that's too much sugar! You turn over all that candy to the grandchildren. There are enough of them to split it, so none of them will get sick—or worse." Grudgingly, Grandfather took her advice: that is, after swiping a handful for himself while he winked at me.

Leaning into that candy bowl to do more of the same, I remembered Mother's warning, "Please don't eat the candy! It'll spoil your dinner!" Her words crashed inward. While I knew gobbling a gob of candy wasn't the best idea, I didn't see how "sampling" one little piece could hurt. And I knew if I set my mind on it, I could easily sneak some and get away with it.

Heck, by the time I reached four years, there was powerful little I couldn't do undetected. I swaggered with my stealth and shroud of invis-ibility. My trick? Youth. I'd stand there, all innocent and limpid-eyed, holding up the wall, as if to say "Who, me?" whenever a hunk of angel-food cake vanished, or when a few lazy coins went missing. No one sus-pected little know-nothing me, and that was the most delicious trick of all. Less skilled folks would be stuck feeling low, far lower than any dreams of tall mischief.

Now, I'm not endorsing petty crimes, but I am saying that when a body is hell-bent on orneriness, then at least have the decorum to do it with flash and style. To do otherwise and get caught demands pitiable apologies, more so for clumsiness than for the actual offense. That ought to make a body feel low. Yet, I wasn't worried about being fingered. No, I worried about the prospects of catching that heinous "sweet water disease" that I'd read about in Mother's nursing books. Folks grew powerful thirsty, their legs swelled, and they blacked out. Their kidneys were shot. Some people lost their toes, and still others went into shock and died. I reasoned those poor people must not have had a Mother like mine to warn them about such danger from sweets.

But, how many pieces of hard candy would a soul have to suck through before the disease struck? My sources were vague on that point. So, no doubt about it, thinking about that dread disease frightened me enough to shrivel my sweet tooth but good.

Well, that particular day, I passed right over the sweets. Not even tempted, I had to wonder about serious habits like smoking. "Now hold on a minute," I told myself. I know a lot of puffing and carrying on, spells trouble. But what if paltry amounts of smoke sneak in a few bene-fits? Then, maybe a small amount is all right. Is the secret control and moderation? Seemed likely. For instance, I knew that powerful forces like electricity may cause death (in an electric chair). However, a small dose of electricity may help a body, jump-starting the heart back to life. Heck, I'd even seen up close how jumper cables hooked between two batteries works wonders, sparking an engine to life!

How about other dangers that most people wail about, like a pack of bloodhound pups deprived of their mother? Well sir, how about drink-ing? I'd read that naughty Sir Winston Churchill had grown partial to brandy. One unsuspecting man asked Sir Winston why he drank so much. Sir Winston calmly chastised the speaker, "Young man, drinking gives back far more than it takes." With startled attention and a deflated nerve, the poor man fled, leaving Sir Winston wrapped in his bliss of solitude.

Might sweets act along those same lines? Although a gob of them might rot teeth or provoke the dreaded sweet water disease, one or two sweets wouldn't cause serious damage, and besides, they gave back a bunch of pleasure. "That's right," I told myself. "I reckon that a drink a day might provoke more good than harm!" Although not many doctors would admit it, a few like old Doc Gately swore by the healthful value of "A Recipe" taken in moderation. Seeing as I liked that old guy, I took his side in the fuss. Then, I giggled about the photo of a St. Bernard that had just tromped to the rescue of some stranded skier. The dog toted a tankard of rum latched around his neck. What's good enough for body lost in a blizzard must be good enough for everyday folks. Well sir, I guessed Sir Winston had been right, thank you kindly.

So, in my youth I assumed the trick might be taking only a pinch of a drink a day. Maybe the trick lies in simple moderation. Now I ask you, why are some things in life that simple, although they seem to peck away at some folks who claim that life is so gosh blame complicated? Beats me.

And smoking! Mother had crusaded against tobacco long before the Surgeon General got in step and followed her lead. She often told her friends—politely but firmly—that tobacco smoke damaged their lungs, heart, and blood vessels. She warned that it caused cancer. "You can't guess how insulted the body is with each puff of smoke," she lectured.

I sure knew its dangers. By the time I reached the ripe old age of four, I had lectured at least a hundred strangers about smoking. Sparing few victims, I often stomped up to a stranger and asked, "Why do you pay good money to hurt yourself? Those cigarettes will do just that!" I usually stomped my right foot to form a cloud of dust, which I pointed at for effect. "That is what you are breathing, that and a bunch of poisons."

When I did this, the stranger grew red in the face, scrunched up wryly, and stood on tip toes. I reckon he looked as mad as a hornet. Then, his face blossomed to shout he was booming mad, as if some fool hornet had flown up his right sleeve for mischief. Man, I didn't know whether he wanted to slap me or spit on me. Either way, inside of a moment his face smoothed out, and he looked like he might crack a smile. I reckon that's because I stood roughly three feet tall and a notch above that in age. Exhaling slowly with a bother, the affronted stranger emptied the smoke-tainted breath from his lungs. My, oh my, a rattling sound hissed out like someone taken to bed with bronchitis.

Usually, a sibling fetched me out of the scene. With gushing apologies for my forward and rude behavior, we escaped. Still, I never told the strangers I was sorry because I wasn't! I was worried for their health, and my concern overflowed my small size. Friend, I knew my duty to help all in need, just as I wanted to feed starving children in Asia or Africa. Smokers were no exception. Every time I plunked a well warmed penny onto the collection plate during special church drives to tackle hunger, I felt warm inside. Likewise, I wanted to cure those smokers of their "tobacco hunger". Well, given my history as a crusader, a soul might appreciate how I felt not long after this.

One summer's afternoon I spied Mother pacing back and forth, puffing on a tobacco weed. Pregnant and smoking, she scuttled along the fence that lined our south road. A crop of angry and well-dusted thistles skirted the fence and sulked in the ditch.

"I might have guessed that thistles would make matters worse, tempting Mother to smoke," I sighed. "They're nothing but trouble!"

The dust Mother stirred up mixed with the ugliness of the toxic smoke that shot from her drawn lips. Inhale, walk four steps, pivot, exhale. Inhale, walk four steps, pivot, exhale. Inhale, walk—I studied her through the living room window—pivot—I must be mistaken, I thought. She's not holding a cigarette. She can't be. Exhale, inhale, walk four steps . . .

Was I mistaken? No, I knew what I saw. There she paced. Mother sucked on a cigarette like a starved lamb sucking on its mother's teat— pivot, exhale. No! I froze, and then I wilted, my chin sinking south. Then a peculiar feeling slithered up my throat. My lower lip hung low, and my upper lip scrunched up. I commenced to quiver, and my eyes pinched shut. Do not cry, I admonished myself. Do not cry.

Then I spun around, and my feet powered up to take me some-where—anywhere—just as long as it was away from the nightmare. Then "thunk", I collided with something tall and solid, like an adult. Grandfather Kearney peered down at me, his lips drawn all grim-like. He'd come to the farm to feed our trees with spikes he hammered near their roots.

"Where're you headed in such a hurry, Sean?"

Not wanting to talk to anyone just about then, least ways not to Grandfather, I froze. He always found a way to tease a body into think-ing gobs. A "humff"and a strong stamp was about all I could muster for an answer. My head hung low, and I crouched to about half of my height.

"I asked, where're you headed in such a hurry? And please look at me when you answer," he said, betraying his faltering patience.

I don't know. To my room . . . and maybe to the closet. Now let me go!" I squirmed to dart around him.

"Oh no, you don't. Not this time. We need to talk about what you saw."

I "humffed" again.

"What do you think about what your mother's doing?" Grandfather began, folding his fingers as if he felt a prayer coming on.

Contemplating one more try at escape, I knew there was no escaping Grandfather when he aimed to talk. Even so, I wasn't going to make it easy for him to make me spill everything. So, I shuffled, turned a circle or two, and tried to stare him down.

"Sean, get to it. I'm waiting."

"Oh, all right then! Mother and I have told people forever that smok-ing insults and kills the body and then . . . and then . . . " Do not cry. "And then there she is," I jabbed toward the window, "doing just that! I . . . I don't understand." My words trailed off, higher and puffier with less wind behind them. I reckoned Mother's cigarette stole my breath, too. Gulping, I held back a sob. There was no need to pile *shame* on top of it all. That wouldn't help, not even a pinch.

"Yes, that's right. She's lectured far more than a few of her friends and

family about the dangers of smoking. You believed what she was saying, didn't you?"

I nodded.

"And now? Do you still believe her?"

"I don't know. I don't know anything!" My chest heaved.

"Listen here," Grandfather calmed me. "Need I remind you that your mother is a professional? She's an RN. She's read a lot about smoking, and she knows right well what she's talking about. I predict the Surgeon

General is ready to announce the dangers of smoking to the country, perhaps by next year. He's just lagging behind your mother, that's all."

"Huh? What's a Surgeon General? And what does he know?" I stammered, although I felt better just the same.

"He's a wise, old man. And he'll tell everyone that your mother is right about how smoking is deadly."

"All right, if that's true, why is Mother smoking now? What happened?"

Grandfather paused, rubbed his cheek, and explained. "Okay. Have you ever seen her smoking before this?" His eyes trolled me.

"Have you?" Gazing up at him, I knew what he was trying to do.

"Well, no." But I did have to wonder if she hid her "smokes" the way Grandmother did. Yet with kids hovering around her all the time it would be mighty hard to pull that off. "And I hope she never ever smokes again."

"So do I. Now, I can't promise you that she won't smoke, but I can tell you she's working through tough times right now."

What does that have to do with anything? I thought. I asked, "What tough times?"

"As you know, your mother is closing in on forty, and she's pregnant with her ninth child. She's getting older, which means she might face more trouble carrying children than before." I understood Mother was almost forty, pregnant, and that she hadn't carried me down our stairs in two months. But that was because I'd grown, right? Maybe not . . . Shucks, was she upset because she couldn't carry me anymore? Was she growing too old to carry even a new baby? All I knew was that something was wrong.

"She needs that cigarette—even though it's unhealthy—to help her. So, I think we need to let her be." With that, Grandfather winked.

"Is that all we can do?"

"That and help all we can. Have you kept up with your chores?" Grandfather asked, his eyebrows raised.

"I suppose, but I could help more," I said. "There's a powerful lot of work to do on a farm." With those words, I knew that I did not feel like I might cry any more. Our talk scolded my tears into exile.

"Then it's settled. You won't pester your mother. Instead, you'll find ways to help."

Grandfather started to leave when I asked, "Do you think the poison Mother is smoking is helping more than hurting her? I mean, is it possible for foul things to help on occasion?

"I can't be sure. But, yes, that's what I hope," Grandfather patted my shoulder. His words comforted me much more than did his touch.

"Since smoking is something she's never done before, and since she might never do it again, maybe it gives something back to her, like Sir Winston Churchill's brandy."

"Like Churchill's what?" Grandfather pulled out a chair. "I think I'll sit down for this. You?" He offered a chair.

"No thanks. It's just that I heard how Churchill told everyone his drinking gives much more than it takes. Do you reckon he knows alcohol's bad for him, but he is willing to drink it for the sake of the good it buys him?"

"You should know, Mr. Churchill has a few problems, and drinking might be one of them. He doesn't know how much alcohol is enough. He may feel better when he drinks, but he may overdo it."

"Okay, so what if nips only a few sips at a time. What if he drinks occasionally? Could alcohol give more than it takes?"

"Maybe, but I don't know."

"But still, I don't know how smoking even one cigarette can help Mother feel well enough to carry a child better."

Grandfather held back a laugh long enough to let it out as a cough. "There are things called hormones raging in your mother, and they make her think and feel different than usual."

"I saw pictures of Pacific Salmon that changed into freakish forms because of hormones." If hormones work that way on salmon, what about humans? Might Mother become freakish? Please, no! But then again, maybe tobacco has a way of keeping those hormones from taking over her body. Maybe *I'm* filled with hormones, because people sometimes think I'm a freak, too. Maybe a freak isn't all bad."

"I suppose not."

"Do you know exactly how Mother's cigarette helps her?" I continued.

"No, I don't."

"Because, now that I think of it, when I first caught Mother outside like that, she looked jumpy, kind of like how I look when I've sucked too much sugar. After a few puffs on that fool cigarette, she seemed to settle."

"Some might say being out there calmed her nerves," Grandfather said.

"I thought about that. Maybe smoking isn't bad for Mother after all. Maybe it's downright fine for her on occasion, if taken in moderation, that is. She knows when to stop, whereas maybe Sir Winston doesn't know."

"Good for her."

"Grandfather! What if stuff that's supposed to be good turns out to be bad? What if what we believe is bad for the body turns out to be good? What then?" I didn't want to face the possibility that I'd had been wrong about what I'd been spouting off to people.

"Many mysteries drift around this old world, and I don't pretend to understand them all. That might happen once in a while. What you're asking might be one fine mystery."

"I suppose so," I said.

"Do you remember carrying on the other day about Medieval physicians who drew blood to drain evil spirits from their patients?

I nodded.

"Did you know doctors used poisons like arsenic as cures?"

"Oh, sure. I read about that in *The Blue Book of Knowledge*.

"What does that tell you?"

Grandfather was wise. He led me anywhere, much the way that a whiff of a raccoon draws bloodhounds toward their prey as they tromp through darkened hills on moonless nights.

"It tells me that our bodies are mysteries, even to doctors and scientists." That idea made me feel a dribble better. Doctors did their best "to do no harm" and yet they made mistakes. That idea drew me.

"But what if Mother and I have been wrong about smoking, and what if we've done more harm than good? The Surgeon General might say that smoking isn't bad. What if I've been wrong about it all along?"

"And what then?" Grandfather asked. I was hoping the conversation wouldn't lean that way.

"Then I'll need to apologize to anyone I lectured. That must be at least a hundred, and most of them are strangers. I don't know where they live, and I don't know their names or their phone numbers or—"

"Hold on now. I'll admit you're the first little boy I've seen tromp up to a stranger to tell him he's killing himself-"

"Excuse me . . . I'm not a little boy anymore, in case you haven't noticed."

"Really? Well then . . . I don't think your intentions were wrong. I'd say most folks understood that you were only a *young* boy with their best interests at heart."

"That's no excuse. I'm going on five, and that's way old. I've been an adult for some time now."

"All right, so you're a big boy. Now what?"

"I need to apologize."

"Are you sorry for being wrong, or for the way you scolded people for smoking?"

"No, I regret the way I lectured them, as if there was no chance that I was wrong." I stepped away from Grandfather. "I feel mighty low."

Grandfather didn't answer. He rose, and we moved into the living room. Mother was entering the kitchen. "Sean? Dad? You men around here somewhere?" Mother called. She was back, revived by smoke. A grin crept over my face as I commenced to feel gobs better.

"Grandfather, maybe I got the best deal of all—owing to what I learned."

"How so?" Grandfather wrinkled his brow.

"Whenever I speak, however well-meaning, I must remember that I might do more harm than good."

"Perish the thought! But thinking this way means . . . wow, you're growing up."

("Ahh, just the words I needed to hear.")

"But here's a piece of advice for you. Even if you're convinced you're right about something, you might be more diplomatic in the way you say so."

"Diplomatic?"

"It's like smoothing the sharp edges off of your words. For example, you might say, 'I know goats take kindly to chewing the socks from the line, just as you do, but I feel that chewing socks is hurting your health, and I don't want to see you hurt.'"

Was Grandfather playing with me? I didn't dare laugh because he rarely joked unless it came to baseball or gardening. Or did he? I tipped my head like PJ did when he's confused.

"Sean, it's okay not to think so much. It's okay to be a little boy—er, a big boy, and be silly on occasion. I was making a joke. Now run along."

Meandering to where Mother had been only minutes earlier, I didn't spy a dead cigarette butt or one misting its last millimeter. I found no straggling smoke—only thistles and dust. Lifting my foot to kick a thistle, I thought better of it. If I was wrong about smoking, maybe I was wrong about thistles, too.

Then, a scary thought seeped into my mind, snatching my attention in one silent moment. Mother paced along that fool fence line, and the thistles that lived there laughed at me. Their purple crowns taunted me in the gusty breezes. I knew that thistles try to crowd out crops. Some farmers thought they sucked up water and minerals that the crops could have used. I knew that most farmers fancied thistles as ugly and prickly eyesores, robbing them of their livelihood. "What if the farmers are wrong, at least a little bit. Do they have the whole story, or is there a finer side to thistles that we don't see? What if there is a beautiful side even to ugly things, one that we miss because we don't look closely enough? Maybe thistles in small quantities are all right after all," I told myself. "Maybe they aren't all bad if taken in moderation. Why, a few here and there might be okay. They might not be all bad. After all, the goats munch on them! Could thistles help teach us a few lessons? Maybe they're all right, provided they're managed, assuming their numbers are controlled. Maybe a few thistles are all right, just as a smoke now and then is all right, too!"

Since I thought I was a big boy, practically all grown up, I fancied that sometimes what we see as the worst part of life might also be the best part because of what it teaches us. Hmm . . . The mystery deepened.

Well, after my talk with Grandfather, I knew I wouldn't cry. I even began to wonder, at least a pinch, if our priest had been wrong about crying. After all, I'd just learned that we can't always be sure about most things. We need to know that we could be wrong even when we feel right. Maybe crying was all right after all. It meant I really cared.

Heir of Mystery

"Bury me with my shoes on," Dr. Redmond muttered in a weary, self-satisfied huff at the end of 14-hour work days. A puff of mystery filled the dusty air whenever Dad spoke of Grandfather, Dr. Thomas Redmond, both a general practitioner and surgeon. For such a man whose life teetered in mists of questions, a man whose actions were tinged with curious contrasts, riddles abounded. "Dr. Redmond wouldn't have it any other way," Dad sputtered, as he puzzled to understand his father a pinch.

So went the life of a kindly but aloof man who befriended his patients, but who also pouted for months on end, refusing to breathe a word to his wife, Grandmother Nessie Storey-Redmond.

"Son, I've struggled to understand your grandfather Redmond, the man who routinely bent down on the kitchen floor to tote daddy long-legs outside to save them. That same man rarely said I love you—neither to his children nor to his wife. I don't know how a man dries up and goes mute for months on end."

I nodded.

"And Mother was special. She was exceptional, suffering so with heart trouble, all the time putting up with Dad. Why, Dad would fuss at her when she grew ill and faint, asking why she had been lazy enough to take to her bed. Maybe he didn't want to believe that Mother was ill."

I nodded.

"Dr. Redmond escaped his mother's Indiana farm for medical school where he finished first in his class," Dad explained. "Then, he struggled the rest of his life to trudge back to a farm. Although he ached to fly away from his family farm in Indiana, I don't think farm life made him restless. No, the farm stood him well. I'm guessing that the people on it riled him."

"Which people, Dad?" I inquired.

"Oh, I don't know. Maybe people like his insane half-brother Jimmie, who was powerful handy with a shot gun. Why, whenever Grandfather and his brother, your great Uncle John, went calling, Jimmie took pot-shots at them, and I mean for real! Lucky no one was killed!" Then there was Grandfather's dad, Great Grandfather James Redmond, who'd been lost following a hail storm in 1884, when Grandfather had hardly reached age ten. Great Grandfather had overworked himself as usual, planting apple tree grafts in his orchard. Then, a hail storm chilled him. Within three days he was gone: dead from pneumonia."

I shivered.

"I reckon that the ghost of my Grandfather haunted Dad. Whenever Dad spoke of his father's passing, he shuddered and went pale."

"What, Dad?"

"Maybe it was his powerlessness and his insane half-brother that gnawed at him. Maybe it was the fact that his mother was his older siblings' aunt."

"How's that?"

"Great Grandfather married his deceased wife's sister. Grandfather was first born in the second family. Should a man ever take his wife's sister as his bride, even if he is a lonesome widower? I reckon Great Grandfather James wanted to keep his business all in the family."

How could anything but unanswered puzzles swirl in mists whenever Dad spoke of the late, great Dr. Redmond, a man of mystery? In turn, Dad became heir of the same mystery.

Dad chased shadows, still aiming to know his distant father a smidgeon. How had he died, this man filled with life yet glazed over with a melancholy and drudgery, this man who labored in his medical office until the day he died, this man who was found slumped over his desk, dead? How could anything shy of billowing clouds of mystery engulf Grandfather Redmond, a man who brimmed with many puzzles about how he lived, died, and whom he had loved?

"Dad took on life the same way that he operated," Dad once retorted. "He did his best with his considerable skill, steady hands, and brilliant mind. He hoped for the best, but often that was not good enough." Thousands of duties left him with dark circles under his eyes, his whitish hair grown bare in large patches. All of that responsibility had taken its toll, and his heart lay weary," Dad observed.

I sighed.

"Dr. Redmond's unswerving aim for perfection wore him out long before his time. Dad spoke of his father's belief, "To retire would be a kind of a sin." So, he literally worked until he dropped dead in his office.

Whenever I heard Dad speak of his father, I imagined he spoke in

hushed tones as he mouthed the words of a large secret. Did Dad fret that speaking more loudly about Grandfather might draw a crowd of gawkers reveling in the specter of one gigantic man who often lived small? I say "small" because that's how I reckon most folks would describe a man who punished his boys for dropping crumbs at the dinner table, a man who didn't praise his boys when they hit home runs, played the lead roles in school reviews, or delivered class valedictory addresses.

And being born left-handed! Was it large for any man to whip his twin sons for writing left-handed? That's how the nuns carried on when Dr. Redmond was a boy, and maybe he thought that was the thing to do! Did he reckon that what the nuns did was sound, even if it meant beating the child for the hell of it?

Grandfather Redmond saw a grand sin in being born left-handed, as if that marked him as damaged goods. I sensed great smallness in anyone who took the nuns at their word on something that absurd.

Yet, there was nothing but largeness in a man who pressed hard on Grandmother Nessie's right hand as she lay dying on her bed at age fifty-five in 1931, dying from ruined heart valves after her bout with rheumatic fever. Most husbands could not have endured it! He watched her and the clock to edge out time until he could deliver another injection of morphine to ease her pain—to take the edge off of it.

Grandfather braved all of that without ever breaking a sweat. His love for Nessie made love as we know it small by any measure. His kind of love wept from the ground up and dwarfed everything in its path. Yet, his kind of love grew so immense that it took company with pettiness and a kind of vicious control that few souls might imagine. Such was the life and soul of Dr. Redmond, who often drove miles in the rain to make a house call on a patient who could not afford to pay him, who often gave up his own supper as well to take the edge off the hunger of the children in the home of a sick patient. The poor parents in such homes might offer only a promise and a thanks for his unmatched service. Such was the life of the aloof Dr. Redmond—magnanimous to his public, petty and distant from his family.

Whenever Dad spoke about Grandfather Redmond, he did so with a sort of sad indignation, with anger tinged in pity, with accusing tones softened by intense longing. Naturally, I perked up and listened. The man and the mystery loomed larger than life. If Grandfather Redmond's soul reflected on a pool, he might be a fleeting image during a storm with shards of light peeking from a patch of undisturbed sky. His sad, longing eyes might lie reflected there, even in ripples that guard against a clear picture of the man: of his life, or of his soul.

With his lower lip softly trembling, Dad often spoke of the day that Grandfather died. "Dr. Redmond died working, this man for whom retirement had never been an option. Yet, he yearned to retire to his beloved apple orchard, his farm that was nothing like the one of his Indiana youth. He ached to retire to a place that was all his own, one that he controlled! As surely as he had longed to escape from the Indiana farm of his boyhood, as surly as he had stampeded to the medical school, so too did he yearn to fly to his apple orchard. The trouble was that he simply couldn't retire. So lay his conflicted mind."

All this felt mighty somber to a five year old child, and I intended to do something to lighten the air. So, one day as Dad related this tale of Dr. Redmond whom he loved to hate, I asked if I could add something.

"What do you want to add?" he asked.

"Well, I know that Dr. Redmond died. It was Saturday, and he hadn't been operating that day. Wouldn't it have made a better story if he died while operating on a patient?" I wondered.

"How could that have made any difference?" Dad wanted to know. I could tell I had his attention because I had already brought him out of his sad, trance-like state as he droned on and on.

"Well, can you imagine it? Some poor man lies flat on his back, waiting for an operation on his intestines or stomach. It doesn't much matter. But the operation's risky. The old geezer doesn't know if he'll pull through it.

"How is that a better story?" Dad asked.

"Toward the end of the operation, as Grandfather began to sew the old man back up, he grabbed his chest, gasped and collapsed smack on top of his patient. Later the patient's nurse said, 'Mr. Jones, I have good news and bad news. The good news is that you pulled through great. You'll make it just fine.'"

"The patient studied the nurse. 'So what's the bad news?'"

"The nurse reported, 'Your surgeon. He, ahem . . . didn't make it.' Whimpering and with her face tilted in sadness, she gasped, 'He's gone.'"

The patient didn't understand.

"We had to pull him off. I think he was dead before he landed on you, so don't take it personally."

About then a hint of a grin crept over Dad's face. A hint led to an outright accusation, and then a flood of laughter filled his face and mouth. A gushing laugh gurgled up from his belly, and Dad began to chortle in hurried bursts of delight. He rushed so he would not delay his next wave of pleasure. He laughed hard enough to weep, and then he laughed more. Then, he stopped.

Drawing himself up and frowning, he lectured, "We must not mock the dead. Now hush, and never speak of this again," he sputtered as he left the room. I don't know where he was headed, but something told me he planned a few more innings of guffaws far away from me. He didn't aim to set a poor example when it came to mocking the dead.

As pleased as I was at helping Dad soften his feelings about Grandfather, at least for a spell, I was also caught up in mystery. Where was the joy and reason for working hard, and what had it all meant if he literally dropped dead at work?

The question bothered me, but I decided not to ask Dad. Naturally, I turned to Mother.

"How did Grandfather Redmond die?" I asked Mother. I tilted my head at an angle, squinted my right eye and peered out of my left eye as if I was trying to make out an image shrouded in a fog. "What caused Grandfather Redmond to die that way?" I began.

"Well, your Grandfather worked very hard and helped many people. In the 1930s he bought a farm and planted 1,000 apple trees. When he was not working in the hospital or in the office, he was out at that orchard. The only trouble is that he worked as hard there as he did in his practice. He often staggered in from the orchard with every stitch of his shirt slathered in sweat. Basically, your Grandfather worked himself to death," Mother offered in a matter-of-fact tone.

"But how does someone work himself to death?" I knew what it meant to work so long that I was tired, but I *could not* imagine working so hard that it killed me. After all, folks often told me work is good for a body, and I couldn't understand how that might kill.

"Well, your grandfather worked so long and hard that his vessels grew hard and sticky. His heart weakened with all that work because it was too much for anyone. Hard work made his vessels grow sticky, and that killed him. That is what stopped his heart."

For a minute I stopped asking questions. I knew what stickiness felt like. I knew what the gooey end of an Elmer's Glue bottle felt like when I stripped off the hardness around the tip and squirted fresh glue onto a piece of construction paper. I knew the feel of honey oozing over the edge of a peanut butter and honey sandwich. (It drips onto the cuff of my shirt.) I knew what stickiness tasted like as I licked the honey from my shirt. But I had no idea that stickiness could kill someone. How could that stop a heart? Could stickiness stop mine?

I reminded myself to wash my hands after touching anything sticky. Stickiness left unattended might edge its way from my hands toward my elbows, to my shoulders, and to my neck. Stickiness might plant itself in my heart and stop it!

Adults had told me to wash my hands often if I did not want to get sick. I imagined Dr. Redmond took ill when he tended apple orchards and left apple stickiness on his hands too long. Since he was mighty busy, he didn't take time to wash his hands.

I spent the days of summer in my fifth year with questions and mysteries to explore like these. My days sped along lazily. With the kids out of school, our days of summer fun melted into one another, the way a clutch of Hershey bars might puddle into a gooey glob on a car dashboard parked under the blazing sun on a torrid summer's day.

Frowning at a small glass jar of heat-treated, store-bought honey one July morning, Mother declared, "I've had it with store-bought honey. It's spoiled with heat enough to kill any goodness. I've had it with junk. Store-bought honey is not the Real McCoy but something masquerading as honey. It's something else entirely, of another family, only distantly related to real honey. Honey you can buy in city stores is a poor country cousin to homegrown honey on Kansas prairies. They are nothing alike, and their taste boldly tells us so."

Armed with Grandfather Kearney's praises for a local beekeeper, Mr. Brooks, Mother visited Mr. Brooks' farm one day late in July. He specialized in clover honey, which smelled as sweet as did his clover. The clover blossomed and loomed redolent, so intensely so that I smell those ambrosial fields to this day. He began with the choicest, handpicked queens, and with the sweetest clover any meadow ever knew.

Mr. Brooks learned the art of honey making from his father who must have tarried with the gods for sage advice. He developed a sixth sense to tell him exactly what his bees needed.

His bees sensed his fine intentions. They were never bothered when he tended the hives. Rarely did he use smoke to urge the bees to gorge themselves on honey—to lull them to sleep or to pacify them. They were already drunk on a sure knowledge that Mr. Brooks would tend their every need. For example, he knew precisely where to place the hives for the best sunlight and shade. He moved the hives near succulent plants that brimmed with nectar. The aroma wafting from his fields and hives can't be reproduced, for they too were a work of art.

Why, you just name it—the sun, the meadows, the plants, the babbling brook, the bees, and Mr. Brooks—all conspired to make honeycomb fit for the gods. To eat his honeycomb was almost a shame. But at the slightest whiff of its delights, few could resist the urge to devour it.

Mr. Brooks usually didn't sell the honeycomb cut from the hive. Normally, he spun it down in his hand-cranked spinner. He peeled the waxy covering from the comb, just as I might peel a fruit. Then, he gingerly placed the bleeding combs into the spinner. Round and round they went, freeing that amber potion from their hexagonal cradles. First a surge and then a steady stream filled one-gallon tins until they over-brimmed with goodness.

After spinning the honeycomb, he oversaw a dwindling stream and captured the last of the golden oozings. You see, even this step was a work of art, requiring sure knowledge of pressure, time, and separation techniques using centrifugal force. Mr. Brooks felt in his guts when to stifle the opening from the spinner: to stop the stream trickling into the pail. He left a trace of "starter" honey in the bottom to prime a later batch, to help mix its flavor with one to come, to tease out bouquets of slightly nuanced flavors that even the gods have not tasted. They hovered in the air, pouting at what had been denied them by a mere mortal. Envy surged.

Mother and I drove to Mr. Brooks' home, and she explained, "I will be a few minutes."

As I sat in the station wagon waiting, I watched the butterflies and bees flitting over Mr. Brooks' clover field. There were shatter cane, milkweed, and musk thistles towering over other plants in a corner along a fence line. Regal thistles with purple crowns stood amongst the plants.

Our mission complete, Mother backed the station wagon from his driveway, and we sped away on the main road. I caught a glimpse of something intriguing in Mr. Brooks' field.

Were honey bees massing around the thicket I'd admired? How odd. Why were bees there? I opened my mouth to ask Mother about it, but she interrupted me, asking what I planned to do that evening after chores. But, what had I seen? Something gnawed at my "gizzard."

It turned out, that "something" made all the difference.

Sticky on Top

The year ripened with action, like a piece of fruit oozing with juices, brimming with flavor. However, our year had been bittersweet. Violence crept into our world, parading boldly, perhaps too ugly to be real. Oh, how queasy we felt weathering the stormy threat of nuclear war the past year (just waiting for the bombs to fall). We had also witnessed the homegrown violence against Mrs. Crocker's poor face. My faithful hound had been wounded, torn and bleeding, before Mother patched him up with a needle, hydrogen peroxide, and dental floss. In the pit of my stomach, I missed the ducklings whose quaking felt cozy. Mostly though, we'd done fine.

I'd felt firsthand the squirminess of knowing folks are sometimes judged by the color of their skin. That left me wondering, "How come? Was Sheriff Cantwell like a mother sheep—sniffing for the scent of her own babies?" Mother had told me, "No, it's more of an illness like a fever. That's what causes adults to act funny." And then there was Uncle Jim. When he was mowed down by wicked men in robes, (as if he was a dusty thistle), unlike a thistle, he didn't return.

Meanwhile, Dad fretted how he might be forced into wage earner's bankruptcy. A skidding cattle market left us broke. That word—bankruptcy—sounded painful to me, maybe like the way a body might feel when split open, the stomach ruptured. Dad's face looked sick a lot that fall, and I thought he might begin to split into pieces, as had Uncle Jim's mind. Tough times came like an autumn rainstorm, powered by mighty winds that may shoot drops right into the face to sting the eyes.

Can troubles melt away as if they're swirls of morning dew lifted under summer sunbeams? Do some problems lead to more of the same? Gazing at white lace curtains that fluttered in the evening breeze one autumn eve, I twirled my forelocks rhythmically with my left hand. Doing that sent me into waking dreams. Those times felt alive and gentle.

There, I craved sunshine, a tonic for a world gone mad.

The Indian summer hung on. Grandma said its loyalty was suspect, like a harlot's fidelity if she takes up with one man for a spell, as if a spell's been cast over her racing mind—one sent to whitewash her racy past.

I had no idea what Grandmother meant. After all, what did a body's floozy past have to do with whether or not she needed a bath? Seeing as how I was no expert on the subject, I still reckoned Grandmother had no certain way to know about a body's washing habits. But her words sounded true enough to remember.

Indian summer lingered that fall, as if the Earth didn't wish to admit the season had ended, one of discovery: the season of my youth. My brothers and sisters crept back to school right after Labor Day. Even worse, my sister Julie began first grade. Feeling left behind, that I was missing out on all the fun, I grumbled, "I don't like being left out, owing to my age. I won't wait until I am six years old!" Alas, wait I did.

Watching the lengthening shadows of an early autumn afternoon, I gulped milk to rinse a glob of peanut butter and honey sandwich from the roof of my mouth. That didn't work. Mum's milk had cooled for a spell in our refrigerator, and its coolness coaxed our too-firm peanut butter to become leathery in my mouth. When no one was looking, I swiped my index finger there to pry loose that peanut butter. A treat of only peanuts and a trace of sea salt, Mother's peanut butter wouldn't have it any other way.

"Kids, will you look at all the hard oils in this junk?" Mother insisted as she read the label of a national brand peanut butter. She ordered "our" peanut butter in half-gallon tins from a natural foods store. She also ordered wheat bread from the same store, stocked with loaves baked in Springfield, Missouri. Marketed in health food stores in both Missouri and Kansas, that bread was the best I'd ever tasted! (I have yet to sample any tastier.) Even though the peanut butter and bread cost more than popular brands, Mother didn't quibble over price when it came to health and nutrition, to say nothing of taste.

Although a peanut butter and honey sandwich is delicious, it's tough to handle. For one thing, when I'm liberal with the honey, it oozes out of my sandwich, onto my shirt, and onto the table. Often, its gooeyness in my mouth calls for coaxing from my fingers. Listen, had I choked to death, my sandwich's flavor and other virtues would not have counted for much, to say nothing of me.

Finishing my snack, I tramped outside for a bit of fun on our swing set, which had been welded by Mr. Randall. He managed the grain elevator and feed store in town, and he cobbled together rusted steel pipes to form our swing set's frame. The seats were wooden planks suspended from metal chains cast off by a local hardware store. Although they were made from seconds and leftovers, that swing set was sturdy, just as was Mr. Randall. On top of that, he charged us a reasonable price: thirty dollars. Of course, even that sum was a fortune for a boy my age. But what price may be placed on freedom and feeling important? All was well.

Walking to the bathroom, I rinsed my honey-spotted hands with warm water. Mother often reminded us kids to wash our hands before playing, especially if we'd eaten anything as sticky as honey. Although I happened to be the only kid who usually listened, I routinely washed my hands before playtime. Mother nudged us to be clean, and her words caused me to take heed.

With a flip of the wash towel, I wiped off the wetness on my hands. Boy, what a job well done, I thought as I hung the towel on its metal rod. Racing outside by way of our kitchen screen door on that balmy afternoon, I knew it was playtime.

The swing set was mine alone, seeing as how the other kids were inside watching television and tending to other truck. As I flung myself onto the nearest seat of our swing set, I felt the sun's warmth on the metal and wooden parts. As reliable as our cistern's gasoline-powered pump, up and away I flew. I labored rhythmically to fly into a free-swinging ecstasy. I imagined that my skill at swinging high and fast rivaled my talent to solve adult problems. After all, I helped Grandfather Kearney figure out how to save our farm. "Grandfather Kearney has a way to help. If we don't take it, we'll lose the farm outright, Dad!" I said.

With that line, I helped to soften up Dad. Grandfather figured out a way to refinance the farm, provided he raked up $5,000 to help. He'd asked me to warm Dad up to the notion. Accepting help, even from a family member, was a delicate subject in the Kansas of my youth. Grandfather knew as much.

As I pumped my swing higher and faster, I remembered that Advent and Christmas drew near. That meant a chance to ask for an ebony toy train. How I longed for a Marx locomotive! To own it might mark me as someone special—someone who could control my life—just as I might control that train as it surged over its gleaming oval-shaped tracks. To own that train meant that I wasn't left out of the fun any more. To own that train meant that I'd be respected, even though money was tight. "Better times must be coming," I mumbled with a faint smile.

Growing tired with the humdrum of swinging, I knew that I needed something else to interest me, and I guessed what that something might be. One, two, three, jump! I timed my launch at the point where the swing's seat glided to its highest spot. Flying over the lawn, I imagined I hovered in the air to defy gravity. With a hollow thud I landed on the freshly mowed lawn. Then, I rolled to a stop. "What a trip," I thought. "Now it's time to fly like a trapeze artist. Now, I'm ready to fly!"

The past year I had seen a circus act with a trapeze artist who flew through the air "with the greatest of ease." Now, if he could do it, so could I. Why not? What he did with knotted ropes and bars, I could do with boards and rusty chains! Success seemed assured.

Before you could say, "Jack Robinson," I shimmied up the swing's metal frame and clung to the top metal pipe. Wow, I must be a big boy, now, I thought. "I am not at all afraid," I mumbled. No distractions, no hubbub, I thought as I dragged my body over the top bar of the swing set.

My legs dangling from the frame, I fancied myself as a trapeze artist, "flying through the air with the greatest of ease." Oh, no. I spied my sister Mary sauntering out to the front porch. She plopped down in the metal porch chair, supported by one curved metal rod which acted both as support and shock absorber. Rhythmically and with an attitude, she began to rock herself.

Great: either she doesn't see me, or she doesn't care. Either way, I don't care, as long as she lets me be!

Time after time I lurched and spun, twirled and flew. All of my daring hijinks thrilled me. Just as I thought! I'm the master of my fate.

"Watch out," Mary cautioned.

"Why can't she let me be?" I growled. My siblings tried to control me, in spite of the fact that I "usually" followed the rules. Take Mother's order to wash after eating any sticky food. I had done what she asked, although I knew most of the others had not. People are hurt when they're careless or sloppy and make a mess, I assumed as I smoothed tousled curls over my forehead. (I was wrong.) People are hurt when they don't think, I muttered, twirling with finesse.

Then, I shouted, "Oh, no! I'll be go to hell!" My hands clenched a section of the one-inch diameter top pipe, drenched with honey and peanut butter. The thought felt fatal to me. Why? Mother's voice echoed, "Grandfather Redmond worked very hard and late, which caused his vessels to grow sticky. Those sticky vessels made his heart sick." I imagined that the stickiness slathered on the swing set might make me sick, too. It would edge through my fingertips. Then, like a guided missile, it would find my heart.

Fury surged. The kids had disobeyed Mother. They played without bothering to wash their hands. The mess disgusted me, and I wagged my head. Anger distracted me sufficiently to provoke a mistake. I pried my fingers from the pipe, oozing with stickiness. I cursed, and then I muttered, "Oh, no," when I knew what I'd done. Falling to the ground, I braced for impact. "It will be like flying out of the swing set, over the lawn, and onto my shoulders," I guessed.

Well, it did not end up that way. This time I didn't roll onto my shoulders. Instead, I landed hard—and I mean hard—on my right hip, which bounced off a large rock. Pain blossomed swiftly, and I couldn't right myself. "Those hellions," I fumed. (Although my infant brother Leo was the youngest child in our family, and although I was only four years older, I didn't see myself as a child. No, I was four years old and going on forty.)

"Oh, no! I've been brought down by stickiness on top," I gasped, writhing on our lawn. Waves of pain shot through me, clouding my thoughts with a shroud of another world. Then, in a second I began gasping, "Heart attack. Heart attack!"

The pain was sudden and unimaginable, like electric shocks arriving in waves so closely spaced that they merge into one other. The waves crashed endlessly, highlighting the yard in super slow motion, one frame of hell at a time. I saw bits and pieces of light, like a halo shattered into a thousand pieces. I might have gone unconscious; everything felt muddled, as if I faced a labyrinth. I had no idea of which passage to choose. My life had changed—unalterably!

Off It Must Come!

My right leg had broken on the rock when I fell from the top of the swing set. Mary hollered for help, and Janice came running to tote me to the garden where Mother was hoeing along the last patch of spinach. Aiming not to cry, I succeeded mostly. However, by that very evening I found my right leg in a cast from just above my knee all the way to my crotch. My right femur had broken in two places near the hip. The doctor in the Paola clinic said, "You'll wear the cast for six weeks." Even for a little boy who's anxious to be done with unwanted companions, six weeks wasn't intolerably long. I'd get by.

Now that cast—a plaster monstrosity—wasn't so bad, except that it was! The worst part wasn't the pain (of which I felt little) but the infernal itchiness that raised the small hairs on the back of my neck until they stuck straight out, as if all that irritation teased them to go airborne. Most of the itchiness lived near enough the top of the cast for Mother to work some of her magic. She toted my yellow bear-handled tooth brush to my bed, and she scratched the living daylights out of my fussy skin. That felt fine, or at least fine enough to drowse me to sleep. Can a toothbrush serve such high estate?

Janice and Paul (and sometimes Mother and Father) toted me around like a sack of russet potatoes. It wasn't too bad, and I was small enough that most folks didn't tease me. If they fussed around and got ornery, I only pointed to the cast, and that hushed them. Although a few of our neighbors were hell-bent on teasing, none of them felt obliged to mock a crippled child.

Registering little pain during those six weeks, I mostly felt that infernal itchiness against which Mother swished that tooth brush under the cast. Otherwise, all was well. Somehow, I reckoned that my accident meant a whole new path to take, one that's mysterious in origin and unknown in destination.

Many folks have felt pain just as commanding as mine that evening. It numbed my mind, as if I entered another world. That kind of pain lives! It lived then, and I reckon it lives even in death. Can that kind of pain startle a body enough to craft memories in every cell?

The most pleasant thing about such pain is the heavenly feeling when it leaves. It did leave after that eventful evening, and I thought that was that. Its absence was a blessing. Right there on the spot, I decided that something that powerful might be useful. If a body can outlast and redirect such pain, it might teach patience.

"It must come off, soon," I overheard. (Suddenly, I thought I could live with the itching much longer.) "We'll cut it off next week."

"Will the doctor give me something for the pain?" I asked. Mother looked surprised as she said, "No, you won't need any."

You see, I thought "it" was my leg. Had the doctors decided to saw it off, just as they had when they cut off an infected leg of another patient earlier that year? That limb had begun to rot, poisoning the patient. So, off it came.

Smiling uneasily, I reckoned Mother thought I was the bravest little boy in the world. To think that the doctor would saw off my leg without giving me a thing for the pain! Mother knows I won't need drugs to soften the agony, I thought. Well, she knows I'm powerful brave.

All too soon the morning crept up when "off would come my leg". Sweat beaded on my face as I whispered to the doctor, "I bet I'll be all right. We don't need to take it off just yet, do we?"

"Oh, yes. It comes off today," the doctor insisted. "You'll feel better then," he promised.

Easy for him to say! Now, what am I going to do without my right leg? I'll be crippled for life. Why can't he leave me alone? I wondered.

Well, *everyone*—even Mother—fussed about how it was best to saw off my leg, and I couldn't get a word in edgewise. Without a say in the matter, seeing as how I was going on five years of age, I braced myself for impact as the wicked whirring of the blade commenced. I can still smell the blade's gritty heat as it whirled through my cast . . . and next, my leg . . .

"All done, Sean," Mother said. "Now that wasn't bad, was it?"

Can you imagine my relief when I figured out my leg would stay put? I blinked away tears before the doctor noticed, seeing as how no boy must ever cry. (Our priest had told me so.) I commenced to grin like a jackass eating briars.

My right leg remained, and I thought all was well.

All wasn't well. One day as I moped around the house, Grandmother said, "Your accident may be a blessing. Why? Because now you'll appreciate standing and walking. Never take anything for granted," she warned. "You never know when it might all up and die," she declared.

"That doesn't feel right, least ways fair," I said.

"Count your blessings. Be thankful for life's unfolding miracles."

Can you believe that happened to me? Say, the vegetable soup is bubbling its temptations right about now. Would you like a few ladles while I finish sharing this story, this *Thistledown Rising*? It might not take as long as you think. It won't be too much longer now . . .

Much may happen in a glimmer—in the time it takes for a wink of an eye, don't you reckon? I am tempted to know what might have been had I not looked absent-mindedly at my hands and then fallen that late autumn eve years ago. Life's complex with countless paths. Just as I knew my life changed completely, I also would have enjoyed knowing what may have happened had I not fallen.

You know, it's no wonder that some opt for a user's guide. Each of us may do only our best as Dad said. We patiently make choices to help our neighbors and ourselves. As Dad showed, we may lean gently into the wind when we choose wisely. We might do more good than harm on balance. By doing this, we enrich our life, and we help our friends. Taking such a path may be the best we can hope to do. It may be all that we can do.

That feeling helps me find my way when important moments arrive, as if the very ground under me rumbles, and when the course of life changes. It's as if all the unquantified mystery and complexity of life builds until there is a release. Life changes dramatically and unalterably.

When that happens, it's like trying to hold back the ocean when its tidal surge pours over me.

I remember wanting to know if those moments happen by chance. On the other hand, maybe we make some subtle choices that lead to those moments. Do we "create" those important events, or do they simply happen, offering us a chance to find meaning from their randomness?

I don't rightly know the answers, or even all of the questions clearly. Maybe the rest of the story will help you decide for yourself. Once you're finished with your soup, we'll head back to the Kansas of my youth. We'll tend to thistles—always the thistles—once again.

Too Sad to Build a Fire

The wind left my lungs as I gasped in disbelief at the scene. Words wouldn't come as I stared at the heap of splintered wood. My lower lip hung low, and my pupils grew large. I imagined if I focused on the sight, I could make it vanish. Running the fingers of my right hand across my eyes, I tried to brush it away, as if I might draw back the curtain of that day and shroud the sadness from our lives.

Our king cottonwood lay in ruins. It lay there on the pasture just northwest of our home. It lay there splintered by lightning: reduced to firewood. Most of the tree was damp from the evening rains driven by gusts of wind.

Looking more closely, I saw whole sections of it untouched—except that they rested on the ground. Those sections invited me to jump aboard as if nothing had happened. "Come on, build a tree house, and let's make a day of it," the cottonwood seemed to whisper through gentle breezes rustling its smaller branches. "Come on, what are you waiting for? I'm here for you," our tree whispered as I stared in shocked grief.

I kicked at the ground, sending some twigs to one side, while a puff of dust and dried grass, shielded from the storm by a gooseberry bush, swirled into the morning air. "Whoever heard of lightning storms in November in Kansas?" I fumed. "This isn't fair. It's not supposed to be this way!" Where was the meaning in the senseless destruction?

The storm had been fierce. A piercingly cold wind had blown from the southwest. Bellowing clouds of white puffs the prior morning reminded me of cotton candy I'd devoured at the Shriners' circus in Kansas City. That candy persuaded my mouth to drool. But then, it made my stomach queasy. The clouds, turning into gray wisps, conspired to unleash similar mischief on my stomach. Feeling ill, I imagined they told me events pounded beyond our control. "Watch out, here we come!" they shouted.

Next, those clouds darkened to violet streaked with black and a pinch of green, the likes of which I'd never seen. The clouds sank steadily lower, moving more quickly as if the ground vacuumed them. After the temperature plunged twenty degrees in an hour, hail commenced. First it came in pea-sized bits, and then it pounded in marble-sized balls. The wind strengthened, and rain fell in great globs. Their sounds swirled together, and I didn't know which was hail and which was rain.

As wind gusts struck our kitchen window, Mary ran to our clothesline to swish down the clothes. Didn't the clothes appear to lie on an invisible table, vibrating to reach a plane parallel to the ground?

Finally, the great gusts sent debris churning around our barnyard. Lightning filled the sky followed by thunder's echoes. We knew we were in for a doozy of storm. Still, nothing could brace us for the loss of our favorite tree. We could not imagine we would lose its wonder.

I don't know if several bolts or just one powerful strike did it. Our mighty king cottonwood splintered from top to bottom, leaving only the trunk intact. The branches that had lived dozens of feet in the air now rested on the ground. Their leaves seemed as green and healthy as they had been for years, yet we knew they would soon brown and shrivel with the rest of that tree. I reckon that tree had convinced me to feel newborn.

Oh, we crafted such plans for that old tree: swaying platforms and viewing decks, elevators and tree houses! Our tree house was an old-fashioned kind crafted of wooden planks or a no-account door hauled up to unsuspecting branches. We fastened it with baling twine and duct tape. Surely, we did not use nails, seeing how that hurt trees and made them bleed. Heaven forbid, for bleeding might doom it! We counted on using a rusted metal drum with notches on the top to haul up our truck. We'd run bailing twine through the holes near the top—two strands on each side for safety—and then find just the right branch to support the rope. We'd use two strands because that old metal drum had a nasty habit of gnawing into single strands. After we found a victim—er, passenger—away he would fly. "Platform two, please, to view the chicken house. Platform three, please, for the best view of Mum and the rest of our Jersey milk cows in the north pasture." Now, our plans for king cottonwood had shattered into lifeless splinters, and we kids struggled to find a way to bluff our way through without those plans.

The past 24 hours were ugly and somber. Not only had king cottonwood met his end, but the kids had been sent home from school early the prior afternoon. I remember Mother sitting in the kitchen in her black wooden rocker that she had used to soothe many of us kids to sleep. She was watching television on our black and white Motorola set. I knew at once that something was wrong because Mother rarely watched television, and she never watched during the day. She'd been listening to the radio in our utility room while she ironed clothes. The light gray ironing board stood erect with a half-ironed shirt dangling from it. Mother abandoned it to run to the kitchen. She turned on our television.

Watching television had been one of my past-times, and I often tuned in for reruns of "Superman", "The Donna Reed Show", or "Father Knows Best." That day I hadn't been watching television. Instead, I was making money--all kinds of bills from US Dollars and Yen to Pounds Sterling, French Franks, and German Marks. I'd played banker, Federal Reserve Chairman, and currency trader on world markets. All those interests left powerful little time for television, I declare!

When I played banker, I first needed a cache of bills. "The bills need a smooth cut," I told myself. I didn't really care how their faces looked, as long as their edges were cleanly cut. None of that jagged jazz for me, no sir.

I said forthrightly to Mother, "Now, I'm fixing to cut some bills. I'll be careful so I don't cut too many. I won't dull your scissors, and that's a fact," I'd promised in a matter-of-fact tone.

Although Mother wasn't pleased, she obliged, reminding, "Remember, every time you cut paper, you dull our scissors."

"Yes, Mother."

"Also, scissors cost real money, not the pretend kind you fashion."

"I promise I'll use them sparingly. I'll make do with the least number of cuts," I huffed. Grudgingly, Mother relented as she handed me the scissors.

Then our living room and stacks of the *Kansas City Star* (from our grandparents) magically transformed into the trading floor of the Chase Manhattan Bank. My twin jobs as bank president and chief trading manager excited me.

Naturally, I doled out bills, and I told my imaginary assistants when to buy and sell other currencies. My interns wore pressed white shirts and smartly buffed black leather shoes. Quotes streamed in from all over the world. On my trading floor, Japanese yen were cheaper to buy in London using Pounds Sterling than if I bought yen with US Dollars in New York. Each time I bid, the spread shriveled, and my profit fled. I could see it happen in front of me, in all those whirring numbers on my television screens.

That morning I hadn't been greedy. I mostly made small denominations. I told myself to be satisfied with less profit since that showed character. Only hogs soaked up all the profits. I also made large bills—hundreds, five hundreds, thousands and ten thousands—just like in the game of "Life". As I did this, I printed the names of the faces on the bills, and I crudely scrawled the person's face, a stick man with frenzied hair. Each portrait looked the same—only the names were different—Franklin, McKinley, Cleveland, and Wilson.

Next came my glorious payoff! I shuffled one-hundred dollar bills into stacks of fifty each. Each bundle was worth $5,000, the amount we borrowed from Grandfather to save the farm. I allowed no mistakes.

After all, people lost their jobs for counting errors. Then, to add a bit of flourish, I fluffed the bills rapidly by my ears, as if to say I knew the number of bills just by listening to them. Detail drenched me with power and authority.

Pulling red rubber bands out of my pockets, I bundled the bills. Finally, I stacked the bundles into my shoe box which I had marked "BANK" with a red crayon. I must have been quite a scene, what with my runny nose and red cheeks, flushed with excitement.

"Wow, what a fine morning's work," I mumbled. I've made a considerable fortune, I reckoned. Now, I can retire the mortgage on our farm. For a few moments all adult problems and cares melted. Did our salve lay tucked under my right arm?

As I walked from the living room toward the kitchen, Mother sat in her black rocking chair. She had simply lost it. There she sat, sobbing and staring straight ahead, her eyes fixed on the television perched on the kitchen table on the south side of the room.

At first I thought she was crying about our farm, about how we lost the cattle and filed for wage earner's bankruptcy. But, we'd solved that problem weeks ago. No, it couldn't be wage earner's bankruptcy making her cry.

So, what was it? "Oh," I gasped as I peered down at Mother's sewing scissors. All right, I got a bit carried away. I cut a few more bills than planned. Maybe I went too far, fueled by the anxiety we felt on that horrid filing day in Stanley. Anyway, the bankers made us feel like criminals, even though Dad promised to pay back every cent. I reckoned those bankers didn't care much about our reputation, though. Did they care only about the bottom line, about how much interest we'd pay on top of what we owed?

I'd overused the scissors, dulling them before their time. Did that make her sad? If that was all, I would come clean and admit it. Maybe she was more worried about my character than she was about that fool pair of scissors. Perhaps she wanted me to keep my promises. So, I decided to walk in there and admit that I overused her scissors. I would!

"There's nothing to feel so sad about, Mother, really. Please don't cry," I said as I slowly walked toward her chair, my head bowed as if in prayer.

She was really sobbing. "Mother, I'm powerful sorry, and I will never, ever borrow the scissors again. I'll save money from chores and flower prizes to buy new scissors. You'll have new ones in no time."

All that didn't help at all, and she commenced to cry with every breath. She shook her head.

"I'm really sorry, Mother," I repeated as I began to stroke the back of her rocking chair. Mother shook her head and kept staring at that infernal screen as she clutched a bunch of tissues in her left hand.

I repeated my offer, but nothing helped. Then, I began to feel scared—right in the pit of my stomach.

Glancing up, I saw the television announcer's face. He looked frightened and sad. I imagined he was about to cry. Of course, I knew that he wouldn't because crying was simply the most awful thing any man or boy could do! Our priest and bishop had told us so. To cry was unforgivable. It meant that you had no character, had no faith, and were weak. To have no character meant you were no one at all. "No one born male may ever cry in public," priests said.

My heart beat rapidly, and I began to pant like an old bloodhound sprawled on his belly to catch his breath after a night of hunting. A wave of terror pounded. Could it be that the Communists had invaded? Were we under attack, the bombs on their way? How long did we have before they hit Kansas? Was Mother bracing herself for the attack, not knowing for sure where the bombs would fall?

"Mother, should we begin praying the rosary? Shall we pray for our country?" I blurted out, remembering how we'd done that one year earlier during the Cuban Missile Crisis.

Mother didn't answer. Walter Cronkite looked powerful sad. He paused as if to fight back the tears. I secretly prayed, "Don't do it; don't cry. If you do, you'll lose your job." I liked Mr. Cronkite, and I didn't want him to be out of work, no sir.

"Mother, are the Communists coming?" I gasped as I peered into her eyes. She shook her head again, just as she had when I had asked her if she was upset about the scissors.

Walter Cronkite announced, "From Dallas, Texas . . . the flash, apparently official, President Kennedy died at 1 pm Central Standard Time, 2 o'clock Eastern Standard Time, some thirty-eight minutes ago." He glanced over his right shoulder and gulped as he spoke that last sentence. His lips puffed out slightly, and I thought I spied a tear in his eyes. He seemed shaken, as if he ached to cry. Before he delivered that last line, he had removed his glasses, and then he snuggled them back on. Had he tried to shake off the horrid news of that day? If there had been a dark curtain lying around, he might want to use it, cloaking the events from our eyes and ears. When he replaced his glasses, he coughed faintly, and his face wiggled a pinch forward. Later, we learned that Vice-president Johnson would be sworn in. Mrs. Kennedy stood at his side, her pink dress splotched in gobs of dried blood. No amount of Amway concentrated detergent would help her. That dress was a goner!

My God, are the Communists coming for us? Did they kill President Kennedy?" I guessed he must've been very brave to stand up to them-—powerful brave. "Mother, if we asked Lucille Ball, she'd tell us that if we must be as brave as the President. Then, it'll be all right. She told me, 'It just isn't that bad, kid. It will be all right,' and I believe her!" As I rambled on, Mother must have tuned me out because my words did no good. My arms began to quiver, and I grew frightened all the way down to my stomach. I must've been trying to calm myself as much as I was trying to help Mother.

I wrapped my arms around Mother's left shoulder and blurted, "I'll protect you with our sewing scissors. They're still mighty sharp. Communists or not, I know one jab to the belly will drop one of them. We won't go down without a fight." Since Mom and I were alone on the farm that morning, I knew it was up to me to protect us. "I am the man of the house now, and I'll protect you. I'll be braver than anyone you ever knew," I comforted her. Those were tall words for a small boy.

Mother shook her head. "Sean, it's not the Communists." I asked her again if we should pray, and she said, "Yes, we need to pray. We need to pray for our president. He was a good man. Bad men, tired and sick in the head, killed him. So, we need to pray for the President, for our country, and especially for all of those sick men."

Later that evening the storm blew in from the southwest. Who knows exactly when the lightning struck? All I know is that it happened during the night. I recall only the wind and the storm in hazy mists as I drifted off to sleep. I'd been worn out—tired slick—what with all the kids home early from school that afternoon. Sister Marie William had been listening to the radio during lunch recess, and she scurried up to the principal's office to let her know. Sister Theresa dismissed school early.

I drifted to sleep that night, not because I felt better when everyone promised me the Communists wouldn't attack, but because I was worn slick by that awful day. The next morning my brother Mark rushed in to pull me out of bed and to throw me to the floor. "King cottonwood is in pieces on the ground, torn apart by the wind and lightning," he shouted into my face. Gone were our hopes and our plans for a glorious retreat. Gone were our dreams of a splendid clubhouse: gone, but not forgotten.

While we inspected the damage the next morning, we tallied our losses. First, our president and then king cottonwood? When would it all end?

The king lay torn apart on the pasture northwest of our house, and there was not a thing we could do about it. If this could happen to our cottonwood, couldn't even worse things happen to us? Couldn't the bombs fall at night to burn us up before we even knew what had happened? That day our innocence and a part of our dreams had perished.

Although we had been brave, we had lost our friend. We died a bit with our tree. Even the birds grumbled and twittered angrily as they left their nests to find other homes. Part of our innocence had been splintered along with the trunk of that old cottonwood. Part of our dreams lay shattered, just as the king lay shattered in our northwest pasture. These were our personal dreams, not those of some stranger.

Our losses seemed specific to us alone.

Paul toted a package of eight Oscar Meyer wieners under his arm. "Come on, it's time to build a fire and roast these," Paul said.

I jeered at him and shouted, "How can you think of eating at a time like this? The President and our king are dead. They're never coming back!" I knew we were too sad to build a fire. We wouldn't be able to roast the wieners. Instead, we gazed off across the pasture.

Paul sputtered, "All right. Too bad. I'll eat 'em raw. Yours, too." I guess that was his way of helping us pull out of the pits.

"No, I'll take mine after all," I shouted. The Oscar Meyer wiener tasted salty, reminding me of the taste of my tears I'd shed in private—away from scorn and contempt. It tasted like the tears that had run down my cheeks after I locked myself in the bathroom so no one could see me cry. I couldn't be sure, though, whether the taste was from the wiener or from tears that had meandered down my cheeks. I withdrew into shadows that shrouded me in the shade of our fallen tree.

Then, I remembered how the cottonwood wafts its fluff-bearing seeds over the pasture during the early summer. Maybe some of those seeds found a home and took root. A piece of our cottonwood could live on as a sapling. There would be more trees and clubhouses, and there would be more days filled with laughter and discovery. We could move forward with courage and hope: with trust in our dreams.

After a few bites I felt sick to my stomach. I wrapped the rest of the hot dog in a napkin I had folded in my pants' right pocket. As I scurried off west from the shattered tree, I placed the wrapped lunch into my pocket for safekeeping.

I needed to get away by myself to think. Spying the pond and its spent cattails, I scampered to the pond's edge to lose myself in its swaying grasses and weeds. I needed to hide there for awhile. As I crept closer to the pond, I dropped onto all fours and crawled over the pond's bank. I entered my "cave" of solitude. Plop went my face in the weeds, grasses, and soil. I rested that way for a spell, and then I turned skyward. The fluffy clouds reminded me of thistledown—like cottonwood fluff I'd seen wafting over the prairie during the early summer. But the summer was long spent. In those clouds and in that thistledown I saw hope for the future. Again, I thought of cotton candy at the circus. I felt those clouds would not turn ugly again—not for a spell.

"Today is our time to rest," I purred.

Wintry Flight

"Oh how cute, the baby's ciphering," adults often gushed. I didn't need that kind of attention. In fact, I wanted to head for the hills, steering clear of that tired prattle. I doubt how "cute" I might have been, although it's true I was powerful busy, what with riddles and puzzles.

Could I understand a piece of the world? Might I find my place in it, not unlike the homes youngsters discover for blocks they insert into holes? Might I craft a language to help me understand and savor my own ideas? Hmmm . . .

Once I learned to tell time, I yearned for 8:45 a.m. daily, the time I could expect Dad to jaunt through our kitchen door. His homecoming became my daily apex. Whenever he ran late, I wondered if he'd stopped at the Manor Bakery for day-old rolls. On those days I caught him at the door, his right hand swaying two dozen sweet rolls wrapped in plastic bags, each one with a yellow or off-white ruffled liner. There were enough for everyone—except for Mother that is. She didn't count, seeing as how she'd have none of it.

"It's junk," she sniped as we yelped for our treat.

"More for us," Paul snapped.

Mother routinely lectured anyone within hearing distance how diet is a "key to health". But no one—not even Mother—convinced our excited taste buds to take heed. We gobbled apple, peach, cherry, or cinnamon sweet rolls with fancy swirls of lacy icing.

"Daddy's home!" I'd yell. Oops, I forgot myself again. No clear-thinking big boy dared insult himself by uttering "Daddy". He was "Dad" to me.

Sure I craved seeing Dad and his treats, but I also luxuriated in watching him hide my coins. This became our special game. Peeking around the corner into the utility room, I often caught him stashing a couple of wheat pennies, a buffalo nickel, and maybe a winged liberty dime under a discarded ice cube tray in our special drawer. (Most people called it a mercury dime, but I knew better.) Harvests, sweet and otherwise, came when the coast cleared.

"Time for school," Mother said, as she took Julie by the hand. The cranking of the engine sounded my green light to share my tales of discovery with Dad.

"I saw the Taj Mahal by moonlight," I started.

"Anything notable to report?"

"It looked like a jewel, one rich enough to pay our way out of bankruptcy."

"Is that so? Hmm . . . You're not funning me, are you?"

"Well, I know what I saw. I'm no baby."

"And-"

And then my mouth overflowed with reports of run-ins with rum pirates and maverick rocket ships, of space voyages and sled dogs.

"I hiked to a camp near Katmandu, and then I scaled Mt. Everest, which was all tucked in with its white sheets of snow and ice. I fell into a crevasse, but PJ rescued me with a rope."

The creaking chorus of floorboards framed Dad's escape to the downstairs bedroom. Tugging at his checkered flannel shirt, I heard myself shout, "I reckon I know where the best dinosaurs live!"

"Where?" Dad asked, drifting toward bed.

"I snatched the idea from the side of Mark's lunch box. There's a space station on it. Maybe one orbits the Earth, and it's big enough to hold dinosaurs, and its far enough away that people can't spot them, and they live there . . . with guess who?"

"You must tell me."

"Oh, with the witch, the wizard, and Dorothy—her shoes ran out of juice, and they need to recharge before they make it clear back to Kansas."

"How long can they stay there?" Dad yawned under the covers.

"Oh, let me see . . . for about six months." I sputtered, twirling my undershirt into one massive knot about six inches in length, like a rat's tail ready to snap someone for attention. "Then they might crash. No one knows if they'll pull through. They might kerplunk into the ocean, and they have no parachute, and that would mean their end, but I don't know-"

"Un-an-angh," killed my ending.

Hushing up then, I scaled the bed, capped with white sheets of cotton.

Oh, not all of my stories came from sides of lunch boxes. There were the older kids' leftover textbooks, and then there were stragglers "borrowed" from the Louisburg Rural Library. And I relied on a 20-volume set of our 1930's edition *Blue Book of Knowledge*, not to mention Mother's nursing school books from way back east (The Catholic University of America).

The kids were home from school on the first day of Christmas vacation, a day that fluttered with our first heavy snow of the season. I decided that I'd be the one to greet Dad, and I commenced watching for him 15 minutes early in case—God forbid—he should show up early. How could I stomach being away from my post?

A half an hour later I knew something was wrong. But maybe not. Sometimes, he worked an extra hour, or he trotted out errands, or he drove to . . . St. Joseph. Mother would raise her eyebrows if he'd done that.

"You know, that's not healthy for you, or us. Stop pestering him. Bill (Dr. Bill Redmond, his brother) is not going to float you a loan."

I also wished he'd stay away from "that place". After all, "I" needed to tell my stories and collect my money. And then of course, there were the sweet rolls.

By 9:25 I began to sweat. What if something went wrong? No, maybe he's shopping for gifts. Maybe that's it.

"I'm going to town with your sisters," Mother said. "You wait here for Dad. Your brothers are in watching TV."

My sisters had visions of fancy fabrics stretching for yards, but I wanted no part of it. Weren't they begging for trouble, like the time Julie dressed the Wallace Park slide with Jean's last 4-H sewing project? Trains of cloth stretched and ripped behind Julie, slowly easing her to a stop near the bottom. Her skirt fluttered in fifteen-feet long strips behind her.

Those traitors, I thought. How could they leave when Dad was missing? Snow fell somberly and sinisterly as they sped away. Snow deep enough to cover a nesting hen had congregated on our chicken shed roof. Will the roof fold and drown our hens? No, I knew better. How much more snow will it take to crash Dad's car? Will he be all right?

By 10 o'clock I grew powerfully worried. Where was he, lying in some ditch with his crumpled 1956 Firebird wrapped around him? What if he hadn't been lucky . . . this time?

Dad's checkered driving past scared even brave folks. More often than not, he fell asleep or glanced away at the worst time. Losing control, he catapulted off of roads. The car totaled, Dad walked away unharmed and without even breaking a sweat. While that had already happened four times in the past year, I hoped this wasn't the fifth. But with each tick of the clock, my inkling of trouble blossomed into full-fledged suspicion.

"I'm worried about Dad. He's late."

"Hush up, we're busy. Woody Woodpecker's on." Mark snapped.

"Should I call-"

Splat, A pillow spanked my face. Swish, another struck my back. "Leave us alone. He's probably in St. Joe again," Paul roared.

Slinking back to the kitchen door, I resumed my vigil. It was a quarter past ten, and Dad was nowhere in sight. Should I phone Grandfather Kearney? Uncle Bill? But Mom said no more long distance calls. Besides, if Dad *wasn't* at Uncle Bill's, what would I say? Uncle Bill might worry. That wasn't the thing to do. Trouble *is*, I didn't know *what* to do.

A few minutes later I spotted a man's head and slowly growing torso edging up from the creek on the east road. The man's head hung low, his shoulders hunched forward, his arms wrapped around his chest as if to comfort the rest of him. Dad trudged home.

Why is he walking? Where's the Firebird?

As Dad groped up the sidewalk, I knew he'd wrecked the car. He saw only me as he lumbered into the kitchen. The spastic laughter jabbing from the living room at a time like this might have shamed even Woody and all of his friends.

"It'll be all right," I blurted. "I know you had car trouble."

"What? Er . . . oh yes. Car trouble . . . that's it. The car's at the creek."

I imagined how his white Firebird jumped the snow-packed ditch, soared over the fence, and sidled up alongside the creek bed as if it needed rest, too.

It was wrecked—maybe totaled—just like the other cars. Of course, I didn't need to check Dad for bruises. He had none, just like all the other times. But then, why did he act wounded?

Sighing heavily, Dad pointed his feet toward the downstairs bedroom. Did he know what to do? Should he go to bed, or should he stay up to explain? Did he want to say hello to the boys? His steps were tentative, halting and unsure. That reminded me of how a stutterer might speak in public. Dad's walking looked like stutter-stepping.

"I'm very late and tired. I'm going to bed," Dad mumbled.

Straightening at the prospect of a reprieve, he crept onward. Our wooden floor groaned his retreat, echoing a gob of wooden sounds: human and otherwise.

"All right, the chores are done. I'll take a nap, too," I said. All that waiting wore me slick, and my right hip ached in spurts. Peering up to Dad's eyes, I said, "Things will look better after a nap." (Things often looked better after rest.)

Pulling the covers over his head, Dad muttered again about some car trouble. Then, he rambled about losing the farm. "I'm tired and scared. Plain tuckered out. And I don't know what to do. We might lose the farm. Wage earner's bankruptcy . . .. declare it . . ."

"The cattle market's down. The skidding cattle market got us, right Dad?"

"Partly that, yes. Partly me. I never imagined I'd make much of a farmer or rancher. But who guessed it'd be this tough? I thought I could turn the cattle loose into the pasture to take care of themselves. Who knew how tough it could be? God help me find a way."

A tired stillness filled the room, a still weariness. Drifting off to sleep Dad muttered, "Today I'm signing the papers at the Bank of Stanley: declare wage earner's bankruptcy. Got to protect our good name, pay back every cent. It'll take a while, that's all."

I was worried seeing as he had signed months ago! Was he all right? And sleep drifted into us. I didn't mind. Besides, my right leg throbbed oddly. Maybe a nap could help me forget that growing ache in my right hip.

It turned out the Firebird did tumble off our snow-packed dirt road, where it went airborne and soared thirty feet toward the creek. It flopped to rest in a soft-pack snow drift. Even with that cushioning, the Firebird ended up a mangled mass of wreckage. But the driver's door and Dad were untouched. Dad had fallen asleep at the wheel, and the crash awakened him. Most people are injured, killed, or at least knocked out in such a crash, but not Dad. He awakened! I imagined that's because he was sound asleep and limp. Others who were wide awake, their muscles tensed, weren't as lucky. I wondered if that was sound advice for most blows, although some aren't easy to take.

Mother and her parents decided it was better if Dad didn't drive for a spell, and he agreed. He took a second job as a janitor—room included—for the Grand Avenue Methodist Church in Kansas City, Missouri. He rode a bus to our farm most weekends, provided he didn't work the extra board.

I suppose this was for the best, but I felt low. As much as I wanted to make sure Dad was all right, I also wanted to see him: enough that it positively stung.

Sunday nights we drove six miles to town to drop him at the bus stop in front of the old US 169 Highway Motel. What a waste. I had gobs of new subjects and adventures to share, and being denied that was the worst part of all. I lived to jabber like a giddy jay as I spouted news to Dad about my day: of discoveries and voyages; of my dreams and plans. Some of my unshared dreams could have been lofty, too. They might have traced a flight path even higher than the one taken by Dad's Firebird the day it sailed from the road and through the crisp air of that snowy winter's morn.

For days I crept past our kitchen door, stopped, backslid, and waited. Cracking it open, I breathed in choppy drafts. I ached for the draft of Dad coming through our door. Pain blossomed in my right leg, and I reckoned it was on account of Dad's absence. I was wrong.

To the Farm to Heal

When a Missouri mule takes a notion to stay put, watch out! Listen, I've heard folks joke about toting a 2 by 4 to rap that stubborn animal upside its head, persuading it to take heed. Sooner or later, the old cuss straightens up. I'll wager that I looked like a dazed Missouri mule as I waited in Doctor Stanley's office. Had someone whacked me upside my head?

Some folks say life sneaks up like a stink bug to bomb a body minding its own business: quite a wake-up call. Sitting in Dr. Stanley's office, I waited to hear him weigh in on my condition. I felt as if I'd been bombed even before his diagnosis stung me. You see, daggers of pain shot down my legs. Would he drop a bomb, one that out-reeks a rotten egg? Maybe I'd stagger like a dazed Missouri mule.

What's taking her so long, I wondered? Dr. Stanley had wrapped up my exam thirty minutes ago, and he'd carried me into his office to wait. That did nothing for me. When would Mother walk through that door to leave? The afternoon stretched, yawning lazily. As I watched afternoon sunlight streaming through the window, I spotted dust swirling in sunbeams. That grew on me. Finally, Mother's voice leaked through the wall from the next room. Great, we'll leave at last.

Back in his examining room, Dr. Stanley and Mother fussed about a new patient. Since Mother was an RN, I guessed she was helping Dr. Stanley. But hold on, Dr. Stanley was an orthopedic specialist, and he must know everything. Latching onto whatever I could make out, I sensed that a new patient was in trouble. Feeling sorry for him, I decided to help. "I'll talk to that child. That poor thing needs help."

"We'll send him to the Shriner's Hospital in St. Louis," Dr. Stanley flatly explained. "They're setup for cripples. You'll see. It's all we can do for him."

"Hmmm, I don't know," Mother pondered. "What treatment will he endure . . . er, face?"

"Oh, they'll test his reflexes and mind after they check his legs," the doctor began with his same know-it-all tone. "Then, I guess they'll cocoon him in a spread-eagle cast. He'll lie as silent and still as the grave for a year . . . or more. He might heal."

I'd heard how folks treated hopeless cases. They're shuttled out of sight, locked on a darkened hospital wing. In this case, the poor thing would be wrapped up like a spider's prey.

"That won't do," Mother protested. "I can't imagine the problems. Think of the atrophy and the bed sores, to say nothing of the emotional trauma. Tell me, will anyone his own age keep him company?"

"Oh, no. Why? The problem's in his legs, not the mind. We must isolate him . . . hope for the best. That's all we can do for the boy. Are we clear, Mrs. Redmond," Dr. Stanley offered in a sardonic tone. "We simply cannot bother him with any kids."

"Doctor, what you blithely call kids are children."

Doctor Stanley only exhaled, sighing long-windedly like a punctured balloon.

"Gee, that would be lonely," I gasped. "How dreadful" A spread-eagle cast is more confining than a cone wrapped around a dog's neck to stop him from nipping his wounds. I'd seen firsthand how that riles a hound, only PJ's cone kept him from digging at his ears.

"No, that won't do. Forget it," Mother objected.

By that time, I had grown mighty sorry for the poor thing. Horrible, I thought. Who could lie there perfectly still: isolated? His fate was akin to solitary confinement. Boy, I'd like to talk to him—to help him feel better.

A stuffy nurse in white uniform flounced noisily into the room, and she snatched bottles from the medicine cabinet like all get out. Without so much as blinking, she began flinging other bottles back into that fool cabinet. Never mind breathing a word like "hello" or "howdy do", she pawed and fussed at those bottles. Well, I didn't pay her much heed, seeing as I was wrapped up with my concern over that crippled child. She fussed and fiddled with her truck as I listened.

"I've told you, I won't put any son of mine through that living hell," Mother's voice echoed. Her words pounded me harder than any 2 by 4. They weren't jawing about some pathetic victim . . . er, patient! They were talking about . . . me.

My stomach fluttered, echoing my gasp. The stern nurse spun an about face as if she'd been raised to alarm. Rushing to my chair, she asked, "Dear, do you need a Kleenex? It's all right to cry, if you need to."

I shook my head no.

"Shush, now. I won't tell. I'm sure they'll understand. No one will blame you if you let loose with a few tears," she promised in a hushed voice, telling me that she didn't want to be overhead. She didn't fancy anyone knowing how she said it was all right to cry. Her robot-like motions battled with her words, telling me that she thought crying was wrong. Mendacity pulsed through the room.

"I'm not going to cry, and I'm not going to St. Louis to be treated worse than a dog," I promised her. "Now, tell Mother we are leaving—NOW!" I demanded with a shaky voice.

As if pursued by a monster, the nurse bolted next door. "Help! Come quickly. He'll throw a fit." I wanted only to be done with that office, and the sooner the better. How can grown-ups be powerful mean and uncaring? If I had children like them, I'd spot "reform school" written all over them. Was all of this merely a horrid dream?

News of my fit were greatly exaggerated. I hadn't cried. Why, I'd acted like any big boy, although I was tired . . . and frightened. If I could only escape. At a safe distance, I wouldn't be bothered by the doctor's good wishes. No, I could do without them. Being cooped up didn't set well with me. Frightening . . .

Mother sent that cussed nurse to fetch my oldest brother, Paul. He'd been in the waiting room where he twiddled his thumbs from boredom, by his account. Mother thought I needed an older boy to talk to me, and Paul was the likely candidate, seeing as he'd beaten the same disease in one hip. While no one had hinted that Paul might need solitary confinement in a spread-eagle cast, he did make it through the same mysterious illness. I heard Mother reason, "Sean needs to talk to Paul. That will settle him." Paul came right away, tagging behind the nurse.

"Sean, Mother says you want to leave. Are you ready?"

No melody ever sounded lovelier. "Yes, but I'm not going to St. Louis. I need to go home: to the farm to heal."

Soon, Dr. Stanley released me. I reckon he was itching to get rid of me, seeing how Mother gave him what for. "You don't know how many beans make five. Your so-called treatment has no guarantee. I'll take him home: to the farm to heal. We'll all help him." Then, just as crisply as a cent, fresh from the mint, Mother ordered, "Paul, carry Sean to the car."

Dr. Stanley breathed all funny, and his face turned red. His lower lip began to twitch, and his face scrunched like a large roly-poly bug. Oh, he was booming mad! I felt sorry for him, seeing as how anyone who's that angry must be in trouble, too.

I wasn't well. In fact, I wasn't well enough to shoo a lame hen from our front porch. A mysterious illness, Osteochondritis in general and

Leggs-Calves-Perthes in particular, had attacked and dissolved the heads of both of my femurs, crippling me. The illness was triggered by the trauma of my fall from our swing set. My condition was rare, and the doctors could not reason why my bones disintegrated, let alone how to treat them. Some researchers reckoned the disease is hereditary. My oldest brother Paul came down with it in one hip after he fell from an apple tree. He struck his hip on a rock in the creek, and the disease coursed freely. However, his illness lasted only one year. Mother and Dad never guessed that I might follow in Paul's footsteps (or lack thereof). Meanwhile, Dad had taken ill, too. Only, his problems weren't in his legs . . .

Mother couldn't be hornswoggled, not by any fancy-talking specialist. She did us proud. Once inside the car, we all knew better than to spout off about anything. Silence felt nice.

We stopped for our weekly groceries, which I knew would mean shopping that stretched into the late afternoon hours. That was fine with me, because I needed time to think after all of that fuss.

Sitting on a wooden bench inside the Buy-Rite while Mother and Paul shopped, I sorely needed time to work on the infernal soreness in my legs, which didn't hurt much unless I pushed down on them. No one needed to tell me that, especially no know-it-all doctor.

Spying lonesome dust bunnies under the gum ball machine, I watched how they danced on the linoleum floor, a few squares crinkled at their edges. Air currents from people passing through the door swirled those dust bunnies any which way. I tried to guess which direction they'd blow as people tromped past me.

How marvelous it is to walk: nothing fancy, only simple strolling. But, I had to stay put, at least until I healed. Then, like the calm before a storm, I inhaled deeply to gather strength for an upcoming storm of hellish pain. Oh my gosh! Maybe I'd commence to hurt even when I don't press down on my legs. What lay ahead if that came to pass? No one knew for sure what might happen, and that went doubly for doctors.

Thoughts pounded wearily with ease.

Children feuded over candy. Some fussed over toys and even who'd sit in the front seat of their car. I wondered: does anyone know what they have? Does anyone appreciate health? I'd be tickled simply to stand so I could walk to the car. Feeling crushed, I cast my eyes toward the floor.

A chubby boy, looking nothing like a cute cherub in paintings, stalked up to me. "Get the hell off my bench, you jerk," he demanded. Before you could say "Jack Robinson," he grabbed me around my chest and neck, choked me, and pitched me to the floor. Knowing I'd scatter all over the floor, I cradled myself like a roly-poly bug to lite on my shoulders—not my hips. That worked, and I landed on my right shoulder before I rolled to a stop. Even though I cushioned my fall, the pain felt like an electric shock—one of horror—that snatched me into another world.

"Get up and fight, you sissy! Get up before I pull off your shoes and stuff them down your throat!" What had ignited his rage? Glancing up, I saw his wicked shadow looming. How could anyone be cruel enough to beat a crippled child?

Just about then, the boy's mother rushed up. "What have you done to my precious, my little Georgie?"

Breathing fire, she huffed, "Did you hurt him, you monster? Why are you picking on my Georgie?" Her eyes oozed her offense. She must have believed her line of drivel, seeing as how she panted with offended pride. Her eyes glistened with echoes of anger.

I could only think how happy I was not to be her kin. Just then, Mother rushed up, saying "My son's crippled, and he can't get up."

Georgie's mother stopped breathing funny, and she ceased glaring at me. Did she have some conscience after all? Meanwhile, her precious— her little Georgie—scoffed, reveling in my illness. He hissed, and an ugly gurgling sound seeped out of his mouth with the poison of a Komodo dragon. Did little Georgie aim to whip the world, one victim at a time? "Such a tall order, so misguided," I mumbled. That made me feel sorry for him. I bet he was confused, and that must hurt, too, I reckoned.

Meanwhile, Georgie's mother was mute, only motioning for her little boy to run toward her outstretched arms. I spied a funny-looking button on her dress. It looked like an elephant with red and blue stripes on it. I wondered if folks loyal to elephants beat up anyone they please, especially crippled children.

Mother had intervened, but I felt poorly. I had hoped to hide my condition, especially from the likes of them. Humiliation soared, nearly excelling the soreness in my legs.

Once again seated upon my perch, I spied the shoppers' frenzied activity. "What in the Sam Hill is so mighty important to persuade them to rush so?" I asked myself. "What can be so gosh darn urgent?" I knew that if I were healed, I would take my time to saunter through the aisles. I'd inhale deeply to suck up every second of freedom—from pain, and to walk wherever I chose. I would take my time and relish all of it, every single second.

Does anyone know how fine health is? (Is it often wasted on those who don't appreciate it?) Sitting on the bench, I guessed the answer: no, not often. When could I go home to the farm to heal?

As our station wagon pulled away from the Buy-Rite Market that afternoon, I knew how worn out I'd grown, and I wasn't sure how much longer I'd stay focused. Could I be as strong and firm as a stone wall? (I'd read about the courageous General Stonewall Jackson, standing as firm as a stone wall.) I might be like General Jackson, except I cannot stand, which is what I can't stand. Burying my face in my arms, I felt sadness pecking like a relentless bird of prey at my "gizzard".

Gazing at my bedroom ceiling that afternoon, I felt my mind drift. The sound of Mother's soft-soled shoes came as a relief. "Mother, how can I be happy while I'm crippled?"

"That's a toughie," she said. "Just remember that happiness—true happiness—comes from within."

I needed to figure out how to be happy. Being crippled might not be my worst problem. If I didn't change the way I thought, I might have larger problems. Will the way I see myself decide who I am? Is any dreariness I see a reflection of what lies within me? If I found my life in Kansas drab, I might see any place the same way. If I found Kansas splendid, then it would live that way. Oh, I got it. The future rested in my hands.

That afternoon I clung to enduring hope. By trying to heal, maybe I'd tap other wonders. If what we see reflects the mind, then I must see sunshine. If life appears drab, does that reflect doubts, shrouded by fear? Wait a minute. No one can force me to remember anything differently from how I choose to remember it. No matter what happens, I decide how to live, and only I decide how to remember my life. Instead of a gray sky, I'd see a blue one with billowing puffs of hope. Instead of dull conversation, I'd imagine splendid voyages to ports of call unknown. It was up to me, mostly.

That afternoon at the Buy-Rite, I had wanted to lie down on the floor to watch dust bunnies dance by me. No one—doctor, priest, you name it—could take that from me. Watching the coils of dust near the door soothed me. Their motion calmed me. Heck, I could spend all day watching dust dance mysteriously. The uncertain journey of each piece enchanted me. Their show felt like I'd eaten something after missing breakfast. That quenched my curiosity. Colors of the rainbow framed feathery profiles of each dust bunny, highlighted in yellow hope.

But was that fear I tasted seeping between my teeth and onto my tongue, parching it? Does fear creep in like blow dirt, swirling under doors and into cabinets wherever it likes, just as it had seeped under the floorboards and inside the walls of derelict farmhouses?

My world echoed colors, particularly in shades of yellow, and they framed hope. My Kansas pulsed as a special place where I could muster peace and calm to heal, in spite of dread and the dim chances experts hissed at me. But, no matter. Mother had told me, "Sometimes I feel that life is one large question mark. Any answers must lie within. No book or lecture can give you that. You must find it yourself, and the answer is different for every single person." The Kansas of my childhood lives in Technicolor memories serenaded by Mother's dancing words.

Hope oozes color-filled images, and I worry about people who make fun of life in Kansas. Some label it drab or boring. Heck, do you remember the opening and closing scenes of "The Wonderful Wizard of Oz"? Filmed in black, white, and mottled shades of gray, its dreariness highlighted vibrant colors of Munchkinland. Anyone who hasn't lived on a farm might think it's drab. I recall Dad telling me, "Although tough, farming can be joy in action." Feeling he was right, I felt honored to help, especially if I might daydream through my chores. If a body's grateful for home (and I mean really grateful), isn't it a palace of light where moonbeams form arched doorways, and where rooftops shimmer with bejeweled radiance? While some folks see a weathered shack with a tumble-down roof, I see a castle that no money could buy. Where some folks see a mound of wet chicken manure, I see riches for soil. That meant a whiff of new life.

Could loving my home and life make me whole, no matter the pain? Could it make up for cancelled trips to foriegn lands? I reckoned it could, and in that gem, hope lived. Hope simply is, then, now, and always. No one can steal that.

As I lay gazing at the ceiling that afternoon, I knew that I owed myself a chance to be happy. Maybe I could find it alone since I wouldn't be going to school anytime soon. Wow, was my mysterious illness a ticket to relax with my own thoughts? That felt right nice. Besides, making my own decisions meant freedom, even if I lay crippled. Freedom makes all the difference—to stay put or to do whatever I fancied. Maybe I could rely on the kindness of chance, seeing as how miracles happen when we least expect them. Doesn't the world open its treasures (like freedom) to any who will welcome them?

I remembered another crippled boy I knew, Billy Crinshaw. He'd been crippled from birth, and his illness wasn't from any fall. Each time I watched Billy, I saw him coping, and that meant he was hoping. When I saw him struggling even to raise his head to smile, I imagined that I saw a movie with hidden messages flickering across the screen. Each time I watched him, my throat felt large and cottony. Billy looked regal, even though folks called him a no-account cripple. Did his happiness come from within?

John Jansen, the old man I'd met in the Kansas City Union Station that night we headed west on the Santa Fe, had warned me that no matter the pain and disappointment, no matter who left me or how they let me down, I must never grow old before my time. "It's poison," he'd advised, "the deadliest poison there is, the poison that makes a person old." That kind of age meant hopelessness.

Suddenly, I smiled. My doctors had acted silly. When they didn't know an answer, they cloaked their missing knowledge with medical babbling (saying nothing and meaning even less). Did they think that they could muffle cluelessness with pretended wisdom? I knew better.

"Enough of this!" I told myself. "If I dwell on it too long, I risk becoming as they are." I'm what I think about. My secret friends will tell me so. They knew how to color my world any which way I pleased. (There is too much living to do. I knew that my legs would heal, despite the doctors' grim assessment.)

The evening I fell from our swing set triggered my mysterious illness, and I felt surrounded by a host of tiny fireflies that glowed in the evening air, filling it with mysterious sparks. My world had slowed, and that reminded me of how something looks under a strobe light. Had I fallen into another world? Can pain craft a whole new reality?

Maybe a light would leave me, like a type of too-bashful light if I was not careful. Maybe colors would vanish. I remembered how color television sets used green, red, and blue. They missed the sharpness of nature's true colors. Just as those colors can't be captured, like the setting sun of a sultry twilight, I felt I might lose my true colors. Did I risk losing life's vibrant colors, reflected by enduring hope?

What about imagination? Losing it would frighten me. To lose my imaginary friends would feel like the flicker of a drab black and white television program of a late-night horror flick.

When Paul carried me to the boy's room, I mumbled, "May I have paper and crayons?" I needed to know if the light had fled. Would my world be stripped of color? I could find out by coloring.

"Sean, are you all right? Do you want some company?" Mother asked.

"Oh, no. I need to be alone for a while," I insisted.

As Mother closed the door, I closed my eyes, the reassuring texture of the paper and crayons in my hands to comfort me. I waited. Then, they slowly appeared: the dancing and twirling images and figures in saffron. Next, I saw the characters in pink, chartreuse, and lavender. But where were the spruce and magenta? What became of my radiant orange? Patience, simply wait a spell, I told myself. Each friend, with a pirouetting partner, trickled onto my imaginary stage. The list included Arabic and Roman numerals, symbols of the Greek alphabet, and the notes of the treble and bass clefs.

There were also playing cards: the deuces, up to mischief as usual; the treys, playing tricks on the sevens and rudely assuming they'd get away with it. The tens pouted in a corner about how they lacked the fancy dress of face cards. The knaves gloated, the fingers of their left hands rhythmically floating up their sleeves. The queens danced and flirted in puffs of jasmine, and the kings glutted themselves on food and wine until their breath reeked. The aces soared over the room with their scent of assured victory oozing from their pores.

One ace had crafted his own version of the Red Baron's plane, and he wore a scarf. His friendly eyes twinkled through his fogged goggles. Each friend hovered, danced, or pranced.

Meanwhile, Omega and Lambda fenced up a storm in another of their battles. Soon I sniffed the salty aroma of fresh blood trickling out of their flesh wounds.

A bloated gamma sulked and pawed at the floor in disgust, smelling of flatulence. Slowly, they returned—all of them.

Then, the symbols began to form answers as they skulked and rose gingerly over the arch of my three-dimensional rainbow ribbon, fluttering in the afternoon sunlight. That ribbon curled just above the foot of my bed. I decided to draw a picture of all this. My pals were back in town.

Outlining my imaginary friends' living forms, I chortled with them. Why, I sketched sixteen different scenes, seeing as how my box of crayons held only that number of different colors. (How could I insult any scene by doing it the dishonor of using a repeat color?) Also, a subdued background noise made me weary. Humming and whirling, that noise felt relaxing at first, but then it grew tiresome—like white noise in an office. No need to wear them out—or me—all in one day, I decided. As I wound down my work, the figures kept right on twirling and pirouetting on our stage to keep me company. Then, along the sides of the sketches, I drew children smiling while adults—like doctors, priests, and police—actually helped the children. Hadn't I aimed high? As a knock sounded on my bedroom door that evening, my playmates scurried for cover, some of them under my covers. A mischievous deuce paused at his hiding place by the door and scowled at me. Sticking out his tongue and blowing hard, he made a funny noise. He'd blown me a raspberry, which floated down in mists and swirls of deep chartreuse and . . . well . . . raspberry. Smiling, he winked at me. Then, he turned, wending his way to hide.

Mother walked into the room. "Sean, are you all right? I know today was rough."

"Who, me? Oh, I'll be all right," I bluffed to make sure she didn't worry.

"It's time for dinner. I'll carry you down to the table." Oh, that: I was hopelessly crippled, at least for the time being. As we left the bedroom, I spied the wallpaper, which looked sad and lonely in its somber, earth tone. Funny, I had always remembered it as a lovely shade of yellow with a green border. Shuddering at its drabness, I wondered if some light had left my life. Had the doctors and priests shrouded my light? Would the vibrant colors ever be the same? Had the hopelessness of the adult experts taken root to grow in my mind?

I whispered a prayer that Dad had read to me from a book about native Americans. If anyone knew how to endure, they did. "Great Spirit, please help me find my way." Please lead me through the pain. Help me find my light. Help me see the Technicolor Kansas I've known. A tinge of fear swept through me as I mused about the color televisions sets which didn't capture reality, not my reality.

I shook my head and sighed. "Oh, I said, "let's carry these scenes with us. I drew them." Mother smiled as she gathered them.

"Wow," she exclaimed. "These look great. WHERE did these come from?"

"Oh, some of my friends helped me draw them."

"What did you say?"

"I mean from within. Of course, always from within." I answered. But of course.

Mourning Those Dry Bones

The skies they were ashen and sober;
The leaves they were crisped and sere-
The leaves they were withering and sere;
It was night in the lonesome October,
Of my most immemorial year.
—opening stanza of *Ulalume* by Edgar Allan Poe

I was hooked from the first picture I saw. Standing there, I heard the chipping of picks and spades that unearthed the men's prize. I smelled a dryness of floating dust, and I tasted its blandness—its nothingness.

Fine powder, like prairie blow dirt, puffed away in whiffs of otherwise still air. Finally, the men unearthed the skeleton of an Alosaur, a smaller and earlier version of the T-Rex. The creature's fossilized remains rested in pieces, leg bones and all. My dinosaur book outlined the creature's curved hip bones peeking out of the dust. All of those dusty fossils heaped around the rock-strewn soil gripped me. The heads of my femurs had shriveled into nothingness, dry and lifeless, just as had the bones of the Alosaur.

Studying images of the Alosaur's remains, I remembered reading that the giants became extinct. Since that happened to a creature with monstrously powerful leg bones, who was I to say that healthy bones were what I needed most? Maybe those fool bones weren't the answer to my problems after all. After being crippled four months, I wondered if my answers lay elsewhere? But where . . . ?

I'd heard stories and songs of dry bones, of how bones remain ever so much longer than the rest of the body. Bones are supposed to be the last to go. I'd read tales of people toting their ancestors' bones with them when they picked up and moved far away. Why had my bones powdered into nothingness: like lifeless dust that streaks and darkens prairie skies? (Weird hazes of orange, brown, and gray tinge the sky ere darkness creeps nigh. Darkness feeds on dust clouds swirling by, shrouding a

215

sun, skulking as they fly.) But why had my bones been the first to go? That wasn't normal, and I fussed to make sense of that. When I learned my bones had died, I felt like something had hit me in my ribs hard enough to knock the breath out of me. Or was it only a cruel joke, one with a punch line in reverse that might suck back my crushed ribs and let wind swish back into my lungs? Well, this wasn't a joke. My very bones had failed me.

What could I depend on without my bones? Had those powerful leg bones conspired to kill that Alosaur and the rest of his kind, nudging the species into nothingness? Our priest wound up each sermon with how pride cometh before the fall, and maybe those monsters had been powerful proud of their mighty bones. Had its skeleton led to its downfall? Now hang on, if my femurs came back to life, who's to say that they might not turn tail, snatch at me, and suck me into the dust, just like our priest predicted? Can a body crave something enough so that when it comes, it spells curtains? I'd always heard, "Be careful for what you wish . . ." Might the same be true for me, and could healing destroy me? If I were healed, maybe I'd die, just as had the Alosaur, and just as had my bones. Becoming extinct for no plain reason must be an unreal joke.

Now, dying was one thing, but feelings were something else altogether. If I walked again, would I feel better? Coaxing myself to sleep with my rhythmic mantra of, "I'll walk again," I took for granted that healthy leg would make me feel a whole lot better. Was I wrong? I remembered how a coyote had taught me that all of us may be wrong about nearly everything.

"Sean, are you ready? It's time to plant the potatoes and summer squash," Mother called up to my room on that June morning. (Although it was a June morning, it was, "night in the lonesome October of my most immemorial year," as Mr. Poe had explained.) No response.

"Sean, let's get a move on! I'm coming up to carry you to the garden. Work's waiting!"

Nothing crept from my lips, and I lay still on the bed. What a change! I'm not myself, I reckoned.

Grandmother snipped, "He's nothing like the five-year old boy who bested sassy jay birds ever since he was this side of two!" How the mighty had fallen.

Setting my book on the night table, I let Mother tote me to our garden. "Sean, scoot along the ground, plop the potato eyes into the mounds I've already made, sprinkle a pinch of fertilizer, and then cover it with soil." While I'm sure I wasn't too much help with the planting, my feelings needed cultivation, and Mother was on the prowl.

Pulling myself from mound to mound, I dragged along a wicker basket filled with potato eyes. As I planted, I imagined each mound was home to a clutch of potato eyes that spied to ensure it was a happy home. Although I was burying them, I knew that those eyes were happy. Why? Because they sprouted out of the earth and grew. Wasn't that their way of "walking" again? My envy towered over each row.

As long as I was careful to keep weight off of my legs, no pain cropped up. Heck, my "scooting" along the dusty ground didn't hurt enough to spit. To keep searing pain at a distance, I invented my special way of dragging myself while my withered legs were bent at an angle to my torso.

Well sir, scooting is simple. My fingers tunneled down into the soil, my hands rivaling any grappling hook. Is that the way President Roosevelt might move if he fell out of bed? Is that the way he might pull himself away from a fire? I knew he feared fire, and that made me feel scared for him, even though he too was long gone.

My fingers edged me along the rows where I plopped potato eyes into each mound. Dusting the eyes with fertilizer, I shrouded them with soil. Lost in reverie, I gazed up to see Mother had left the garden.

She'd been planting carrots two rows to the west. "She must have run into the house to make a call," I reckoned.

Suddenly, I glanced up to see ugliness churning in the morning sky. Black clouds swirled toward our farm. (As swiftly as early summer storms brew, they often drop their fury faster still.) A gust of wind and the musty scent of the soil warned of the storm's approach. "Mother will be right out to carry me back indoors, I'm sure."

A crack of lightning and a peal of thunder echoed danger. Then another crack and another peal sounded. And another . . . and another in rapid fire. My stomach began to quiver. Would I grow ill with dry heaves?

Breakfast had been a stranger.

The storm didn't scare me much. It felt like a bunch of wind swirling dried leaves, and that's how my innards felt. Sad about losing my legs, I didn't care who knew it. I needed to cry for my dead legs.

I ached to cry because doctors and priests had failed me! I felt like crying because my playmates had fled, although they popped back the day I came home to the farm to heal. (Those were imaginary ones, and I knew it. Knowing that felt worst of all.) Had my playmates gone because light and color had left my life? I felt utterly alone. Gone were my comforters, as if fierce winds had blown out lamps posted on a rocky, windswept shore. Those lamps had shone their light to warn me of danger. After those lights faltered, my tutors fled. I lay alone.

Sadness, worry, and fright built in my stomach, pounding up into my face like a tidal surge. Where did Mother go? There was no stopping it.

I was simply aching to cry, and that might mean the dry heaves.

Too sad to care, I didn't mind if anyone saw me. "You simply cannot cry, you know! No man dared cry anytime, anywhere." To do so was a sin since it meant you had no faith and were weak. To cry meant you did not trust God, and that wasn't a small sin, either. No sir, any man who cried damned his soul! Our priests frightened me when they grew red in the face and breathed all funny as they spoke. A crash of thunder, a gust of wind, and spray of rain splattered my face.

"You'll go to hell," the priests and nuns giddily promised. They repeated their fiendish mantra. To cry meant disobeying the most important commandment the church taught us. It meant being weak without faith, and that was a sin! It meant defying the priests and nuns. To cry was the worst sin of all, and it meant hell! There was no denying that in the Catholic Church of my youth. Well sir, the only ones allowed to cry were women, and then only in private.

"Sean, we double-dead-dog dare you to cry today. Do it, and you'll go straight to hell! If you collapsed and crumpled to the floor, you'd be in hell even before you hit it," I imagined our priests and nuns panted as they hovered over me in the garden that stormy morn. Swirls of madness echoed from their bloodshot eyes.

The storm was almost upon me. Mother! Well, that was just too bad. Feeling so puckish, I couldn't help it anyway. "Besides, if I let loose with a few tears, maybe I'll feel better. I might heal! There's no use talking about it," I told myself. "I'm going to cry. I can't help it anyway, and I don't care who knows it. Why, I'm fixing to cry so hard with such globs of tears that I'll be shielded from flames there!" Smiling, I imagined, "I'll extinguish those fool flames. Well sir, I'll cry so hard that my tears will grow their own faces and eyes! Those eyes will weep their own tiny tears, too small to be seen!"

"But you'll go to hell, straight to hell!" the priests hissed and fumed, skulking in for their kill.

"Oh, is that so? All right then. All right. Then, I'll just go to hell!"

"What, you'd throw it all away just for a chance to cry?"

"Yes! I can't hold my low feelings any longer. I can't help it, and I'm simply set to cry . . ." Then, like a great quake where rocks strain and then shear, there was no holding me back. Sobbing came reflexively, and I didn't care who heard it.

Silently, I pawed at my cheeks with my dirt-caked fingers, as if sadness made my face and fingers lonesome strangers to each other. My scratched and broken fingernails had become dirt-packed from working the soil. Slowly rubbing my cheeks for comfort, I knew my meltdown neared, like the point of no return in a chain reaction—when control rods have no show.

Crack, kapow, split! A bolt of lightning splintered one of our hedge apple trees. A large limb cracked right off and lit on the tarnished barb wire fence lining the hedge apple trees. The storm took no prisoners!

Where was Mother? Had lightning struck her, too?

My lower jaw began to tremble, first slowly and softly, but then with increasing vigor. I wasn't scared! I was powerful sad. As if saving strength and wind for the main event, my sobs rose silently at first. Slowly and imperceptibly, they knew their voice. My lungs ached to power my cries. I had all the time I needed to do it properly . . . to build slowly in volume, and then to feel a grand release.

Spidery fingers of lightning sparked in the distance, waging a spectacular, fiery display. Ribbons of light showcased fluffy clouds, and then the clouds draped like curtains over towering pillars that fired at will. As if the storm's strength had been caged, it needed to make up for lost time. Mighty bolts filled the sultry morning sky. Then it happened. First mists and then sprinkles of rain fell. Where is Mother? She'll be back soon to fetch me, won't she?

The Kansas winds, my old tutor, returned. Kansas, "The Land of the South wind People", is blessed with ample winds. They began to sing through the worn and broken stones, echoing mournfully with a melody that howled down the valley.

Did that wind carry shrieks of a tormented soul? Its screeching matched the volume of my full-throated moans, grating from my lungs, like a despairing accordion in disrepair. The wind and my cries swirled and merged to became one as they rumbled into our valley. Mother was no where in sight.

I sat there, my weight supported by my right arm with my clenched fist driven into the moist soil. Repositioning, I lifted my left arm to my face again. I felt disoriented like a punch-drunk boxer. Was I fending off unrelenting blows? I needed both protection and comfort on that windswept morning of my blustery youth.

Lifting my arms and hands, I strained them skyward as if to touch the very clouds. My shouts and sobs, muffled by the wind, melded with it. Shaking my fists at the sky, I writhed in pain, my body trembling like ice-laden wires shivering in an ice storm. (Those wires vibrated like a snake set to strike.)

Tears mingled with the first drops of rain. Mother had told me that rain drops are heaven's tears. "They fall to earth, which holds them in deep, cool springs. After resting, they spring to the surface to quench our thirst and to carve out streams and brooks. Those tears gurgle to the surface to seep over moss-covered stones that luxuriate in cooling comfort," she had told me. I imagined that these tears from heaven had mixed with my tears that morning. While comforting me a bit, the rain could not calm me down as I was too hurt—too betrayed and angry—to be calm. I hadn't yet begun to wrench all of the pain and agony out of me.

Like a traumatized animal caught in a storm, I continued to writhe and to tremble. (I had watched some injured coyotes twitching to relieve their pain that spring; they would either heal or perish.) I once again stretched my arms skyward, and I felt as if a great trauma lifted. I didn't know what lay in store for me, and I DID NOT CARE. I felt better. Pain drifted up, like thistledown buffeted on windblown prairies. I could feel the weight release, as if I had entered a warm pool of water to soothe and to help heal my legs. President Roosevelt had done that in Warm Springs, Georgia. It felt fine.

In response, the Kansas wind picked up its howling volume. Would I tumble back into despair? My state became as unstable as a wobbly top, warped and off-balance. Dad had advised me to lean gently into the wind of hardships. His very gait and posture told us so. Reflexively, I did as he advised. A gust of wind shifted to push me off balance. Although I sat on newly worked soil, I splattered onto a potato mound, my face resting smack on top of two potato eyes. Pulling myself up with my hands, I smoothed mud from my face. Then, I clawed into the loosened soil to steady myself. The ground felt powerful and alive! I dug in harder, which I sorely needed. Heck, I wallowed and lurched in that Kansas soil, and I don't know how long I lay there. My sobbing began to weaken. Then, the storm's fury was suddenly spent.

Rushing outside, Mother shouted, "Lordie, what a sight!"

I smiled up at her and said, "It's a wonderful day. I love this day! It's a marvelous day to cry, and I don't care!" After shouting those words, I laughed with wild abandon, and then I laughed harder still. My joy was a gut-wrenching laugh that feeds on itself, like the water that primes a pump. Laughter choked up from my soul and from that Kansas soil.

"Sorry, Sean. Mrs. Knuckle phoned just before the wind knocked over our trash can. When I heard that, I dropped the phone and came running." (Mother must have thought that I had lost it, because she ran to scoop me up.)

"Please don't catch cold. My, your clothes are filthy! How did you slather yourself with mud so quickly?"

I didn't answer; I laughed louder and harder that day than anytime before or since. I was happy.

Why I was as happy as an old bull frog a'wallowing in Missouri mud. That kind of mud feels rich and velvety, cool on any sultry summer's day. And, why was I happy? I knew I'd be all right after all. I hadn't been forgotten, abandoned, or betrayed. I'd heal! The Kansas winds in my youth had told me so.

The Kansas winds became my special friend. Unlike the windy bone specialists, the priests, the sheriff, and most adults, my special friends would help me find a way to heal. They cared about me enough to help. Had sadness forced them away? Maybe. Gladness might lead them back to me: to help me find my way home, to help me find a way to heal.

Nearly breathless from laughing, I spied a little deuce lurching and skulking beside the tendrils of a raspberry bush. That mischievous deuce, crouching near the row of red raspberries that Mother was fixing to fertilize with manure and straw, scrunched up his face at me. Then, he stuck out his tongue and blew me a raspberry. That was all right, seeing as how he meant to make me laugh, and that would make me feel better.

His playful insult swirled and drifted up to form amusing images in a charming shade of raspberry, I reckon.

Chartreuse and raspberry misted into the air. What a welcomed sight to warm me! He grimaced at me, squinted his eyes through the mist, and blinked to clear them. Tiny drops clung to his eyelashes, even after he swirled his face to shake them loose. Then, he smiled to take his leave.

My friends were returning, and I laughed once again. Well, I knew one thing for sure. I'd make it! I'd be all right! Although I knew little else, that much I did know. I felt it, and that meant I knew it!

Sure enough, my friends had told me so.

My, Can That Man Dance!

CBS led the networks in summer ratings, partly on account of swarms of folks who knew what we craved. My family counted on CBS to air a movie that grew mighty important to us Kansans, "The Wonderful Wizard of Oz."

After many telecasts of the film, programmers needed a fresh format to perk it up, and they usually drummed up one movie star or another whom they decked out in a smart-looking suit and black shoes with a sheen rivaling that of Dorothy's ruby red slippers. The star introduced the movie in new ways, some of them catchy.

I was in luck the summer Danny Kaye hosted, swirling us on a magical journey to the Land of Oz. As far as I was concerned, he was the perfect host. Of course I may have been biased, seeing as how he already mesmerized me with many tales: "The Ugly Duckling," "Thumbelina", and "The Red Shoes", not to mention his over-the-top charm in his LP version of Hans Christian Andersen's Fairy Tales. When Danny Kaye got to the part about the roasted chickens in "The Tale of the Nixie" (with his musings of "So juicy! So oochy!") I tasted every last roasted morsel. Melted butter with herbs trickled freely.

Do you remember how Danny Kaye had his own "Yellow Brick Road"? It commenced in concentric circles spiraling outward like a nautilus. Next, it straightened to run smack into the back of the stage. It seemed to climb into the clouds as it passed near a rainbow highway that led "Somewhere Over the Rainbow".

When I saw that yellow brick road stretching upward far enough to pass clean through the clouds, I shouted, "Look, look . . . it's real! It's real after all! I told you all it was!"

Of course, my older relatives smirked, confirming what I'd long suspected: that they were all wet when it came to set designs and journeys to exotic lands. Why, the nerve!

If the road was only a clever television set like "they" said, Danny Kaye would have glided right up it, easy as you please. But he didn't.

(That might have been owing to his talent as an actor and dancer.) Either way, it looked powerful tough for him to make it up that steep yellow grade. Oh, he pranced and half-tripped, sometimes trotting in time with the music, and all the time keeping up his spirits and speed.

Just how far did that road run, anyhow? That's what I needed to know. Sure enough, I glimpsed an answer. You see, when Danny Kaye danced up that road, I was with him every hop, spin, and hitch-step of the way. And why shouldn't I be? His smile and agility told me he was the same as any of us: even me. His radiance and wit were housed in the body of a grown-up, that's all.

Then, a thunderous idea hit me. I sputtered, "My, can that man dance." And that was it.

No different from me, Danny Kaye also wasn't crippled, and that meant I wasn't crippled either, right? Oh, my legs were only on a long vacation. Danny Kaye knew the truth, which is more than I could say for most people.

Naysayers—especially priests and doctors—loved to "tsssk" at me and quip, "Hopeless. Simply hopeless. Ship him away, fly him away, or even float him away—it doesn't matter—just be rid of him."

Danny Kaye would never hiss such nonsense. He couldn't. And dancing along side of him, I felt as light as thistledown that twitches free, puffing and drifting to take flight.

Ahh, what might I do after all this dancing with Danny Kaye? Run outside and play ball? Skip rope under the apple blossoms on the tree? Chase a ferocious goose and hiss in "its" face for a change? What might I do?

"Well anything, of course," Danny Kaye would say. "That's how hope is."

From my living room couch, I flew to Liberal, Kansas to reconnoiter Uncle Henry and Aunt Em's farm. I walked along the pen fence housing funny hogs: nervous hogs, and probable playmates. If I tumbled into the pen, Bert Lahr as Hank, the inimitable and half-frightened hero, would be sure to yank me out.

Peering skyward through the window, I searched for the spot where bluebirds darted through transforming tapestries of color. I became Dorothy's shadow, sharing in her fun without anyone the wiser. If our doctors and priests knew what I was up to, they'd order their flunkies to, "Find a deep pit and give him a shove, then cock your hand over your ears to hear his 'thump' as he hits bottom. And if it looks like he's going to make it back up, shove him back into the pit."

And besides, why shouldn't I travel with Dorothy?
After all, if birds fly over the rainbow, "then why, oh why, can't I"?

Whenever Dorothy skipped along the Yellow Brick Road, she took two steps forward followed by two sliding steps to the side, and maybe even a hitch-step to boot. I'd be stepping forward and sliding sideways as well when I joined Dorothy, Scarecrow, The Tin Woodsman and, of course, The Cowardly Lion to sing, "We're off to see the Wizard, the wonderful Wizard of Oz."

The director knew enough to yell, "Make room for that boy!"

Once we reached Oz, I'd ask for "working" legs. And if the wizard was too busy to fuss with me? Why, I'd ask his front man, Danny Kaye to take the job, then. Danny Kaye would see to it that I was "normal" and not the "ugly duckling"—or a freak, as many folks labeled me. He'd know I had run behind, what with all of my delays in worlds to explore, boats to sail, and pirates to battle. He'd know about the treasure chests to spot—the ones over-brimming with sparkling gems and spanish doubloons—and he'd know how I yearned to gallop race horses. Danny Kaye would also know how I might be destined to step into a soupy fog, one that echoes the baying of blue-tick hounds running full-throttle to gobble up a ghoulish prey.

It was about this time I first heard the song "You'll Never Walk Alone" from the musical "Carousel". You remember the lyrics, "Walk on, walk on, with hope in your heart, and you'll never walk alone. You'll never walk alone."

I misheard the words. I thought they were, "Walk on, walk on with hope in your heart, *or* you'll never walk alone," words telling me that without hope I'd never be able to heal or walk.

When I heard those words, I ached to be normal, and I knew that somehow I must keep hope alive, no matter what, for hope was life itself. Mr. Danny Kaye would have agreed with me.

Like Danny Kaye, I crafted stories. Sometimes I adapted them into plays in which I shared the playbill with a full cast of characters, imaginary friends included, who devised ingenious ways to restore my bones. In those plays, hope always healed. I dreamt that my bones would knit together just as the green raised fabric was knitted together on my grandmother's fancy furniture. And every time I glanced up at the clock to see how much time I had left for healing that day, I would peer back down at that raised green fabric on Grandmother Cloddie's upholstered furniture. It bent down to meet me, warping to echo the pull of gravity on my body. Can't time also warp, slowing down to allow for more healing?

One morning my grandmother caught me mouthing my latest play. "Look out, Scarecrow, we're coming into the landing strip on the space station too fast. Slow down, or we'll warble out of control-"

"Sean, enough of that. I know what you're up to."

Scarecrow had to land without me.

"Tell me, what will you do with your legs once they heal?"

Wasn't it obvious? Why, I'd run and skip and play, just like "normal" kids. But somehow that answer embarrassed me, so I said nothing. I needed to think for a spell.

How might I best use my legs? Hmmm. I'd take charge of more than only myself! To serve others, relieving their pain? Yes, I'd help. Maybe the wise Scarecrow would advise me.

I guessed Danny Kaye's dancing tapped a great big yes to these questions. "Yes! Yes! By all means, Yes!"

I recall the day Danny Kaye died. I was finishing my first year of MBA school at Cornell University's S. C. Johnson Graduate School of Management in upstate New York. Bittersweet sadness gnawed at my "craw" as I strolled the Cornell campus. It was May 1987, but the afternoon's brisk air cut through my clothes. I ached knowing I'd never realize my life's dream to meet him.

Pausing to gaze across Lake Cayuga nestled at the foot of the town, I spied light shimmering from the lake. It dazzled me, just as had Danny Kaye. A gentle breeze wafted across the lake's surface to tease tiny ripples. Crinkled leaves from the past fall fluttered onto them, rocking up and down in their wake. A yellow light carved a path across the water, one resembling a . . . Yellow Brick Road.

A flock of Canada geese honked overhead, and I remembered how Danny Kaye told the story of a hungry servant who had gobbled up chickens: "So Juicy! So Oochy!" Was he bidding me farewell? Tears froze on my face as if I'd walked into a freezer.

"Now, Mr. Sean Redmond, *why* are you crying?" asked Danny Kaye.

"I'll never be able to meet you. I'll never be able to thank you for everything."

"Come, come, you know there's no such thing as 'never'. That exists only in the tired minds of grown-ups. Just remember this: If birds fly over the rainbow, then why, oh why can't you and I? I'll wait for you there."

And then his presence poured out across the water.
"Sean?" trailed back to me.
"Yes?"
"Remember to bring the chickens: the juicy—so oochy—chickens."

There is a rhythm to dancing, to music, and to healing. Maybe if I found the right wavelength, one stretching and reaching high enough to heal, I would be all right. Is there a rhythm (some might say an energy) to the universe, not unlike that of verse and music? It whispers to me, and I sense a world overflowing with music, sometimes silent, and often-times only a vibration. And it's free to anyone who will hear it. The world and our universe plays on with a chorus too glorious to know fully. A twitching energy takes shape, knotting into strings. We need only to stop: to sense it, to hold it, and to feel it. It beckons to us, "Know me more deeply."

The Goats and I Helped!

Whenever Mother began planning her gardens, we all knew spring drew near. Each year her master plan called for her garden's blossoming in the number and length of rows. By the time I entered my sixth year, our garden had swelled to more than an acre.

The first year Mother had us tending bush beans and onions, russet potatoes and butter squash, leaf lettuce and Swiss chard, cucumbers and sweet corn, watermelon and tomatoes. The following year, rhubarb, string beans, raspberries, strawberries, and Virginia peanuts got the nod. Mother sprinkled her swirl of cow and goat manure, tinged with straw, to persuade any plant that it lived in tall cotton. Our southern legumes didn't fare well, though. They may have suspected Kansas was not Virginia, rebelling against the trespass of dwelling in our Kansas garden. Those peanut plants didn't amount to much, nothing more than paltry nubbins along their roots. Had they taken ill?

One Saturday evening, early in the spring of my sixth year, Mother plopped her red pencil (hardly more than a stub worn round and smooth from use) onto plans she'd sketched on several sheets of scrap paper. That too-short pencil looked like a toy as I watched Mother lay it down and inhale. Gathering wind to explain her tall plans, she declared, "We're expanding this year. We'll sow seeds north of the house around the clotheslines. It will be our satellite garden." Gently patting her stack of plans with her right hand, a tinge of triumph in her voice, she also said, "Of course, we'll enlarge the main garden to an acre."

Staring in disbelief at Mother, I reckoned that she must be kidding! After all, April Fool's Day wasn't too far away. How could she be serious, what with all of our work the previous summers? I grimaced to recall lines of sweat trickling down my face and back. That salty aroma clung to me like a cocklebur that first makes a snatch at and then tangles itself in the curly mane of a long-haired dog. We kids cringed.

That news wasn't the worst of it. Heading her list of new garden tenants, Mother scrawled the words "beets and turnips". Well sir, beets were one thing because we could steam them or pickle them, or eat them raw: as tasty as all get out. But turnips? Oh my word, they were a different story . . .

While not much tastes better than beets tended with cow manure and goat dung, turnips tasted nasty no matter what! In fact, most of us held turnips in contempt, prepared anyway you pleased. "Has Mother taken leave of her senses?" we kids fumed. "What is she thinking?" Beets may have swiped some traces of sweetness from the spring water that rested and aged for a spell in our cistern. That water must have tempted beets with a siren call: "Here, little beets. Sip of me, and you'll taste finer still." But not even cistern water stored enough know-how to make turnips taste anything other than nasty.

Still, there was no dissuading Mother once she had made up her mind. She had it all planned, and that was that. We'd tuck the beets and turnips into hoed and fertilized rows in that patch of ground north of our house. With water and liberal hoeing, Mother predicted a bumper crop. Well, we kids wanted none of it! Fouled taste buds spurred my siblings to run away whenever Mother asked for help with the turnips.

With the list of candidates dwindling, Mother wondered who'd do the work. Well sir, it all boiled down to Mother and a crippled farm boy: yours truly. While everyone else scurried away, I was caught daydreaming. I was too slow to drag myself away to escape, and Mother caught me as I neared our kitchen door. With no one left standing, and with me scooting, I became the likely victim . . . er . . . , one to help. I begged Mother to let me tend the beets. Surely, my poor feelings would find their way into the turnips, rendering them less tasty—if it's possible.

Beets and those fool turnips were going in north of our house where we'd pastured goats the past year. That plot of ground sure fed our "characters". You see, goats nibbled and gulped just about anything in their path. They also delighted in climbing on anything they took a notion to, and they insisted on showcasing their skills for any and all audiences—visitors on our farm their specialty. I don't know if they aimed to amuse our guests or if they simply wanted to outdo themselves. Either way, visitors risked their car: a toy for naughty hooves. Unfazed by the general flatness of Kansas, our goats found their own ledges with ease. Our goats pranced along car fenders and over hoods for no extra charge.

The little fiends also nibbled willow trees, clothes fresh off the line, and anything with a ripe aroma. What they did to Mother's weeping willow tree is a crime. You see, Mother kept a keen eye for willow trees near our creek, and she painstakingly transplanted one of them near our mailbox. My, she'd smiled at that willow. She called that sapling her baby. And the little tree did fine—that is, until the hellions had their say.

Turns out, Mother's willow lasted nearly two weeks before a billy goat slurped it for an afternoon salad. Within an hour he'd stripped the tree bare, its trunk peeled like an onion.

Mother fumed at first, but then she labored to contain a giggle that stretched into powerful laughter. Watching her, all of her helpers wondered what she might do next. Laughing harder and louder, Mother took it well, and her levity grew on each of us. Before we knew it, we were all laughing hard enough to cry.

"Those little hellions," she fumed. "Those hellions!" Then, she wiped her eyes and sauntered back into the house to tend to dinner.

Those goats ate things which no sane animal would fancy. One day a nanny goat nosed her way into a trash can to nibble paper and plastic. I watched her munching away, as contended as a bull frog wallowing in Missouri mud, and I wondered how sick that would make her. Do you know that she never missed a beat, as if all that junk had been on her preferred diet? Well, she did belch a few times, and I thought she might heave. Far from it. That belch said how delicious the meal had been, just as some folks in foreign lands burp to compliment the chef.

One day the past summer saw a few goats devour a patch of musk thistles, prickly points and all. Gulp!

That sight made me quiver and scratch. How a goat is able to eat something as unsavory and testy as a mean old musk thistle is beyond me. I mean goat innards must be coated with some kind of gooey lining; otherwise, thistles would have sprung leaks inside them.

Their milk tasted and smelled gloriously odd. Did its flavor seep from all of their weird food? Their cream formed a layer on top, which I thought looked like skin. Dad marveled, "Our goat cream is thick enough to slice with a knife." Their cheese also tasted insane, enough to make me feel queasy. Goat cheese has a way of persuading its scent to linger on one's skin.

Thistles or not, those goats digested their food and routinely left droppings. Dad had told me how that helped "enrich" the soil. Goats turned thistles into fertilizers and managed their utter contentment to boot.

But this year those hellions were not welcome on that spot of land. We built a fence to keep them away. That land north of our house had burned several times, the victim of range fires raging out of control.

Usually the fires began in the valley. About once a year one of Mr. Knuckles' steers died. He didn't find it until the next day, and that was only on account of help from his nose. (He'd decided to burn the carcass near our creek.) Well, he'd forgotten himself and how dry pastures might explode into flames, especially during dry spells. He'd failed to watch the fire until it burned itself out. His fire swept and crackled up the hill and through our pasture.

Mary had spotted smoke coming our way as she hung clothes on the line. That fire meandered close enough to our farmhouse to scorch the paint on its north side. We kids stopped the flames a mere ten feet from the north face of the house by beating them back with gunnysacks drenched in water. Furiously holding off the flames, we prayed for the rural fire department to arrive. "This is the last fire I set that'll bother you," Mr. Knuckle promised.

Since the dry spell meant that only the weeds had done well in our pasture, he hadn't really done harm.

The flames burnt weeds, helping the soil with all those ashes. Even though Mr. Knuckle assured us there would be no other pasture fires, he held an encore each year. Well, some things never change, and Mr. Knuckle set more fires. How do adults get along with such short memories? For three years in a row our racing bodies and hearts pounded away to halt the flames, a mere spitting distance from our already heat-crinkled farmhouse, the lingering strips of paint curled and frayed on the edges.

So, after torrents of goat dung, range fires, and shooting stars—yes, shooting stars—our beet patch prospects were rosy. (As far as the turnips were concerned, I wagered they would grow just as well with our without our efforts, seeing how they're ornery and bitter.)

One evening as I spotted a shooting star overhead, I asked Mother what it meant. "Those shooting stars are meteorites. That's another way that heaven blesses the soil." Our soil relied on help from the skies, too. What if once upon a time, 3,000 years ago (which is a long time for adults, and an eternity for children) a hail of shooting stars darted across a cloudless sky in a dance of fire? Native Americans gasped at the show, and they wished on those shooting stars. Who knows? Maybe folks in Europe watched other shooting stars, too. Perhaps ancient Greek poets penned poems about those nighttime voyagers, too. Hmm, . . . I wondered.

Dust, sea water, and goat dung would help Mother's beets and turnips grow. And so would I, dragging myself along to plant their seeds. I scooted to the cistern and pulled the hose from it to let the thirsty rows drink. As the meteorites plummeted to earth, they toted a bunch of minerals with them. There were phosphorus and iron . . . and, a bit of calcium as well. Other minerals fell to earth from those shooting stars—from that "stardust"—helping the soil grow richer.

I remembered our priest saying, "Remember, man, you come from dust, and unto dust you shall return."

I reckoned he meant stardust. Does the Earth itself owe much of its nicer parts to stardust: millions of shooting stars? Although meteorites are often small, vast numbers over millions of years did improve our soil, just as had prairie fires. The remains of meteorites mixed with soil to enrich it. Meteorites took a lot longer than range fires to help, though. As those meteorites fell apart with rain and winds, their minerals helped to build the soil. After the wind, the rain, and the glaciers crushed the meteorites into dust, that dust gave us minerals for life. Kansas prairies grew richer. Once part of an ancient seabed, those Kansas prairies were rich enough to feel like they were walking in tall cotton.

The seabed grew shallow, and the salt water that had seeped into the ground percolated there after the sea retreated. One day the ancient waters that were filtered in the earth gushed forth from springs, just like the one in our valley. We pumped that water into our cistern, and we used that filtered sea water in our vegetable gardens. Those waters helped bring life to our living rows. Well, that's what I think. But I was a child and doubtlessly wrong.

The beets grew into a bumper crop, and I felt connected to them because I had planted them. Also, we all came from the same stardust and filtered sea water that had fed those beets. Oh, how I sprinkled the seeds into the soil—into the dark and musty soil—where they could rest for a spell. I covered them with some other fertilizer from a bag, one that Mother bought in town. After I finished in one spot, I pulled myself along, being careful not to put any weight on my legs. That would hurt. Well sir, all of that dragging and all that dirt worked wonders on my britches, too. I wore out more clothes that way. But Mother gave no mind to it, seeing as she had asked me to help.

I wondered if ancient Greek poets knew any warriors...like me, for example. Prepared for battle, I sat under the night sky . . . waiting. I wore clothes crafted from leather and cloth, and I toted a shiny brass shield and a long, pointed stick that folks called a spear. (Being crippled meant that I naturally imagined myself as an athlete ready to fight.) There were shooting stars, and I wondered if the gods were sending me best wishes for my battle ahead. I think they were wishing me well, and that made me feel cozy inside, mostly.

But I felt a little sad, too, because I knew that far away villagers would die the next day. They would die all right, provided my fellow soldiers and I lived. (Heck, maybe we'd all die at once. Who knows?) But, the gods were wishing me well, and I breathed a prayer of thanks.

My mind drifted as I dragged myself along rows to plant those beets. The soil—made of stardust and helped by prairie fires and goat dung— was moistened by filtered sea water from distant times. The soils fed by stardust came from shooting stars perhaps seen by ancient peoples. Had they made a wish on those same shooting stars? Had they welcomed those stars and imagined that the stardust would help grow vegetables to feed a crippled child? Did ancient people know that I would think of them one day? Had a Greek warrior known I might drag myself along these rows as I thought of him: of his life long ago? I'd wondered what that warrior might have thought about me. Had he guessed I might be thinking of him as I worked? Had they seen shooting stars fall to earth to help make our bodies?

So, I found a pen pal across time, only we hadn't written letters. We simply imagined what the other felt and thought. I am fed by and made from the same stardust and sea water as were the Greek warriors. The sea water coursed through his veins, just as it does through mine. The stardust that formed his body made mine, too. Those common threads of life unite all peoples. I reckoned that each of us are alike (one part stardust and three parts sea water). Humans the world over and throughout time are pretty much the same.

Maybe I as a Greek warrior had heard of the famous Greek poets whom Dad had described. I don't know how well they knew their poets back then, but I bet this one was the talk of the town. The one I fancied was known as Aeschylus. He wrote that pain falls drop by drop upon the heart, until in our great despair, against our will, comes wisdom through the awful Grace of God. As I watched meteorites skipping across the night sky, I had imagined those lights might be tear drops from heaven falling upon the earth, upon a communal heart beating as one. That thought made me feel mighty lucky. Did the life from those meteorites along with sea water give us all a start in life?

What pain had they known in their lives? Maybe the ancient Greek poets knew a bunch more about us and all generations. Maybe their ideas apply to all of us even today. Then, by knowing pain, would we find wisdom through the awful Grace of God?

Could a Greek warrior or poet have thought about all of this as he beheld a shooting star on some cloudless, smokeless eve? He might have seen the shooting star at night before going into battle at dawn. Had his army won, the way I had imagined? We might have traded dreams that way. Since each of us is fed by the same stardust and filtered sea water, it might be common to trade such thoughts.

Both of us could have shared daydreaming as a way to cope. Who can say whether or not dreams and imagination from two people might be shared just by each thinking of it? I guessed that if two people tend to dream enough, they might be able to imagine what the other thinks. After all, we are all connected in many ways.

For weeks I watered, weeded, and tended the beets to work up a storm! Then, it happened: the beets sprouted and grew . . . and grew.

One day in the late summer, Mother exclaimed, "My, what a bumper crop! It's a tribute to your hard work and skill, Sean. You planted and cultivated those beets. Great job!" she had told me. Well, after such accolades, I savored eating those beets even more than usual.

When I ate them, I used the same fingers with which I had dragged my broken body along the rows: the same fingers that I had used to dig into the soil and to cover the beets. I had used those same fingers to pull weeds. In that way, I had connected with the life in those beets, just as I had connected with ancient times. I had found an unlikely friend in the mists of a distant past, in a land far away and amongst a people known to me only by books and daydreaming.

Along the way I delighted in vegetables too tasty to say. Why, I've never found beets to equal those beets. I might have guessed as much since they were flavored by the filtered sea water, stardust, and prairie fires. I reckoned that burnt thistles and goat dung added to their flavor. Did the thistles add magical seasoning to the beets, favoring them in ways that shamed any ambrosia meant for the Greek gods? I declare, the goats also helped whenever they munched musk thistles, turning them into droppings. Well sir, even after being burnt, those thistles strengthened the soil with their charred remains. And do you know that those prickly wonders often survived, their roots tunneling deep into the rocky soil? Also, their thistledown puffed away to promise a new day after most other plants withered and died.

My, oh my . . . those ingredients swirled to create gloriously-flavored beets. Yes, the goats did what they did best, and I helped.

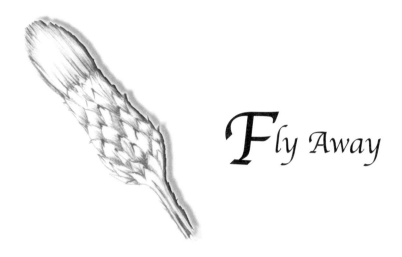

$\mathcal{F}$ly Away

During all the years of my mysterious and crippling bone disease, Mother worked part-time evenings and most weekends at the Osawatomie State Hospital and at the Paola Nursing Home. But on weekdays, I reckon Mother had a hen on. You see, after we dropped the kids at school and finished chores, Mother and I often headed out for a day of Amway sales.

"Time to open a window and make a fresh start, Sean," Mother declared, earning a trickle of money to help buoy sagging fortunes. The sight of large sliver coins—Franklin Halves and Washington quarters glinting back at us from her opened purse-—felt like freedom minted on shiny planchets. From my boyhood days I reckoned that those smiling profiles of Benjamin and George meant they cheered for our freedom, although some folks claimed they looked somber.

Her Amway sales meant dribbles of money on top of freedom from hospitals and from Dad, who often declared, "What do you think I am, an walking cash register?"

After finishing the breakfast dishes, Mother tended to the chickens, goats, sheep, and cattle. While I could only watch, on a good day I scooted across the barnyard to help fill feed pails. While that didn't make me feel poor, had any strangers seen me I'd have liked to dry up and blow away.

After chores, Mother loaded up our station wagon with cleaning supplies. As we headed out to call on customers, I thought puffs of dust on our dirt road might be a magical mist to wing us to our fondest desires. Can such dust whisk a body to a place where no money worries bellow and where no pain lives? Maybe so.

"Mother, can that dust help us earn a shower of money? Can money make the loan officer at the Bank of Stanley dry up and blow away?"

"What? Please, hush. I need to watch the road. Don't make my mind wander."

Even on days we planned to work around the house (and I'm sure I was not much help), we sometimes got a hankering to see her folks. Oftentimes we combined trips into a swirl of business and visiting--or do I repeat myself? Mother had a charming way of making work feel like a time to chat over news, especially with prospective customers. And in Osawatomie we even managed to wrangle over business with Grandfather Kearney who loaned us $5,000 to help save our farm. (Well, that was before the wage earner's bankruptcy settlement and the new terms that Dad signed to repay the Bank of Stanley every dime plus interest).

Sometimes Mother dropped me at Dr. Hoffman's office for a checkup. Since I rode with her on those errands, she didn't need to worry about finding a baby-sitter for me. I'd told her, "Who, me? Need a what? I'm nearly grown. And why would I need anyone watch me read?"

Mother would have none of that, insisting that I never stay home alone. If I really needed to get out of the car, I might be able to hoist myself down to the ground where I could scoot across hard-packed dirt.

I usually waited in the car while Mother conducted business. Some waits stretched into late afternoon. Even with stacks of books and puzzles, I often grew bored. Then, I peered at the front door of the customer's home, and I fussed about when I might catch sight of Mother. Cracking open the door and with her back to the car, Mother stood there as she spoke to a housewife. Could I guess how long she'd need to stand there to "wrap up" her sale?

Many times a farm dog trotted up to the car to check on me. Most were friendly, whimpering at me as they licked the glass. "You want to play, don't you?" (Their wagging tail and floppy tongue said so.) A few weren't so nice, and they jumped up on the car to lean against the window, their jaws snarling as they rocked the car to deal with me. Even then, when I made eye contact with them, they hushed. "Now be still, puppy," I purred. Were they calmed the way some people settle when birch leaves rustle on autumn breezes?

A natural talker, Mother probably took more time with customers than did most other Amway distributors. Mother's sales style stretched my waiting time. The bother was worthwhile, seeing as how Mother earned a splattering of money. "Here, follow the instructions," Mother told her customers. "Soak the stain with one part LOC to three parts water after dinner. Rub for a spell, and the stain will dissolve. You won't need to scrub your clothes." When she served customers, she sounded larger than life and twice as natural. Each lady stood with her chin headed south, her arms dangling, and her eyes glazed.

"But I prefer washing clothes in the morning so I can let them dry on the line all day," one lady insisted, her right shoulder leaning against the driver side of our car. Mother had inched her way from her house, down the walk, and into our car. Mother hadn't escaped the woman's questions. She trailed Mother the way a baying bloodhound trails a coon.

Some of the ladies fidgeted with a ten or twenty dollar bill they were fixing to hand Mother. They folded each bill a bunch of different ways, and then they refolded them in the shape of wrapping paper flaps on gift boxes while Mother wrapped up their business. While their folded bills looked funny, they spent equally as well as did crisp, new bills. Finally, they handed Mother a few bills.

"Here's your receipt. Thank you. I'll return a week from Tuesday," Mother said after she scribbled a receipt in her sales book. Then, we were off to another customer.

As Mother waved good-bye, each women's chin sank, her eyes filming over to look like smoked glass.

I'd have thought she'd gotten her fill of Mother, what with following her to the car and carrying on for fifteen minutes in the driveway. Their talks stretched on to the very second of Mother's last wave as she backed out of the driveway.

Soon after Mother started her Amway business, she decided to earn money faster by recruiting distributors. She asked her better customers if they'd like to report to her. "I'll train you and show you how to demonstrate the supplies," Mother said. "But, seeing as how you already know all you there is about these products, you'll be a natural. Come on, we'll have fun," Mother cast her line . The look on her candidate's face said she was rearing to go. Her eyes were wide, her face was flushed, and her head was tilted.

Her breath came in spurts. Inside of a minute, Mother turned unsuspecting candidates into the likes of a largemouth bass set to strike her line.

"Lola, I know we're friends, but why are you doing this for me?"

"Because I want you to share in our business. You believe in these products, right?"

"Yep."

Mother cajoled, "Besides, you'll earn money and product discounts. Come on, it'll be fun. We'll have a great time."

"Oh, I'll need to check with Fred. He'll need to okay it."

"Fine. And if he has any questions, send him my way."

"Much obliged, Lola."

"Glad to help. Let me know what you all think by a week from Friday, okay?"

"That soon? I thought I'd get longer to decide."

"Well, I need to make some decisions quickly. I want the best sellers working with me, and that's why I need to hear from you before I ask Mrs. Peters. I can train her, but working with you will be a natural."

In return for working with Mother, each of her sales people forfeited a small portion of their margin. That is how I understood it worked then, and I reckon not much has changed today. "If Mrs. Jones asks to help, you might consider letting her work for you," Mother would say. She'll report to you, and that means you both will roll up under me. The larger our organization, the larger our discounts and profits. You'll earn a nickel on the dollar for all of Mrs. Jones' sales. Think about it, and talk about it to anyone whom you think would do well."

Six months into her business, Mother had recruited three ladies. One lived in Osawatomie, her location handy since Mother called on her whenever we drove there to visit Grandfather and Grandmother. Another lady lived in Kansas City, and that meant a larger number of people to serve. Mother checked on her every week when she drove to a sales meeting with her manager, the one who recruited Mother. The third lady, Mrs. Barbara Borden, lived near Drexel, Missouri and drove a white Ford station wagon. She filled it with cleaning supplies, making it her mobile warehouse. Mrs. Borden racked up more than 40,000 miles a year, buzzing around several counties to make sales.

Mrs. Borden also had her hands full with six children and a husband with a checkered work history. All of her kids were enrolled in the combined Wea Elementary and High School—except for Ricky, her youngest boy. I'd have been a classmate of her youngest girl except for the fact that I was crippled, meaning I couldn't go to school. Instead, Sister Henrietta tutored me.

Sister Henrietta lived in the Queen of the Holy Rosary Convent. She drove to our farm every Wednesday in the convent's black sedan. Seeing as how I already knew how to read, write, add, subtract, multiply and divide, she let me read during most of her "lessons". Then, she remembered herself and focused on catechism to set me up for First Holy Communion and Penance (or Confession). Pleased with my work, Sister

Henrietta carried on about me every time she taught her class at Wea. Those lessons lasted a month or two for each of the first and second grades. The rest of the time I was on my own to read and wonder as long as I wished. Maybe I finished grades one and two quickly in order to spare time to daydream and to read . . . in that order.

One fall morning during my sixth year, Mother decided to swirl up some oatmeal and raisin cookies.

Making the dough from scratch, she'd already baked four dozen cookies when a knock sounded on our kitchen door.

"Lola, are you there?" Barbara Borden called, peaking in her head. Behind her walked her youngest boy Ricky, age four and nearly that many feet tall. His clothes were threadbare: scrubbed with SOC, a leading Amway detergent.

"Can you spare two bottles of LOC?" she asked after Mother greeted her, inviting her in.

"Sure, Barbara. Take a seat," Mother said as she walked to the utility room where she stored her small inventory. In a minute she handed Barbara two bottles that she happened to have on hand.

"Thanks," Barbara said. "Add them to my purchases for next month, if you don't mind. I'd like to pay you for them then, if that's all right." Barbara had run short of LOC after a screw driver rattled loose in her car and punched through the plastic skins of two of her bottles. That left a stream of syrupy soap to dry for a few days before she'd discovered what had happened.

"The back of my station wagon sure got a working over, Lola. It's clean now, I guarantee," Barbara sputtered. Was it really clean? I suspected she'd swiped at the stickiness only a time or two and called it good. "I need these bottles for an order five miles west of here."

"Sharp thinking, Barbara. Good idea to restock while you're making rounds. Questions?"

Barbara often asked nit-picky questions, but Mother nearly always had the answer at her fingertips. More often than not, she wanted to know how to explain SOC's cleaning power.

"Tell the customers to use only one scoop, and it will clean as much as four cups of Tide," Mother began. "These supplies aren't pumped full of all the fillers and gunk. They do the same job with about a fourth of the volume. Plus, they don't pollute as much."

Barbara scribbled notes, and then she thanked Mother kindly.

While Mother and Barbara chatted, I watched Ricky coast over to the oven. Prancing and darting about like a wild stallion kicking up his hooves during mating season, he drooled. Did he remind me of a Miller moth flitting around the light above our stove? He hovered there on his tiptoes as he sniffed at all of the baked goodness.

"Lola, may Ricky sample your baking?" Barbara asked, patting her left hand. "I must confess, we were rushed this morning, and I didn't fix much of a breakfast."

"Sure," Mother obliged, and Ricky made a beeline for the tray of cookies that Mother had pulled from the oven minutes ago. Since they were still steaming, Mother warned, "Now Ricky, these cookies are hot." He nodded okay. Did he delight in steamy gooeyness?

Mother might just as well have spoken to our maple tree on the front lawn, seeing as how Ricky registered nothing. In one single swoop of his right hand, he snatched the whole front row of six cookies from the tray. In another motion, he shoved three of them into his mouth. Would he yelp in pain from the steam? No, he didn't even blink. Instead, he munched rapidly, moving his head from side to side. Would he spit out the cookies, like a grasshopper spewing tobacco juice into the wind? No, he gulped to let a wad of steaming cookies slide down his throat. That looked like the bulge that black snakes form when they suck eggs down, the lumps outlining each one. Then, without hesitating and in a rhythm that mocked the pain he must have felt, Ricky pumped the next three cookies into his mouth as he commenced to gulp.

Was I watching a gifted actor? Heck, anyone who could gobble all that without missing a beat must be talented. Glancing over at Mother, I saw how she stood staring at Ricky, her mouth agape. When she tried to move her eyes away after Barbara asked again about the concentrated cleaning supplies, she could not. Ricky had her transfixed. I'd broken my stare only to check on Mother's face, and in a moment I also looked back at him. After devouring that first half dozen cookies, he snatched at the next row of six victims. His total stood at a dozen cookies, gulped down without milk inside of three minutes.

What in the Sam Hill is he doing? While I knew better than to insult him by asking, I bet my face shouted the question. Mother had managed to break her stare long enough to look at Barbara and to answer her questions. However, after Ricky finished that second row and started on the third one, Mother asked Barbara, "Please tell Ricky not to eat any more cookies."

When Barbara obliged, not even her words took. Ricky was already well within the third row and rounding it off as he headed for home: the fourth and final row on that once steaming sheet of two dozen cookies. When Ricky took no heed, Barbara pretended he had stopped.

By that time I scooted on our kitchen's linoleum floor to watch Ricky. How could he eat that quickly? Would he heave and run to the car? While I thought he might, nothing about him hinted that he was about to slow anytime soon. Each group of three oatmeal raisin cookies met the same fate as he steadied himself for his next victims. If he did heave, I imagined that the cookie dough would steam its freedom, seeing as how they'd been inside of him for only a spell. That reminded me of how PJ bolted down a one-pound package, still chilled, of hamburger. My

brothers chased him through the house until he vomited the cold hamburger on the steps.

Ricky added a certain flair to his feasting, like a swaggering scalawag who downs tankards of rum. Soon, he looked unsteady. For his fourth row of cookies, he changed his mode of attack. Instead of chomping first, he chewed even less and gulped more globs of waded together cookies. They oozed between his fingers as he crammed them into his mouth. Panting, he lapped up the treats, swallowing them whole. Did he even breathe, and would he choke? He'd clutched one handful of cookies in his right fist, while his left hand smeared cookies into his face. But he ate these cookies with a rhythm that belied the speed. Watching him, I thought that I must be seeing a fine actor—an artist in his prime— sticky hands, torso, and all. For his last few handfuls, the still-moist cookies in his hands looked like cookie dough once again, steaming and seeping between his fingers and around his fingernails. They oozed out of his steely grip the way Silly Putty splutters through a nozzle.

Once again I peered over at Mother. She'd been trying to ignore it all while she talked to Barbara. I knew that I must not utter a word, but it all overpowered me, as frantic as all get out. For once I felt speechless. Can anyone fully describe it, a moment that lives that sublimely?

As Ricky finished off two dozen cookies, Mother asked, "Barbara, please . . . that's enough."

When Barbara told Ricky, "Stop", her words didn't register.

Mother moved to the mixing bowl where she had finished stirring up another two dozen cookies. She told Ricky, "Now if you help me lay out these cookies, I'll let you lick the bowl. But first, wash your hands."

That didn't set well with Ricky, judging by the scowl on his face.

"Barbara, will you please take Ricky to our utility room to wash his hands?" I knew that was Mother's way to pull him out of the kitchen and away from the second batch of cookies.

Barbara obliged, and Mother worked extra fast to lay out those two dozen cookies on the sheet that she'd already lightly dusted with flour. Muffled cries of pain echoed from our utility room as Barbara scrubbed off layers of filth and cookie dough, mixed in a paste with his spittle. That filth had been clinging like another layer of skin to Ricky's hide.

By the time Barbara and Ricky tromped back into the kitchen, Mother had plopped that batch of oatmeal raisin cookies into our oven, and she'd moved the second tray of two dozen cookies to the top of the white Fridgidaire refrigerator to protect it, the way she might have moved a canary in a cage up there to protect it from a feral cat.

Gingerly, Mother offered Ricky the mixing bowl and a large slotted spoon. In a second, the sound of a faulty engine with perhaps a broken piston took to the air as Ricky pounded his spoon against the mixing bowl, stripping away any dough. His arm and that slotted spoon whirled in a blurred haze of noise, punctuated by his spasmodic fits and starts.

Once he got what he could with the spoon, he commenced using his fingers, which he wadded into his mouth. Could he even wait to swipe each finger into his mouth completely? Each one caught on his lips and teeth to be raked clean before he gurgled his mouth shut, his tongue slurping up any final hints of dough.

For his finale, Ricky buried his face in the bowl and lapped at its sides the way a famished hound downs his supper. I can still see his tongue sweeping the sides of that glass mixing bowl.

All the while Barbara acted as if nothing was amiss. That alone made me wonder about what her home life must be like if her boy carried on that way in another person's home. That got me to wondering . . .

The next Tuesday evening Mother, Barbara, and her tagalong husband planned to ride to a sales meeting together, and I asked Mother if I could stay at the Borden house while she went to her meeting. "I'll stay out of the way. Maybe I'll read in the living room," I promised Mother.

Secretly, I planned to watch all of the action.

Barbara put her oldest daughter Helen, a senior in high school, in charge. Barbara ordered, "Watch the kids, wash and mend the clothes, clean the house, and tend to the chickens and goats." Dinner would be a chicken and noodle casserole that Helen baked from scratch, including the part about killing, cleaning, and boiling a hen fresh from the barnyard. As the oldest sibling, she was expected to take charge.

"I haven't had an afternoon off in a year," Helen told my sister Janice. "The only time I get for myself is during Sunday Mass." Was Sunday Mass her idea of a fine time? At least then she could relax for an hour and let herself be.

With no time for herself, Helen's studies suffered. Janice told me, "Helen's teachers sent home a note that said Helen might not graduate—on account of failing grades." I wondered if her parents cared. Would the shame of their daughter not graduating matter to them?

Helen told Janice, "My parents cringed when they read that letter." They accused, "Why aren't you doing better in school?" The question came almost before her parents walked through the front door, leaving no time for Helen to think. Struggling to wring the water from the sponge, Helen didn't know what to say.

Janice reported how Helen huffed, "All I could say was, 'I'm doing my best.'"

Of course she was. Janice told me how Helen always did her best. And she wasn't dull, either—no sir. In fact, Janice said Helen was "naturally bright."

Helen's mother answered, "Well, you're grounded, my dear. And that's final until further notice!"

Barbara spoke the words deliberately, with a precise diction and rhythm. Helen asked Janice, "Did she mean I wasn't ground before?" Was Helen too tired to be sad?

One night Janice slept at Helen's house. Janice stayed with Helen to help her with chores. Just after midnight, Helen left her bed for the bathroom, and when Janice crept by the bathroom door thirty minutes later, she found Helen slunched over her school book and scribbling answers. (Partial credit would be better than no credit at all, and she mustn't be late with her homework.)

She'd snuggled into the corner between the bathtub and the wall next to the linen cabinet. Would she be punished for working on her lessons? She might if her parents caught her and asked why she wasn't able to finish the work before bedtime. Maybe she loved her parents and didn't have the heart to tell her mother that she had too many chores, and that she couldn't touch her lessons until after midnight.

Helen said to Janice, "At least I'll finish some of my assignments. Maybe Sister Theresa won't send home another note to warn Mom about my incomplete lessons."

Janice didn't utter a word.

Then, Helen sobbed, "I'm frightened—trapped or lost—and no seems to care. Well, maybe you do . . ."

"Do you need help with your lessons?" Janice asked.

"No, Sister Theresa will notice different writing. I'll work for another thirty minutes. Will you check on me in thirty minutes? If I fall asleep in here, there'll be hell to pay."

"Sure."

The prior week Helen fell asleep while she finished an English composition. "Were you sleep walking again, young lady?" Barbara Borden asked her daughter.

"No, ma'am. I was trying to get my lessons, that's all," Helen declared.

Not listening well, Barbara quizzed, "Who in their right mind sleeps in the bathroom?"

"Helen keeps going by eyeing her goal," Janice said. "She'll be eighteen in three months, and she plans to be free when her time rolls around. She'll be able to do as she pleases, then." Her freedom lay in doubt.

Roughly thirty minutes later Helen finished her math assignment. "She stumbled back to bed and slept for a few hours before morning chores," Janice whispered. There were two cows to milk, chickens to feed, and hogs to slop. She must fix breakfast for the entire family and pack sack lunches for her sisters and brothers. If she didn't finish on time, there'd be hell to pay.

Somehow, she'd muddled through Tuesday morning. She'd even remembered to pack a sack lunch for herself. With her math assignment done, she needed only her book report for her English literature class. Mercifully, Sister Theresa extended the due date until Friday. Helen didn't face another incomplete-—not yet, not on that day anyway. No letter would be sent home regarding her progress. Well, no letter might come until Friday. She might hold it all together if she got a move on and finished her book by Thursday. Hope blossomed eternal, and maybe she'd squeeze in a few hours to finish. Could she read enough to bluff her way through a report? After all, most of the reading was predictable, and Sister Theresa was getting on in years. Maybe she wouldn't notice that Helen missed the details, and Helen might work faster.

Maybe Helen could hold on for a few more months to finish school. She'd be free to do as she pleased, then. She'd live free if she could hang on for a few more months. That hope kept her going when she caught her breath and wondered how all her bother might end.

All of this happened the week before I rode with Mother to the Borden's home. That evening while I arranged myself on the living room sofa and Mother returned to the car to wait for Barbara, I heard Barbara warn, "Don't forget to work on your sisters' hair. They were teased again at school. Come up with a hairdo that suits the other kids, or else."

The trouble was that the kids at school might be teasing Helen's sisters because their hair was too fancy compared to their clothing.

So, that evening Helen scrubbed the kitchen floor, tended the animals, washed and braided her sisters' hair, and killed a hen for supper. Her siblings yelped, "What took you so long?" as she cleaned the hen and then baked it in the oven. They ranted, "We'll tell Mom you were late again."

Seven o'clock seeped into eight and then eight-thirty as Helen turned up the heat on the pot of noodles. The hen had roasted, and she finished boning it. The pot of noodles bubbled on the gas range. Helen stopped a moment to catch her breath. Sweat beaded up on her forehead, and she looked dizzy. Lack of sleep, constant demands, and accusations had worn her down. I knew it. From my watching place, I heard her whisper, "If only I make it through until May; then, I'll be all right."

At nine o'clock, Helen and the kids finally sat down to dinner.

As I watched Helen, I noticed dark circles under her eyes, and I wanted to know why no one else seemed to care. Why doesn't anyone, except maybe Janice, offer to help her? Scooting to the kitchen, I asked, "May I help you scrub the floor?"

"No, that's all right, dear. I'll finish it myself. Thanks for asking," she smiled at me. As I sat in the corner of the kitchen, I watched Helen toiling as I heard and smelled the pot of chicken and noodles grumbling on the gas range. Did I sense her thoughts? Maybe I knew what she planned. In spite of what Janice said, I guessed Helen might not stay and struggle until her high school graduation. Although she labored to hold on, maybe she'll set out on another course. Maybe she'll run away before then, I reckoned. But where would she go?

"Helen saves all of her pennies and nickels, and she picks up pop bottles from ditches for their refunds," Janice confided in me. She'd saved money that she earned each summer by baby sitting. Maybe that totaled enough to buy a one-way bus ticket to a distant city. Did it matter which city as long as it was far away?

I hoped that she'd make it. Rooting for the underdog, I sure cheered for her that night. I silently recited a prayer for her. "Help her find her way." I whispered. "Help her find a way."

When I didn't see Helen in Mass that following Sunday, I knew that something was wrong. Later that day, I heard Mother say, "Helen's gone missing, run away. Her parents teared up when they read the note she left. It said only, 'I love you, and now I must go. Good-bye.'" That was the last Helen's parents or any of us ever heard of her. I had seen the pain in her eyes, and I had noticed the courage she summoned. Somehow, I knew she'd be all right. She'd survive, and I reckoned she'd be all the stronger. Tunneling down into the rocky and sun-parched soil, she'd endured with nothing left but hope to sustain her.

Would Helen recall her days of forced labor with bittersweet memories? I doubted it. Sometimes a soul needs to start all over and not look back. Sometimes a person needs to leave to find one's self. Just as that pan of noodles boiled on the gas range, Helen had boiled for years until she'd simply wept over. Most people would not have lasted nearly as long as she did. Leaving after her pot had bubbled over, she began her voyage. Her feelings had simmered from years of toil and slavery.

I knew she'd made the right choice to leave—to start from scratch, unfettered by past chains. She'd be free, and that thought warmed me that spring of my seventh year.

I wonder if that's what thistledown does when it wafts into the distance to find a new home. Isn't it free when it drifts to take root in richer soils?

New Neighbors

Vacant homes on Kansas prairies have a way of snatching attention, as if their wooden frames grow lonely for company and moan, "Will new tenants ever move in?" Did the long-abandoned ones yearn as Emily Dickinson had, to send a "letter to the world that never wrote to me"? Lying windswept and creaking, those shells whispered tales of all that once had been.

The Crocker farmhouse had rested silently for more than a year after Mr. Crocker took off, and his family moved to town. Then, the owner rented it to the Crawfords. Even before Mother began her Amway business, she took it upon herself to visit new neighbors. Introducing herself, she'd say, "I sell Amway, detergents a specialty." The Crawford family was no exception to her welcome routine, and within a week of their arrival she declared, "I'll pay a visit to our *new* neighbors." No doubt, she'd say, "Welcome to the neighborhood! I'm Lola Redmond, and I sell Amway . . . detergents a specialty."

As our Pontiac station wagon pawed its way up the rutted dirt lane to the Crawfords home one sunlit morning in August, I didn't give our visit much thought. As usual, I sat in the car while Mother wrangled business. Being crippled meant that I couldn't leave the car until someone offered to carry me from it. Since this was embarrassing in front of lurking strangers, I didn't mind waiting. In the Kansas of my youth, being crippled was a dark secret *to be kept*. Most of the time I daydreamed peacefully, which I fancied.

As Mother eased our station wagon into park, she leaned over to say, "I won't be long. I'll offer them a sample, and I'll be right back."

Mother mostly showed newcomers that Amway detergent hadn't been tainted with fillers and other "gunk" common in national brands. "One scoop of this 'concentrated' detergent does the work of *four cups* of the national brands."

"All right, Mom. I'll read," I mumbled.

A flash of light caught my eyes, and I spied a strange sight on the front porch of the Crawford home. A scrawny looking woman in a raggedy dress and straggly hair echoed from the creaking house. There was something about her . . . was it the way she paced back and forth or twitched her arms, folding and then freeing them inside of a breath?

More flashes of light reflected from the porch door as she opened it. Standing on the top step of the wooden porch, she propped the door open by leaning against it with her right shoulder. Without meaning to, I stared—and it lengthened—my lower lip drooping while my gimlet eyes burned into the scene. Light framed her lined face, scrunched up and *soiled*. She looked roughly Mother's age, and judging by her tawny face, I reckoned she must work outdoors a lot.

Peering back at me, the woman dangled her right arm while her left hand clutched at the pleats in her dress, wadding up a piece of it. She curled it as if she hid a secret weapon. Did she conceal a tear she'd meant to mend?

When the woman spotted Mother walking her way, she flinched. "Heck, what's worrying you," I wanted to say. "Mother's friendly. She's welcoming you to the neighborhood with a sample of Amway detergent."

But that look on her face—half puzzlement and half fright—made me squirm. What's she hiding? I wondered. Did she suspect that any stranger who came calling might unearth her secrets?

Her right eye squinted at me, and she cocked her head to one side. Her eyes whirled to the edge of her sockets to connect with me. Had she never before seen a towhead with curls and blue eyes? Her shoulder-length hair was stringy dishwater blonde. It only half-hid her brown eyes. Her face was *smudged*, her skin oily. Had she freshened up with kerosene instead of water?

Mother *commanded* that we wash before and after every meal so that we wouldn't fall ill. I wondered whether *her* mother had forgotten to tell her to do the same. Might she be running a fever or something? Had I looked like that sitting at our kitchen table, Mother would have scolded me—and rightly so. Even a child knew better than to look like *that*.

The woman stiffened as Mother shook her hand. Was the woman brittle enough to break? (That didn't bode well for Mother's sales.) But Mother could talk her way into anything—even a thief's secret lair where *no girls* were allowed. Why should I be surprised that she talked the untrusting woman into opening her home? Heck, she might even thank her for the trouble.

Although the squinty-eyed woman standing on the top step of the wooden porch that morning frowned, Mother charmed her, coaxing her way inside the Crawford home in nothing flat.

I wondered if I ought to worry. Maybe that woman escaped from jail, and bloodhounds tried to track her, but she lost them in the creek. Does she live in that rickety old place because Sheriff Cantwell *can't* trouble himself to track her? The fact is, he didn't trouble himself to do much of anything—except bragging and eating grease-sopped food. He was partial to sounding his windy tales at the US 169 Motel Grille and Coffee Shop. Apart from that, he puttered around in his squad car and carried on like a big shot. Dad had once told me, "Sheriff Cantwell looks like a bullfrog puffing himself up during mating season, except his bloat is farther south than his throat—clean around his waist."

I couldn't remember a time when Sheriff Cantwell had worked. Had I grown forgetful at age six? No, I'd have bet that if Jesse James and his gang had shot their way into town, the sheriff might have kept right on blowing hard and slurping his slop. He wouldn't have caught on. Law enforcement in our town meant a windy show: well greased, with nothing much to show for it.

Mother said, "Sheriff Cantwell's mind burns with fever."

"Huh? You mean like when I had German Measles?" (I'd been sick the year before.)

"Sort of. His mind is fevered—plus he can't spell to save his life." I knew what Mother meant. Although he whined that he hadn't written it, we all knew he had. "Niger, don't let the son sat on y'urn bak," was wickedly scrawled in crimson paint on a withered sign.

Within a few minutes, the front door snapped open again, and Mother scooted through it. "The woman" yanked it shut faster than all get out.

"Mother, are you all right? What's going on?" I asked.

"That's sick. Simply sick," Mother muttered. Without another word she shifted the car into reverse. She's miffed, I thought. I knew better than to talk to Mother when she was riled. But that didn't happen often. It took a doosie of an insult to get Mother going, and I itched something fierce to know what set her off.

A few days later, I rode with Mother to Osawatomie. Bored blind at the prospect of afternoon talks with Grandmother and Grandfather

Kearney, I guessed on that day I'd live by keeping my ears open for mention of the Crawford family. Silently, I sat with Mother and my grandparents in the living room. I ached to hear why Mother had said, "That's sick. Simply sick."

Mother said to Grandmother Kearney, "Mom, the other day I welcomed *new neighbors*, just as I always do. They moved into the old Crocker house."

Go on, I whispered.

"You know, the family that moved to town after Jim Crocker ran off? You remember how he showed up at our house toting a shot gun, giving us *quite* a scare."

"Oh yes . . . yes, I remember. The fellow with a nasty drinking problem," Grandfather said.

"Drinking problem, my corset," Grandmother said. "He was a mean-eyed drunk, and I wouldn't be surprised if he goes to hell straighter than a blue-winged hawk."

"Too bad. I rather liked him. He seemed anxious and drank too much, I know. But, it's too bad he took off like that." I wondered if he did the best he could do.

"Now John, enough of that. You barely knew the man. Why would you feel sorry that he's gone?" Grandmother Kearney quipped, her right eye stabbing at Grandfather.

Grandfather pulled his hands up toward his neck and lined up the fingers of his right hand with those of his left hand, tapping the tips together. When he pointed his fingers that way, he looked like a little boy trying to stay out of trouble. "Well, I liked him. It's too bad he ran away short of facing his problems, that's all."

"Anyway," Mother continued, "I met the Crawfords. They moved into the Crocker house."

"Well, what about them?" Grandmother asked leaning forward to gather up swatches of news as Mother laid them round about her.

"It's sad. I hate to say it, but the family is white trash. The house is a wreck, and the kids are *filthy*. The mother—if you can call her that—is nearly as bad off as the kids. Her face is *smudged* with dirt and grease. When I offered her a detergent sample, she acted as if she'd never seen anything like it."

"Never saw store-bought soap?" Grandmother growled. "Why, even a poor person *knows* about soap and water. What's her excuse?"

"Makes her own soap, and by the looks of things, she isn't very solid at it either."

"Maybe she makes soap only on special occasions, like one Saturday a month whether the family needs it or not," Grandmother needled.

"Whew . . . " Mother waved imagined stench away from her nose. "I declare, even the air in *that house* smelled foul, like a blend of sweat and mold."

"If a body doesn't know enough to keep clean, that's just plain sad," Grandmother said. "But I don't know if that makes them white trash."

"Maybe not, but get this. The mother is the children's half sister."

"My God, how horrible," Grandfather spat.

"Yes, it's hideous. The father and or grandfather is a no-account drinker who hunts and makes his own 'drink'."

"Moonshine."

"I suppose so."

"Probably as bad as the soap she makes, but I'll wager he makes it a whole lot more often," Grandmother teased.

"What a diseased, incestuous old bore," Mother declared. Since I had no idea what she meant, my mouth hung low as the mystery rose high. My stomach hurt with such low words.

"You mean . . . you mean . . . the old man bred his own daughter?" Grandmother asked.

"Yes, it would seem so."

"How do you know?"

"She told me so, and I hadn't asked . . . blurted it out the same as if it was her job."

"And what happened to the girl's mother?"

"Ran off years ago after her husband began taking up with his oldest daughter. That heap of crap got his daughter pregnant at least twice. Her girls call her 'Sister Mom.'"

By this time, I felt what had happened. While I didn't know how children happened along, I knew that for any man to "take up with his daughter" was wrong—shameful in anyone's eyes. I could tell by watching Mother's outrage. I studied my grandparents' disgusted looks.

"And the poor thing wouldn't take the sample of soap you offered her?"

"Nope. Since she makes her own soap, maybe the real McCoy frightened her. I told her she was welcome to a sample, no charge. 'Mrs. Crawford' shoved it away, told me she'd never accepted charity before and wasn't about to start." Mother huffed and brushed at her hair. "And then—can you believe this?—she told me to leave."

"And her two daughters call her 'Sister Mom', huh?" Grandfather asked. "What are their names?"

"Nancy and Linda. Sad, isn't it?"

The room sat still for a moment as Mother's words yawned for company. Then, Grandfather began to carry on about his hibiscus. He had a habit of stretching the size of the blossoms by pulling at the edges until they nearly tore. Then he "lined up" the ruler in a way that overshot the the edges by an inch on either side.

News of the Crawfords didn't resurface that afternoon, and that was the last I heard of our new neighbors for quite a spell.

As I often daydreamed about first one subject and then another one, I'd been musing about the Crawfords one morning that summer when Mother casually advised that we'd have a new neighbor on our pasture. Bolting upright in my chair, I imagined that some other wayward family planned to camp there. "Who are they, another family with a Sister Mom?"

"Sister mom . . . ? Huh? Oh, no . . . Sean. The new neighbor will be a *horse* from town."

"A horse from town? Is he special?" Why else did he need a new home on *our* farm?

"Yes, he is. He's a retired thoroughbred racehorse."

"Thoroughbred?"

"Oh, that's a horse that's trained to win races."

"What'll he do here? Run around all day, I reckon?" Gulping sadly, I yearned even to stand.

"Well, yes. But he'll also start a new family."

"How so?"

"The owner will stud him out here."

"You mean to help him build a floor or something?"

"No, he'll bring a mare around from time to time, and the thorough-bred horse will sire a foal."

"A fool?"

"No, a foal."

"What's a foal?"

"It's a baby horse."

"How does a thoroughbred sire a foal?"

"The male horse rubs up against the mare with a special kind of seed. Then, the mare commences to grow a baby. And after awhile, she'll give birth to a foal. The owner will let the baby grow strong on our pasture. One day, that baby may also race."

This sounded like a "likely story", but I was too embarrassed to keep asking questions. I had *no idea* what Mother meant by all that talk of a seed, "special" or otherwise. In fact, I wondered how a horse could handle seeds, say like a potato eye. How could he plant it? *Maybe* he could, provided he rubbed his hoofs up against the ground. He *might* be able to plant potato eyes in a mound. If Mother only knew what I was thinking . . .

Seated in a metal rocker on our front porch, I waited, knowing the thoroughbred's owner would walk him through our yard to our northwest pasture gate. I'd eye him as he walked by, and that suited me just fine. New neighbors felt swell, whether they were the two-legged or four-legged variety. I felt drawn to *anything* that ran, and that went double for a thoroughbred racehorse.

Dad first saw racehorses when he was a few years older than I was. Grandfather Redmond had taken his family on a trip to Chicago, and they had seen a race at the Arlington Heights racetrack in 1928—just one year after it opened.

Dad ambled out to the porch that morning to let me know about horses. "I'll tell you about thoroughbreds," Dad began. "Man alive, can they run—free and quick, zipping like the wind."

"How can they run that fast, seeing how large they are?"

"It's a *wonder*. To watch them is like watching a poem in motion."

Not knowing what he meant, I wondered, "How much does a horse weigh, anyway?"

"Somewhere between 1,200 and 1,500 pounds. The jockey weighs no more than 110 to 115. That doesn't seem like much, being a small fraction of a horse's weight. It's less than ten percent."

"Does the jockey ride with a special saddle?"

"Yes. And he rides in a certain way to help the horse run."

"What way?"

"With his boots *wedged* into metal stirrups so that he can crouch over the horse like an anxious guardian, or like a comforting spirit. He spurs on the horse. A fine jockey urges his steed to give his all, *by George*—when the time's right, that is."

"And when is that, Dad?"

"When the jockey spies an opening on the track, he nudges the horse and urges it to break loose. He asks the horse to dig in, to do what he's meant to do: cross the finish line first. If he's a *true* champion and a natural leader, he'll lead the other horses to the wire, too."

Taking one look at me, Dad knew he'd snatched my attention. "The thoroughbred pricks up his ears, flares his nostrils, stiffens his tail, and digs into the track. Dirt spears up near the jockey's head and shoulders. Can you picture yourself riding?"

Dad took on an announcer's voice. "Wait a minute. From out of nowhere, waiting patiently, it's . . . Thistledown! That's right, Thistledown *Riiissinng* piloted by Sean Redmond. There they go, tearing around the backstretch. They're flying around the clubhouse turn, and Thistledown is pulling away. Now they're rounding the final turn while the other horses are falling back. They're zipping down the homestretch, and with less than a furlong to go, it's Thistledown stretching his lead. Zooming ahead, they're pulling away now, breaking for the wire. And it's... *Thistledown*! By seven and three quarter lengths!"

"Dad, I'm *crippled*. Remember?"

"Yes, I know. To ride means that you must heal first. It'd mean you'd walk again after *years* of longing."

"Yes. My God, wouldn't that be *grand*?" I bristled with excitement. "I've thirsted to walk again, but could my dream ever be real? How could I know it was real, even if I crossed the finish line first?" My right hand patted my left "paw" to reassure me that it might happen. Was my wish to walk more than a pipe dream?

"Oh, you'd know if you were first to cross the finish line, believe me." Then, with *that* voice again, "Sean's steed is racing down the track, sweat glistening on his withers, and mud spurting in streaks. The wind's streaming through the jockey's curls. Oh, wait a minute, Sean's wearing a cap, but his forelocks are dancing in the breeze, and his horse is pounding for the finish line."

Dad switched back to being Dad. "You'd be free, not just because you could walk again, but because you'd be flying."

"*Flying?*"

"Yes, you'd whiz through the air as if borne on wings. And that's how riding *is* like flying. Marvelous, huh? Few things are grander than walking or running after praying to do so, and few goals are more noble than waiting patiently for a cure, for a *miracle*."

"Sounds mighty fine, Dad," I murmured, my mouth watering. "Sure feels right nice."

"Yes, and I'll give you something else to remember."

The 'voice' began, "Sean's coaxing his champion steed to break. He's waited until the right moment: not so soon that his horse gets tuckered out, and not too late that some smart-assed horse takes a great lead."

"Not too soon, not too late? How'll *I* know when the time is right?"

"It's in the blood, and you'll feel it. It's training and a pinch of mystery thrown in. Trust me, you'll know when to ask the thoroughbred to break for home. You'll know."

"But how would I *feel*?"

"Like you're balancing. There's a trade-off, which is a trick. The right moment moves with the specific track and its condition. It depends on the other horses and jockeys, on you and your horse, and on how well you work together. It's the jockey's job to sense all of this, and *much* hangs in the balance."

"Wow, that's a bunch to keep track of."

"There are many signs to read. A fine jockey must be a speed-reader, and he must make his move if and *only if* everything is lined up right."

"I didn't know riding a thoroughbred race horse was *that* tough."

"It's tough because it's worth doing, and most things in life worth doing are tough. It takes practice and good judgment, training and a pinch of mystery. Riding a thoroughbred is like a *wedge* of life, and life *is* complicated. And you need confidence in your ability, in your skill to focus on what's important. Keep faith in your talent to read these conditions."

"And I imagine my horse would feel better sensing that I'm confident?"

"You bet. There's *no* faking it. There's nothing a horse delights in more than a sure hand. He must *feel* that you're in charge. You and your horse must swirl into a single, thinking entity. You must feel each other's thoughts as they become one.

"Someone might not be able to tell where the horse left off and where the boy began, like the Centaur Chiron. Didn't he help tutor Jason and Achilles?"

"Yep, but you know Chiron's only a myth. Supposedly immortal, he doesn't *really* exist."

"Yes, I know. Well, what if somehow I'm tricked, and what if I don't read the signs right?"

"Life can be a trickster, just as the Native Americans believed the coyote is a trickster. But a champion senses the traps. He sniffs mystery while he taps into its energy."

"That's funny." I giggled. Into my mind flashed Wile Coyote, plugging himself into an outlet with a monstrously long orange extension cord. Predictably, electricity seared the poor thing into a charred crisp, his smoke drifting skyward.

I said after a few seconds. "So, life's like horse racing for some folks?"

"Sure it is. I reckon God handed out special gifts. He hopes some people will lead. He makes some people like thoroughbreds to race home and lead others there, too."

"That's some gift."

"Yes, but with that gift comes a cost."

"Like what?"

"Well, for starters, they must *use* their gifts. They aren't allowed to squirrel them away."

"But what if they do squirrel them away?"

"Then, like some jockeys and horses, they won't break at the right moment."

"Sad. How does that happen?"

"Maybe they haven't read fast enough to know the "right" time, or maybe they're frightened, or maybe they don't trust. Maybe they can't embrace the mysterious unknown. Maybe they can't hear themselves say 'yes' to life amidst the thundering hooves racing along the track. Maybe they're simply spooked by mud geysers that spurt along the way."

"I sure can understand being afraid. The unknown might spook a bunch of people." My chin drooped. *I* would *not* be riding a thoroughbred to victory anytime soon.

"Sean, you don't need to crouch over a thoroughbred race horse to win. In fact, you needn't ride a horse at all to lead others home. There are other ways—if you use other tools to win."

"Like what, Dad. How can a crippled boy win?" I kept my chin down.

Dad smiled. "With imagination a body can win without a horse wedged beneath him. If he tries hard and has a little luck, he *might* lead others home gracefully via his writing."

"But, Dad, you're the writer, not me. How could my tale amount to anything?"

"Who says I'm talking about you? All I know is that a crippled boy *might* help people."

"Whom could I help?" My eyes fixed on Dad.

"Anyone who's working through tough times—nearly everyone at one time or another."

"How?" I crossed my arms over my chest.

"Most people like to hear about how others have dealt with hardship. Humans are partial to that because 'misery loves company'. If a body tells a story with a certain intention, the audience may go still." Dad commenced to whisper. "The lights dim, and we feel a presence. Folks catch a glimpse of hope, and that means healing commences."

"People might laugh at such a boy because he doesn't know how to tell stories the way his dad does," I whispered softer than Dad did.

"If the boy is a fine listener and remembers what he feels, and if he relates those feelings to other folks, then there's a foundation. After that, it's practicing, watching, dreaming, and striving to drive for home. I imagine talent *might* be involved as well. It's in the blood, waiting to pounce when the time is right." Dad winked at me.

As Dad spoke, I stayed still, wishing to feel what he said. He breathed rhythmically, and he began to rub his right wrist as if to soothe himself. His manner cast a spell over me.

"Swell writing takes all of this and something else. It takes a pinch of unknown—the mystery you can glimpse from the corner of your eye. A fine writer needs to snatch that. Words will fly into the air, spurting hope. The audience will hear the tale, and their nostrils will flair: to sniff the *wonder* and *mystery* lofted into the air."

Was Dad funning me? How could anyone tell a story that well? Well, maybe Mr. Zettle . . .

"They'll sniff the story, and they'll stand to cheer the author as he clatters homeward, as he gallops his story toward the finish line. And he'll be riding high—flying, really—with forelocks (much like yours) flapping in the wind and sweat glistening on his brow."

"A crowd will *stand* to applaud what a *crippled boy* says?"

"Yes, the crowd wants only the best for you because *your* story is *their* story—provided it's told well. Yes sir, it's everyone's tale then. In fact, I'll bet that *no one* will know who's telling the story and who's listening." Dad paused, and then he added, "And you'll hear the crowd roar. You'll *feel* it, sniff it, and *drink* it in."

Catching his breath the way a winded athlete does, Dad drove home his message, "And all along the way, the wind will shove at *your* back, gliding tufts of thistledown a few lengths in front of you, almost like Thistledown Rising! That sight will nudge you closer to the finish line.

"Dad, why a race?"

"It's a mysterious voyage. Such a voyage opens a window and offers a chance for new life and new hope. It hints that a dream might be born on a wind of words. There you'll be ready to tell your tale at a fitting moment." Dad paused. "Say Sean, have you heard this quote from Thornton Wilder? He said, 'the stuff of which masterpieces are crafted drifts around the world waiting patiently to be clothed in words.' "

"What does that mean?"

"*Your* thistledown may be such a drifter, naked and waiting to be clothed in words."

"*My* thistledown? Why not *your* thistledown? Like I said, you're the English teacher, not me. I'll be laughed at for trying."

"Enough of your reluctance—you won't know if you don't tell this story. Just listen for the rhythm of words, like the beating of hooves.

Think of writing this way: Nouns are jockeys hunched in their saddles, and verbs are the flurries of the hooves pounding the track. Pronouns are nicknames jockeys utter to steady their steeds, and adverbs are the curved motion and the speed of mud as it spurts into the air."

"And whips?"

"The whips are adjectives, telling readers of feelings. How does the horse feel when he's coaxed to run faster?"

"And interjections and conjunctions? What of them?"

"They're the way jockeys wiggle horses through sudden twists in tight lanes, and then how he 'connects' with his lane, joining himself to an opening as he finds a clear track in front of him."

"And the way jockeys steer horses through tight spots?"

"The way a writer uses words to convey a precise feeling."

"What about the way jockeys talk to horses?"

"Those are the appositives, cooing to the thoroughbred."

"And the way a jockey brushes his hand against the horse's neck?"

"Those are prepositions to show direction."

"What about the signals jockeys use?"

"Why, they're the story's climax. He suavely delivers it at the right time. The parallels are manifold, and the wonder they conjure hinges on an appreciation of mystery and how all things swirl into a gigantic masterpiece of music, of poetry, of motion, and of hope."

I began to understand what Dad meant, quipping, "A racing horse *is* a poem in motion, isn't it?"

I sped through grand adventures while I sat waiting all afternoon to spot the racehorse parade by our porch. I felt what it was like to race with the wind streaming through my hair, and I tasted its *delicious* freedom.

When the truck and horse trailer pulled up to our farm, my eyes raced to catch sight of a chestnut stallion leaving his trailer. I stared gimlet-eyed, my lower lip drooping. "Maybe my new neighbor knows I'm in awe of him," I said to myself.

As he drew closer, he eyed me too. I felt as if I watched a god. Stopping in front of me, his nostrils flared as if to say "howdy". I felt he might have added, "And what in the *Sam Hill* is wrong with you? Why haven't you jumped up to greet me?"

I was too embarrassed to tell him I'd come up lame, but I sensed he knew anyhow.

As I sat watching him, I knew what it might feel like to run as a champ and to win. The deep mind and feeling of that horse raced into my eyes that summer's afternoon. And I knew what it meant to stand, to walk, and to run—what it felt like to be a champion. That was a spicy feeling, one that I lapped up as the horse stared back at me. Did he wish to send a letter to crippled boys like me who never wrote to him, in a manner similar to what Ms. Dickinson mentioned?

The owner gently pulled on the stallion's reins to move him toward our northwest pasture gate. Although I wanted to walk and run with him, all I could muster was a letting-go of my chin as it settled on my chest. The great chestnut horse stopped, pawed at the ground with his right hoof, and neighed.

I suppose he felt sorry that I'd come up lame. Maybe he wanted to say, "Cheer up, boy. Even racehorses feel hobbled sometimes." Maybe he spied a painful desire in my eyes.

It really went without saying. Most of what saddens folks need not be spoken. It echoes in eyes, and no words are needed. A body senses it in eager stares and on desperate, *smudged* faces.

Artisan of Soils

Mr. Finesse's knotted knuckles and calloused palms spelled his devotion to potato fields with a capital "D". His leathery skin fissured deeply, reminding any who would notice that a topographical map nestled there. It showcased his bare-handed years of digging, hoeing, and cultivating "tasty" spuds. In fact, I couldn't look at Mr. Finesse or his potatoes without sniffing a plate of redolent food, the steam wafting from golden butter, chives, and herbs. Mr. Finesse's genius misted potatoes with an otherworldly wisdom and love.

While I cannot say what accounted for their savory flavor, I have my ideas. Potatoes grow well in loamy, well-drained soil, just as do melons. In skillfully chosen lots, they lick up the flavors of compost and manure. Mr. Finesse knew what mixture to apply—enough to add flavor and minerals, but not so much that it spoiled drainage. Somehow, he embodied a heavenly taste with a golden halo over his russets, just as a premiere wine maker elicits angelic bouquets in wine by employing soils right for his grapes.

One autumn I watched him warily breaking sandy soil with his four-tined pitchfork. Lifting potatoes, he gingerly sifted the spuds from the soil, freeing them to breathe. Then he shucked the clinging soil from them. Next, he sized and separated them into piles. Finally, he scooped these spuds into musty hemp bags that smelled like the damp earth. We called the bags "gunnysacks", and they worked well for potatoes, seeing as how they let the potatoes breathe. As Mr. Finesse filled the gunnysacks, tiny piles of dirt puffed onto the ground. With choppy puffs, didn't the tators grumble warnings against rotting?

One day the following summer, Mr. and Mrs. Finesse watched me while Mother called on Amway customers. Mother dropped me off at their farm, and I "scooted" out to Mr. Finesse's field along his east fence where I watched him plant. Although crippled, I'd grown skilled at pulling myself along the ground. My hands became grappling hooks for clawing into the damp soils.

Mr. Finesse's overalls were worn, oftentimes sporting small holes in need of patching. "Oh, he's too busy to be bothered by such things," Mrs. Finesse said nervously, offering her excuses, her right hand rubbing her left arm with a rhythm to match the meter of her voice.

Mr. Finesse merely smiled without apology and said, "I like my potatoes, and I—like my potatoes—need to breathe."

While the untrained eye might think his ways slatternly, I knew better. His overalls sure needed all of those holes.

Rarely wearing gloves while he worked, Mr. Finesse needed to feel the musty soil and crops. He brushed against their dampness and warmth, and he held their powdery dryness. Did he capture their life, the way an artist captures the moment, rendering a version—albeit feeble—of beguiling truths? Is that the way Vincent van Gogh felt as he swirled his masterpiece, "The Potato Eaters", in which his subjects' knotted knuckles and calloused hands tended the soils. Their hands also raised the soils' fruit to their mouths. I watched Mr. Finesse swirl fertilizer, lime, and soils to form mounds for planting the potato eyes—wedges from sprouting potatoes cut for seed. He moved as carefully as a skilled artist who loads his palette with shimmering paints hand-mixed right on the spot.

Mr. Finesse spied me watching him from my special spot at the northeast corner of his east fence. Sticking his shovel into the soil, he called out, "Sean, would you like to help?"

How did he know I was aching for such an offer? "Sure!" I said as I commenced to scoot.

Mr. Finesse rigged up a peck-sized apple box with a strap of twine for me to drag. Dumping a pile of eyes into the box, he said, "Sling this around your neck." Then, looping the twine over my neck, he directed, "You go first. Place four eyes, about two inches apart, into the mounds. I'll follow to cover the eyes with the lime, fertilizer, and loam."

These directions were music to my ears. In the fall, I'd be invited to help watch Mr. Finesse's wonder, and no honor felt richer. I'd sit as straight as a pin and point at his crop, exclaiming, "And I helped!" That hooked me.

Carefully placing the eyes face down in the first hole, I felt their cool stickiness. How does such bounty sprout from scant beginnings? Tiny clumps of soil clung to my fingers. (Force has a way of convincing soil to stick to skin.) With a whiff of inspiration, I reckoned I'd leave a bit of myself in each mound. So, into each one I brushed the soil that clinged to my fingers. Mr. Finesse buried every potato eye with a piece of me: my hope for a fine crop. Was each soil particle a holy grain of dust to bless the mounds? I imagined that "blessing" worked its wonders in darkness and in damp earth. Didn't those eyes need to slumber in their dark tombs before they sprouted life? Would my well-wishes urge those tubers to grow?

"Remember, man. Dust thou art, and unto dust thou will return," Father Schudders reminded grieving families at funerals. Was I sprinkling "someone's" dust over the eyes? Did the dust I stirred up hail from Wea mission pioneers? Might their dust have swished all over the prairies and onto Mr. Finesse's field, the way Mr. Zettle claimed the dust of Ponce de Leon had spread? Was this what Dad thought when he read to me from Walt Whitman's "Song of Myself"?

> "I bequeath myself to the dirt to grow from the grass I love. If you want me again, look for me underneath your boot soles. You will hardly know who I am or what I mean. But, I shall be good health to you nevertheless, and filter and fibre your blood. Failing to fetch me at first, keep encouraged. Missing me one place, search another. I stop somewhere waiting for you."

I reckon Mr. Whitman was pondering dust and grasses much the same way I was thinking about dust and potato eyes. I remembered graveside family members picking up dirt and sprinkling it over the coffin as it was lowered into the ground. I got to thinking, wouldn't it mean more if that sprinkled soil came from the shoes of the person who'd died? That would sure personalize things.

I'd read about gunslingers in Dodge City who asked to be buried with their boots on—alive one moment and gone the next. Did they want their dirt buried with them? Maybe they aimed to prepare for whatever came next.

I reasoned that sprinkling dirt onto coffins was more of a way for the living to say good-bye, not so much for honoring the person whose life had moved into another realm. Maybe funerals are more for survivors who wonder about their own mortality. Dad probably would have told me so, had I asked. Just the same, if funerals are meant to honor the dead, why not sprinkle dirt from the shoes of the departed, not the no-account dirt we snatched at the graveside?

When lowly potato eyes are buried and blossom into fine harvests, are they reborn in a way? Does all life come from death? Could death and life be pieces of a grander mystery that our fogged vision won't let us see clearly? What might happen to the body and the soul after the coffin is buried? Maybe there is another voyage of rebirth waiting for the spirit of the deceased, just as the Greeks and Egyptians imagined.

Life goes on, and the connection that Mr. Finesse and other farmers crafted with the earth showed me so. Farmers begin and end each day with the earth, with their fingers drenched in soil. That connection does not change. Don't we all begin our friendship with the earth at birth, and don't the lucky ones of us keep that friendship alive until we die?

After brief months in the dark and musty earth, Mr. Finesse's crops sprang forth. When I gazed toward the fields on their farm (Mother again left me with Mr. and Mrs. Finesse so that she could deliver Amway.), I felt like I drifted to sleep, but I was wide awake. Mr. Finesse's work did that for me.

The potato plants needed compost, and Mr. Finesse himself prepared it. Folding together dirt, straw, manure, and secret ingredients, he crafted mixtures with distinct colors.

Aha! The dirt in Mr. Finesse's fields had distinct colors, too. Were those colors on account of his toil—all of his work to swirl those soils until he found the right mixture for his compost? Was he able to change straw, manure and, dirt into a living palette? Did alchemy create his wonders? Of course. Mr. Finesse borrowed soils with slightly different colors and textures to form his masterpieces. But doesn't nature use winds and rains to do the same? In that way, maybe creation carries on ceaselessly. Maybe Mr. Finesse only helped.

About that time, I'd read in a science book about how a few inches of topsoil form in the space of thousands of years. So that meant Mother Nature makes new life with top soil. I wondered if she created a certain kind for potatoes, and other kinds for corn, milo, and alfalfa. Maybe the color and minerals in the soil tell us a lot about how suited they are for certain crops.

My long thoughts led me to wonder: could soil colors and textures help predict crop growth and yields? I muttered to myself, "If light in photographs captures a person's image, why can't the hues and textures of soils yield clues about crop growth? Don't plants reflect the soil, and visa versa?"

When Mr. Finesse worked the dirt around his crops, he hoed with effort-less strokes, his hoe crinkling the earth with his angled thrusts—some short, some long. All came with a rhythm, much the way a maestro wields a baton. But, while even a maestro borrows help from a metronome on occasion, Mr. Finesse needed no such help. He timed his strokes perfectly, and I reckoned I might write a melody based on his steady motion.

Watching him, I had to breathe in choppy breaths. Wasn't I witnessing genius at work? Although I yearned to jump up and dance, I melted into the soil, my chin drooped in stunned reverence at the miracle I beheld: one of life, of hope, and of love. Words can't capture the full-fledged feeling and meaning of such moments, too radiant to describe.

"Sean, make your way over to the fifth row west," Mr. Finesse said. "There're tators ready for harvest." They were from his first crop, and he harvested at least two each season. Did he sense I felt hungry?

Eagerly, I did as he asked.

Digging into the soil and finding a choice spud, I rubbed it against my hands. I shucked the clinging dirt off of my skin along with the dirt holding onto the potato. Then, Mr. Finesse stuck it on a stick in one piercing motion. He'd mastered that detail as well.

"Roast it in the fire over there, where I'm burning trash. A fresh-roasted spud will keep you going," he promised. I guessed he held a bunch of experience with hunger. He knew how to feed little boys with runny noses, racing minds, and fizzling energy. Maybe he knew that children like I feel gummy and tired in the arms long before we're filled inside.

Well, that spud tasted nothing like any I've tasted since. Anyone who roasts potatoes over a campfire will certainly know what I mean. Never mind the trace amount of dirt left on the skin. That adds flavor. Besides, the heat sterilized the dirt. (My first dealings with scorched earth weren't anything like the kind M&A folks on Wall Street fancy.)

As Mr. Finesse joined me resting by the fire, I glanced back at the east fence line. There were no traces of weeds there except for a thicket of thistles six feet in length. Some of them were meshed in the fence, and I felt that looked like a net to cradle them in the wind.

"Why haven't you whacked those weeds?" I pointed to the thistles. "I don't see them anywhere else on your farm."

Mr. Finesse turned to the thistles, and then he turned back to me. "Some folks think thistles are meant only to be killed. I reckon I hold that opinion . . . mostly. But when I think for a spell, I wonder if I'm wrong. Maybe there's something special about them—something that I didn't see before. After all, I've gotta respect anything as ornery as those prickly critters. They sprout new life and return no matter what. Heck, I need to leave a clump of them to remind me of who's in charge. Lord knows, I won't be after I'm gone."

"Yes, sir."

"Besides, there's no telling what's hiding inside those tough hides of theirs."

"Sir?"

"There's no telling what kind of blessings are inside of their thorny hides."

"Blessings? Mr. Finesse, there's no blessing inside thistles. There's nothing good there." I shook my head, wondering if he'd taken too much sun.

"Well, like I said, there's no telling what might be hiding inside. Take artichokes, for instance. Did you know they're thistles?"

"Nope. What's an artichoke?" The word sounded scratchy and breathless.

"It's a vegetable. Mrs. Finesse totes a batch back from Salinas County, California every Thanksgiving. Her cousin gives them to her. And, without fail, every New Year's day my wife cooks them up fine—roasts them with oils and spices."

Ugh, roasted thistles, I thought.

"You don't believe me, do you? Well, just ask the Missus. She taught me how to scrape the meat from the artichoke leaves, you know. De-e-licious, with a capital D."

"If you say so."

"I do. Son, even in the meanest and most unlikely things on earth, there's something pretty to see, or taste. I reckon that's a kind of balance, you know?" Mr. Finesse sighed.

Janice's botany book spouted about how thistles are "noxious weeds". It also said that thistles churn out nectar, even during dry spells. Was that goodness? And thistles keep doing what they're supposed to do. They make nectar until it drips from them. Maybe some of the farmers I knew were the same. Although tough and sinewy, they might be beautiful inside. They endured.

Then it hit me: Mr. Finesse might be right. Maybe thistles weren't all bad after all. Why, I thought, if there's goodness in something as ornery and as prickly as a no-account thistle, then there *must* be goodness in everything. Did I need to dig deeper or look closer to find it? Maybe I did.

Came Calling a Stranger?

My innards felt sore, a dull ache commencing in my stomach to sound an annoying rhythm. Pain hummed, leaking upward to pester me as it blossomed, especially when I pushed down on my legs. It swept on waves, like a salty tide striking a forlorn and windblown shore: desolate and lifeless. Tuckered out, I felt sad, and I waited for nightfall. (Life felt better then.) A crisp evening breeze and the night sky—punctuated with fiery dots—soothed me. The breeze felt like a wet cloth on a feverish forehead. The twinkling stars against an ebony tapestry helped me focus. On one particular evening, the sliver of a crescent moon felt like a beacon of hope. I sat for a spell on our front porch, seeing as how I didn't know what else to do.

Gazing into the starry night, I felt a coziness: still and solemn. It seeped into me, and I didn't ache as much as a hush fell.

I mused about my pain and sadness. While I had a powerful problem in being crippled, I didn't know how to solve it. How might I heal? Lights twinkled. Father Shudders assured me the Bible says if we have but the faith of a mustard seed, we may command a mountain to move, and it will. He was saying—more or less, "So what's your problem, boy?"

My imaginary friends drifted in to help me find a way. One evening as I sat wondering and searching for an answer—any answer—my ears caught a faint rustling on the lawn, as if a breeze had crinkled dried leaves, swirling them in an otherwise still blackness. I heard a slight groan, as if someone in pain drew near. A snugness seeped in to calm me, as if I knew that whoever drew near might understand my problem.

From inside my night dream, a warmth glided over my right arm. Looking up, I saw a gaunt and drawn face, etched with pain-drenched lines. The man's face overflowed with grief, as if his family had been killed in an accident from which he had managed to stagger. His face was toughened, almost leathery, with blotches of faint yellow and greased tones, the whites of his eyes jaundiced. He reminded me of someone with hepatitis. I knew all about hepatitis, seeing as how Dad and Uncle Jim contracted it their first year at the Christian Brothers' School in Minnesota. A rat fell into a barrel of peaches in heavy syrup, and it drowned.

The syrup grew heavier than the brothers wished, and hepatitis came calling. Dad told me that their bout with the illness was the most pleasant part of their stay.

As the man drew closer, I could see he wore soiled clothes and a tattered straw hat, as if he had been traveling for some time. His eyes were a sparkling blue, and I imagined the fiery night sky might appear in shades of amber as it shimmered in them. His eyes were highlighted by the light from the porch lantern that Mom had set behind me. (Mother had grown partial to hanging lanterns on a wooden hook on our porch, and that lantern swayed gently: revealing more then less, less then more of my visitor's face.) Pain in his eyes pierced the still air that starry night.

"Please have a seat, Mister. You must be tired." His clothes were soiled and tattered, and I guessed he might have been prowling along dusty lanes or through dry pastures for a spell. Did his unending search and grief ooze from his pores? Did that sadness frame his haunted eyes? His very breath, wheezing in fits and starts, led me to guess he was tired.

The man thanked me, exhaled wearily, and fell gently into the chair next to me. Rocking, he rested for a spell.

"Where're you headed? Visiting family in these parts?" I asked.

"No, no. Hmm . . . they're long gone." He smiled demurely. "I have no family." He mumbled shyly, nuzzling his chin near his chest as if it were a chick being tucked under the warm wing of a hen. "Theo is long gone, and I'm far from home. I'm only passing through."

"Just visiting, huh? I thought so because I don't know who you are, although your face looks familiar. I know those eyes. Since I know most folks in these parts, I took you for a stranger. I know I've seen you somewhere before, though. Your eyes are sad: somehow, familiar."

"I suppose they are."

"Are you famous, someone I'd know on sight?" Although no one in town had eyes like his, I knew those eyes.

The mysterious stranger smiled softly as if puzzled. "Me? Famous? Not hardly. Nothing I did worked out."

"What did you do?" I asked.

"Oh, I tried preaching and then painting and a bunch of other things. I failed at all of them . . ."

"Would anyone recognize you?"

"Well, maybe my brother Theo would, but he's long gone. He was an art dealer. Did you know him?"

"Nope, I didn't know him. An art dealer, huh?"

"Yes, and a fine one, too. I'm weary and sad, that's all," he mumbled. The stranger glided his left hand to his right one to rub it soothingly.

"I know I've seen your face, your eyes. Please lean into the light."

As soon as the stranger leaned into the lantern's light, a chill flew down my spine. What did he want from me? Despite what he said, this man was indeed famous. He sat with crinkled eyes. He sat quietly, and I stared, not daring to ask.

It's him! I thought. (His right ear lobe had been lopped off.) I felt a chill fly down my spine. "Why had he come visiting, and what did he want? Why had he come to see me, a crippled boy?" I wondered.

"As I said, I'm no one famous, although you might say I've 'failed famously.' I'm also tormented. I once married a woman with a past, and that didn't last. Had trouble with women," he mumbled, pointing toward his mutilated ear. "Tried to impress one, and here's what . . ."

I nodded and leaned forward to hear his story.

"She took her child and left me. After that, I ached for company. Before that I tried to preach, but my parishioners would have none of that. I wanted to love them, but they could never love me. I failed."

All I could do was nod for him to continue.

In my disgrace I took up sketching and painting."

"I'm glad you did. You're a marvelous talent!"

"Who, me? Oh, well some folks, including my brother Theo, fancied my work a pinch. Theo advised me to paint with more realism. I understood what he meant, but I was drawn to bold strokes in shimmering colors. I still am. Is that wrong to see life in ways that make it more hopeful?"

"Nope, I reckon it's a way to survive."

"Well, Theo advanced me on possible sales . . . thankfully. As far as I know, he has never sold one. The world would likely smirk at my paintings, so that is for the best. I failed at preaching, at romance . . . and even at painting. People wanted nothing to do with me. I wished to touch people's hearts or to show them light inside. I failed, and that's that."

"You didn't fail at painting. You're work is brilliant, and I can't stop staring at it!"

"How old are you?"

"Seven," I said as I stretched up in my chair.

"I see. Listen, I know better."

"I don't think you heard me clearly. I'm seven years old . . . and that's way old."

The stranger only shrugged.

"Well then, what kept you painting?" I asked.

275

"Painting calmed me as I drew furiously in bright hues of yellows, blues, and reds against a white canvas. I swirled the colors, and I stroked them onto the canvas in globs, bearing my torment and sadness . . . my pain. I wanted to succeed, and yet I failed. I felt overcome by pain and sadness. I saw the world in swirls of chaos and even madness."

As he spoke, his eyes reflected the light from the swaying lantern on our front porch. The amber light glistened in sharp contrast to his pale blue eyes, glinting in the evening mists. His hands quivered. I was drawn to his tormented soul. "Don't draw too close," I cautioned myself. I don't want to be scorched, I thought.

"Painting calmed me," the stranger whispered. I wanted to tell him that drawing with crayons did the same for me, but I didn't fancy him seeing me as a baby . . . which is how I felt next to this master painter. Still, I was drawn to this mysterious man. You see, through all of his pain and grief, through all of his torment, I sensed a quiet peacefulness. A solemnity waited to leak free. Although he looked and felt tormented, I felt a deep and abiding peace, a sad resignation, seeping from him with his every sigh and patient glance.

After catching his breath, Vincent huffed, " I dreamt and felt that people have noble hearts, warm and filled with love. That's why I fancied sunflowers and daisies: any flower that radiates yellow and amber. You're lucky to live in Kansas with all of its sunflowers.

"It feels fine. The state flower of Kansas is the sunflower. Did you know that?"

"Well then, you're lucky on that account, aren't you? Anyway, I say yellow is hope: bright sunlight piercing a bleak world. Now I wonder if anything will lighten my world. Maybe I'm a fool for hoping light will appear." The man lowered his eyes, and his breath deepened into a peaceful rhythm.

"It will be all right, you'll see." (Hope said so.)

Mother called through the porch screen door, "Sean, are you all right?"

"Sure!" I answered.

"Okay, then."

The stranger smiled, "your mother?"

"Uh-hunh . . . If you don't mind my asking, what is your name?"

"Vin-"

"Vincent! I knew it."

"Why would you know me?" Vincent asked.

A tinge of misty sadness layered over his eyes, reflecting the lantern's amber glow, perhaps magnifying the contrast between the blue and the amber. Gazing into his eyes, I felt what real sadness must be. It's a kind of grief that overflows with fear bordering on panic, like I simply need to heave up and run somewhere unknown (where a body may bawl unseen and unheard). It's the kind of sadness teaming with pain that is remembered even in death at the very molecular level, as if the orbits of the electrons themselves are slightly warped in the presence of crushing weights of sadness. (Is that the way gravitational fields might bend and fold space, warping it?) That kind of sadness lives eternally and is remembered that way for what it is: simply profound. Vincent's voice sounded full of the kind of grief that shakes the soul like a ragamuffin, leaving an animal's teeth marks deep in the body and doused with grimy saliva, sticky to the touch. It's the kind of grief that leaves a residue of stench like stale and decaying food, both slimy and withering to its host. I watched him with my right eye squinted, my head cocked slightly to the right, my lips pursed, and my jaw clenched. Vincent's hands trembled more sharply and subtly, with frantic pain and with soft peacefulness. He reminded me of his paintings, filled with unrest in violent swirls, yet which also pictured peace in a beguiling way.

He had not yet answered my silent question: why had he come to visit me? Then, he shifted gears to answer me. "Sean, I knew your uncle Jim Redmond. I visited him in the state hospital."

Did this have something to do with why Vincent was sitting on my front porch?

"You need to know the truth about what happened to him."

"Dad says I'm too young to know 'everything' right now, but he's whispering pieces of the story whenever I am old enough to hear them."

"All right, I'll get to the point. Your uncle didn't die from tuberculosis or from a collapsed lung."

"I suspected as much. Dad hinted that he died from a broken heart."

"Yep. Likewise, I didn't die because of a bullet that pierced my lung . . . No, we both died of a broken heart."

"I see."

"I suppose your father told you that after he found Jim dead, he grieved alone. Likewise, Theo stayed with me after my 'accident'. I lingered for a day, and Theo comforted me by reminding me that my agony was ending. What a relief!"

"You poor thing. Are you still-'

"Tormented? Not that way. On Earth I didn't find any salve to still my madness—except through my painting. Oh sure, doctors tried to cure me, but they failed. They didn't understand my mysterious illness. They kept hounding me to confess what I'd done to cause my sickness."

"That's the same story doctors spout off around me: 'Son, we don't know how to fix your legs.' And the priests tell me it's my fault . . . about how only a true believer will be healed."

"Sorry, son. I found the only relief I could for my illness, one no one understood or for which no cared to help—except my brother Theo. As I lay dying, he assured me that my agony was ending soon. I hoped to leave this mad world, and so I did."

"You're still alive, aren't you?"

"Well, yes. . . . in a way. But, I failed at staying alive. Success would be my ending of it all. I took my own life." Vincent closed his eyes and appeared to leave me.

I stopped squinting out of my right eye, my head cocked to the right, my jaw clenched, and my lips pursed.

Thinking that Vincent could not hear me, I mumbled, "Is there any way out for me?"

Hearing me, Vincent gasped, "Yes, there is a way. There is a way for anyone with a mysterious illness—one which the doctors and priests neither understand nor care to understand."

"What's the way?"

"Never give up. Yield nothing. Never give up—and, oh, by the way, are you listening?!? NEVER GIVE UP!"

"Yes, sir. But why did you give up?"

"Well, my illness grabbed me. It seized my mind, shaking me. I couldn't endure it any longer. I searched out many doctors and asylums for a cure, but I found no help . . . no hope. Relief came only when I painted. That's why I fancied those bold strokes in swirls, and that's why I painted in magnificent shades of yellow and amber, gobbed onto the canvas in violent strokes. While I felt that inside, I also ached for a cure to my illness. One never came.

"I'm sorry."

"Thanks, my dear. Then one day I couldn't handle it anymore. I was tuckered out, and all hope had fled. I craved peace . . . an end to my madness. I saw no hope."

"But you hoped for a cure, right? You searched for a doctor and for an asylum that might help."

"Yes, I did. But do you know where I didn't look for my cure?"

"Where?" I asked.

Vincent thumped his chest to say, "The wisest doctor sits within the heart of each person, waiting to break out and to craft a miracle to heal the one afflicted. I simply could not find that source, even though my painting brought me close to it, even though my painting reflected it."

"Could that reflection of the healer within that you painted be an echo of that inner doctor, a feeble echo of the healer within each person?" I ventured.

"Yes, it is. That's precisely what it is. That's why I felt some peace when I painted. My painting brought me nearer that inner tonic, that source of inner healing and peacefulness. That's why my madness—my agony—abated whenever I painted."

A hush filled the evening air. (I was going to need to think on that for a spell.) We heard only a muffled chirping sound of crickets and the droning of locusts from our silver maple trees in the copse of our front yard. Their monody stirred the night.

"Sean, you must take a journey, a voyage-"

"If you mean a trip to the Shriners' Hospital for Crippled Children in St. Louis, forget it. I'm not going, and that's final. Mother said so. No, I'm not going to St. Louis, and if you're my friend, you won't mention it again," I panted, my heart pounding as my chest heaved.

"Not that kind of journey. I mean one inside you . . . deep within . . . to find a source of healing."

"Really?"

"Yes, and most folks need to make an inner voyage. It often happens when folks are older, oftentimes when they are full-grown. You're lucky to take your trip while you're young and resilient."

"What do you mean by resilient, Vincent?"

"Not even strong winds of trouble can rip your innards. You'll hold on, bend, and adapt. Others who are older and more rigid might break."

"Yes, sir."

"You need to take this voyage now while you are supple enough to survive. That doesn't mean others don't take a similar voyage later in life."

"What do they need for their voyage?"

"Their heart and feelings must not be hardened. A journey like this is best taken when the person is young at heart."

"Why so?"

"Brittle branches snap in the breeze. Trunks break and crash down if such a journey is taken when a body is old. Bon voyage," he quipped.

"Well, I may be young, but not as young as you or my parents . . . and everyone else seems to think. And, I'm powerful sorry that I snapped at you about St. Louis and all that truck."

"Don't mention it, son."

"All right, I need to tell you why I don't fear pain...much."

"Tell me."

"I'm learning to control it. If I'm careful, and if I don't push down on my legs, they don't hurt much. Although pain comes in waves if I do slip, after a spell the waves grow weaker and smaller—like the waves in a pool. They grow smaller as they ripple from the spot where a worn stone kerplops into a deep pool. Similarly, pain lessens."

"Hmm, interesting," Vincent said.

"Mother told me pain is carried on tiny nerves . . . strands like fine rope."

"Yes, I remember a little of how it was when I lived. Please continue."

"The nerves connect to my legs. Can tiny nerves also fray like strands in a rope? Maybe all of that pressured pain wears them down until the pain eases up. Maybe the nerves fray like a rope. It snaps strand by strand until the rope falls apart. The pain eases up, seeing as how the nerves can't carry a signal anymore."

"Fine work," Vincent said.

"Well, that's what I've noticed, and that's one way I aim to manage pain."

Vincent held a half-smile. "A nerve—or a soul—can handle only so much pain before it stops working."

"True, but I also try to be careful not to slip or to press down on my legs. Well, I daydream a bunch, and sometimes I forget. I've been told that's being 'absent-minded'. When I do forget, I hold on for minute after minute, knowing that the pain will wear down after a spell, like a rotting rope in the barnyard, one that mildews from spring rains misting dust from its surface."

"I see." Vincent said.

"Yep, and as I wait for the pain to lessen, I sometimes poke my arms to direct some attention, some pain, to other places. That way, I might divert pain from my hips until the nerves wear down." As I spoke, Vincent tilted his head to one side, his right eye squinted, and his jaw clenched to help bear some of my pain. He understood. He pursed his lips, maybe so as not to interrupt me.

When I had finished, Vincent looked me right in the eyes to say, "Most folks are alike."

"How so, Vincent?"

"Well, take us, for example. I aim to handle pain by painting. You control yours with imagination. Maybe both ways are similar."

"How so?" I asked.

"They swirl us nearer to an inner source of healing, one we both crave," he mused.

I had to agree with him.

"Art weeps up from an inner source, one of truth, expressed the best way we know how."

"Yes, sir."

After a meaningful pause, Vincent said, "Sean, you told me you aren't much frightened by pain, but you are afraid of St. Louis. You fear that spread-eagle cast. Are you afraid of being crippled . . . different from 'normal, walking' children?'"

"No, not really. I've been different from most folks from the start. I seem to feel and see the world in ways different from the ways most folks do."

"Then, what is it, Sean? Why are you afraid of St. Louis and that spread-eagle cast?"

"Well, I suppose because I need to run wild all over this fool world and to see all the truck and all the doings here, there, and everywhere. I need to view wonders with both eyes: head on, with two separate shows before me at the same time. That saves time. And I'd be viewing a third show within my mind while I watched the other two, don't you know!"

"You said it."

"Yep, and I reckon I'm in a powerful hurry to see what there is to see, to learn what other folks know, and to feel what they feel. I must be free to see it. Maybe I'm a vagabond, brimming with wanderlust at heart . . . you know, like a butterfly. If someone aims to pin me down, I'm frightened. And being entombed in a spread-eagle case in solitary confinement riles me most of all."

"Why?

"Heck, I'd squirm and throw a hissie fit. I'd burn with a mad desire to escape. If I couldn't leave, I'd simply explode."

"Too much!"

"I must run to parts unknown. I wouldn't want to miss a minute of whatever there is to see."

"Bravo, my dear!" Vincent smiled his first broad smile. Some of his pallor lifted.

I shifted in my seat. "I suppose curiosity has it's price. It's a tall responsibility, and it means I cannot rest."

"Right."

"Solitary confinement for me would be like asking a painter to give up his eyes. It would be like asking a singer to lose his voice. That frightens me, Vincent."

"Hmm, I understand. But let me ask you this: If you explore the world with imagination, could you ever really be confined?"

I cocked my head and squinted one eye. Was he funning me?

"Granted, Sean, you'll have plenty of external chains to consider, but how strong are they compared to imagination?"

"So, you're saying I might use my imagination to travel, to discover, and to explore? In that way, I may heal myself?"

"Yes, you can sit still on this front porch with its swaying lantern, or you can be confined in St. Louis in a hospital or a bedroom, and it wouldn't matter. Anywhere you are, you're as free as birds are floating on evening breezes at sundown. You could soar on wings of imagination, even though you lie grounded and crippled. You might do all of that as you search inwardly for a cure to your mysterious illness—one which the doctors don't understand and can't be bothered to know—one that the priests want to fling away," he consoled me.

"Yes, you're right!"

"And don't forget 'The Spirit of St. Louis'. Lucky Lindy took off early one morning for Paris. He flew the Atlantic solo. Folks in St. Louis wish you well, too. They know you must explore."

"Wow, I reckon you're right, Vincent! By taking an inward journey, I'll freely travel anywhere!" Vincent's images of freedom sparked and then flamed within a few seconds. As I spoke, the crescent moon peeked from behind a lonely cloud that cloaked it in the otherwise clear and starry night. The moonbeams calmed me, offering solace to help bind up festering wounds.

"I can fly anywhere I choose. By taking an inward journey, I'll ramble anywhere I fancy. I'll be free!"

Glancing at Vincent, I noticed he was as taken as I was by the crescent moon. A mist rose from his shoulders and melted into the clouds. Was that his pain?

"Vincent, I'm planning where to travel. With that, I began to describe the hidden lands in shrouded mists . . . even before I knew what I might say. Picking up the pace, I tipped my words with staccato punches more rapidly but with a certain rhythm: one, two, three; one, two, three; one, two, three, four. Through it all, Vincent tried to pay attention, but I must have carried on for quite a spell, drowsing him to sleep.

"Vincent?"

No answer. He was gone. He must have slipped away while I rambled. "Not even a farewell?"

Then, I spied a small strip of his tattered shirt sleeve. Had he left it behind to remind me of the power of imagination and of dreams—to remind me of the strength and healing power that lies within? The faint beams of the crescent moon shone on the ragged strip of cloth, reminding me of Vincent's stormy life.

Reaching down, I was careful not to apply downward pressure to my legs. Clasping the strip of cloth in my right hand, I cradled it over my chest. I prayed for all tormented and lonely souls, for all who have lost hope. I wished they might feel the comfort of an inner source of hope, an inner tonic, from which all life and healing might spring. I whispered my prayer, and I finished by asking that life be kind. May it be more gentle to any who struggle, filled with grief. I cast my wish under the crescent moon as the gentle evening breezes rustled the crinkled leaves and dried grasses on our lawn that starry night. I wished this as I heard the rustling sound of Vincent's departing sough.

"Well," I told myself, "I reckon that Vincent did say good-bye. He bade me farewell in his own special, shy way." Exhaling with resolve and with newfound strength, I felt, "I'm on my way."

In the distance, the hooting sound of a screech owl echoed from the valley. I imagined that wise owl searched for food to nourish it on a nighttime voyage that starry night.

Ripples of a Mysterious Universe

From childhood's hour, I have not been as others were;
I have not seen as others saw.
I could not bring my passions from a common spring.
From the same source I have not taken my sorrow.
I could not awaken my heart to joy at the same tone.
And all I lov'd -- I lov'd alone.
(excerpt from *ALONE* by Edgar Alan Poe)

Gazing out of our downstairs bedroom window, I felt alone. I knew better—that no one is ever really alone—but I sure felt that way. After waiting and hoping for a cure, I clung to the thought that we're all connected: never alone. For more than a year, flights of fancy buoyed my spirits, and I began to feel that I might be able to heal myself. Now I was about to undertake a voyage inward (one of discovery), as described in my fanciful visit with Vincent. I would explore with my imaginary friends, including Lambda, Omega, and the Deuce. My story teems with mystery and adventure, which is the way I like it. I hope you like it, too. Welcome to my saga. I'm tickled to share it. By the way, help yourself to another ladle of vegetable soup. (Later, we'll steep mint tea.)

Gazing at lace curtains fluttering in the afternoon breezes, I reckoned that folds in the curtains danced to form random ruffles. Outside the window, sparrows twittered in a lilac bush, bees droned around summer roses, and feathery white tufts of thistledown poised to twitch airborne for parts unknown. Might I also fly away, or at least stand up and walk.

"Well," I mused, "the experts didn't help, even going so far as to join the other side by assuring me that I'll never walk again." Dr. Stanley wanted to isolate me in a spread-eagle cast in St. Louis. That idea piled torture onto torment, especially as it did not assure healing. I convinced myself that in order to heal I must reach within, viewing and feeling each and every "step" along the way.

While no two-legged varmints could help, I marshaled a host of imaginary allies to do just that. Which ones will help me heal? I puzzled. As I sped on my great adventure, I dreamt of ways to heal.

Hearing from the musical notes, I wondered if I could depend on them for help. While clamoring to sing along to any tune, they seldom stuck to one idea long enough to know it well. Although brilliant, those notes were too fleeting. They lacked staying power. Oh, a few could hold their voice tolerably well, but none could muster the kind of endurance needed. No, I thought, while those notes are lovely, they won't do.

Next came the Arabic numerals. While full of potential, their loyalty lay in doubt. For example, I knew the ornery treys relished playing pranks. If caught in mischief, they pouted and fussed, raising sullenness to an art form. Oftentimes, the treys stood aghast if I dared to correct them. Did they deserve pardon for their misdeeds? I thought not.

Interrupting rudely, the ten of clubs boasted how it was the key to our number system. I felt obliged to remind it, "Any number would have been fine. Maybe ten was chosen owing solely to the fact that humans tote ten digits on their hands and ten toes on their feet."

My counsel silenced them for only a spell. But then, the ten of hearts lamented about how he'd been cheated of regal finery lavished on face cards.

I began, "Let me tell you about those face cards. The queens flirt and pander while wearing cheap perfume puffed over their graceless limbs. The kings boast between each gulp of food or swig of wine as they glut themselves, their breath reeking."

While illustrating the face cards' debauchery eased the ten of hearts' feelings, my words also rested me.

Sadly, I disqualified all of them on account of weak character and paltry self-control. Tall indulgences dwarfed their short restraint.

The knaves, on the other hand, held potential. As they fluttered in the afternoon breeze, I wondered if I might use their alleged bravery. Could their courage help me find a way to heal? Perhaps . . . But the knaves weren't consistent, and that meant trouble. They wavered between nobility and self-indulgence. Hot one day and cold the next, they could not be relied upon. I needed a steadfast temperature to gauge reliability on my loyalty thermometer. Why, how could I think any other way? Besides, the knaves didn't even have an assigned number! That left me guessing their point value. Did it match the value of other face cards? If so, that did not impress me. And another thing: why did they defer to royalty? What kind of half-baked power was that? Nevertheless, I might have counted on them if they hadn't earned a wild reputation.

Finally, who knew about the one-eyed variety of jacks? Did they have another eye hidden on their dark side, or had that second eye been gouged out in a hellish street fight of their making? Those jacks seethed with a hidden fury that seemed pointless, settling nothing.

Too many questions, and too little information, I decided. They're all out, on account of their foibles and flaws. In order to help me, my friends must be loyal.

Next came the mischievous Deuce. Although he delighted in teasing, when troubled times arose he rallied. In the end he pulled through for his friends. The Deuce sensed what ranked as truly important. If I really needed him, he whooshed in to my rescue. Simply dressed in white slacks, a sports jacket, bow tie, and a straw hat, he peered somberly at me—right into my eyes—assuring me that he'd do all that he could do to help. I likened the Deuce to leprechauns, mischievous but loyal. When they tired of playing pranks, their help made a difference. The Deuce made the short list of friends to help me find a way to heal.

"Mr. Deuce?" I began. He moved like a vapor, misty and nearly invisible. Even his clothes blended into the background, the way a chameleon changes colors to camouflage itself. I caught a glimpse of his wispy face and form as he passed out of a shadow, helping to outline him, and as he hovered near my bed. I couldn't see him unless I stared right at him, contrasting his form with shadows on the wall. His stealthy movement and appearance helped him avoid detection.

"What, whhhuut do you wwhishh? Whhuut do you wwaant?" he whistled in a soft voice at me, reminding me of words huffed by an old man, words muffled by the wind as it whips across an open prairie. I strained to hear what he whispered my way.

"Mr. Deuce, will you be my sentinel, standing guard to warn of intruders? After all, our plans must be kept secret until we know they have worked."

Without a word Mr. Deuce nodded in agreement. His serious nature assured me of his intentions. Mr. Deuce understood what lay at hand.

"Just as you wwhishh. I'll be your gatekeeper, watchhing whhaat waits beyond your wonder-filled world. Before unwelcomed wanderers crash in, I'll warn you. I'll keep a balance between your world of imagination and the rest of the world. Then, you'll work on ways to heal without wondering if anyone might guess whhaat you're doing."

"Much obliged, Mr. Deuce. I don't wish to be embarrassed if our plans fail."

"You'll stay balanced as you try different ideas. You'll be balanced, and you'll keep right on trying until you find one that works."

"Thank you, Mr. Deuce."

"I'll help you balance those two worlds, like a tight rope walker using a balance rod. Without that balance you might tumble into a world darkened with despair. With that balance you will tote hope to keep trying for a cure until you do find one."

"I can't thank you enough, Mr. Deuce. Hmmm, may I ask you for one more favor?"

"Asssk away. I know you need help, and I'm here for you."

"Well, it would mean a great deal to me . . . I mean I sure would be grateful if you would let me call you . . . Well, it's kind of embarrassing, really, but may I call you . . ."

"Out with it, son! Whatever it is, don't stammer. Say it!"

"Well, if it's all right with you . . . golly, I'm blushing just to ask you this . . . but, may I call you by a pet name?"

"That depends on how poor it is. What do you have in mind?"

"Since you stood so small the first time I spied you next to the raspberries—you know, the day I reckoned it was all right to cry—may I call you the 'Little Country Deuce'? If you don't think it's too sorry."

Sighing wearily, he relented, "Oh, I suppose. I've been called much worse, don't you know. All right, the 'Little Country Deuce' it is."

Well, tickle me pink! The Little Country Deuce's kindness had me hooked.

The Little Country Deuce turned, the color of his torso brightening as he puffed into a wisp. He whisked toward the bedroom door to take up his post. Nearly invisible, he commenced his vigil.

Next, an array of Greek symbols flitted by me. Bored silly, most seemed to be along for the ride. Still, there were a couple of standouts.

Presently, I witnessed a sword battle between Lambda and Omega. The scuttlebutt was that Lambda had riled Omega, stinging her with a zap of high-frequency energy. The battle ended abruptly when Lambda struck Omega. That let a bit of blood from a tiny flesh wound. As the salty aroma of that blood wafted through the air, Lambda's face grew ashen. Had he really hurt her?

A grin spread across Omega's face as she said, "No serious damage. It's only a scratch." So, the battle continued, rising to new heights. Their single-minded devotion to a task told me that I could trust them to help find a cure.

Now, if I could figure a way for my fool pain to work for me, I'd be set. It swept in with unrelenting shock waves, coursing through me and echoing within. Like shock waves from fault lines in an earthquake, hellish daggers of pain grew unmanageable. Unlike shock waves from faults, I could predict my waves of pain. They came only when I put pressure on my legs. By contrast, shock waves from faults came randomly, releasing pent-up stress. I reckon that I needed my waves of pain, for without them pain might soar to unbearable heights. Since I needed my shock waves to keep me from exploding into fireballs of pain, I wondered if my waves of shocking pain might be useful for healing.

"Ha! Pain, help me? I must be silly to reckon so," I muttered.

Listening to the wind's melody whistling over the prairie, I heard its echoing monody. Then I knew that I was mistaken. (Oh my, I wasn't hearing the wind. Rather, it was the voice of the Little Country Deuce.) "Recall the windmills, stooped and rusted from age and service. They harness the wind's energy. That kinetic energy powers pumps. Why not use pain's energy to power your healing?" wafted his whispered words as he hovered in a windy wisp over my bed.

Mother had spoken often of raindrops, water and windmills. She had told me how pumps are powered by windmills. The pumps suck water from the earth to fill silent cisterns, dark and slumbering. "The waters fall to earth from heaven's tears," Mother affirmed. "Then, one day the waters spring forth after filtering through ancient rock layers of sandstone and limestone. Those waters inspire new life for soils. Those drops from heaven's tears seep up after they fall to earth, drop by drop upon the heart," she taught me. The drops reminded me of pain falling drop by drop upon the heart, pain which cannot be forgotten, as the Greek poet Aeschylus had spoken. "And even in our sleep, pain that cannot forget falls drop by drop upon the heart, and in our own despair, against our will, comes wisdom (and healing) to us by the awful grace of God." Dad had quoted Greek poetry often. Might pain help me find wisdom to power my healing?

"Now think," I muttered to myself. "May I harness pain by changing its wavelength? Maybe pain is another side of joy. Maybe we don't see it because we're too rigid. Is pain part of a wholeness? Are joy and healing pieces of a whole? Can pain help me heal?"

After pausing a moment to consider the opportunity, I asked, "Might I learn to harness the might of my pain? Maybe I could focus it somehow or other. Could it be a catalyst to help heal my legs?" I wondered. After all, the one thing that the doctors knew was that my fall acted like a catalyst for my illness. My fall acted like a mechanical catalyst, promoting my illness that attacked my bones. That rendered me sorely crippled.

Maybe I could learn to use pain as a catalyst for healing just as in our body cells, where certain enzymes act as catalysts to control the rate of certain chemical reactions. I smiled as I remembered the struggles of the ancient alchemists who kept right on trying to find ways to change base metals into precious ones. I thought, It might work, if I can control the pain in the correct intensity. By focusing it, maybe I'll turn base feelings into warm ones, precious to hold!

On and on I mused over dusty ideas. Soon, I commenced thinking about earthquakes. I imagined that the shock waves from earthquakes force rock strata over one another to release unimaginable pressures. After building, the pressure stresses rocks to the breaking point, far beyond their resiliency. The forces seemed unknowable, beyond anything

I could imagine. Given the pain I felt, I presently felt sorry for the rocks that framed my dreams. (Hadn't I read that the 1906 San Francisco quake exerted a force of 10,000 atomic bombs?)

Next, I gazed again at our ruffled lace curtains fluttering in our bedroom window. While most of a curtain billowed outward, some of the curtain floated inward, even as a gust of wind tried to persuade them otherwise. Watching the medley of motion, I remembered a book I'd read about cosmology. It covered the creation and evolution of the universe which began billions and billions of years ago. I mused about our exploding universe, which might expand outward forever. Then, I struggled to reason just how large infinity might be—a powerful tall task for a small boy of seven years. I knew the universe had been growing since the first nanosecond of the Big Bang. With all of that material and energy exploding outward, I guessed some of it might prefer to tarry. Might the fabric of space be tearing and creasing, like a piece of elastic material, with parts of it folding in different places? If there are ripples in the cosmic explosion, then folds might accelerate back on themselves in a headlong plunge, even while the rest of the fabric explodes outward on its endless quest. Those lacy curtains and their motion prodded me to imagine multiple motion—mostly outward, with creases folding inward upon themselves.

If that happens, then space may be collapsing back on itself in places. Might my legs be similar in the sense that my bones could commence to gather material to re-ossify heads for my femurs? I imagined that their disintegration parodied the expansion of the Big Bang, and that their eventual healing might parallel the acceleration of the universe back upon itself. In a crude reflection of that motion, I might be healed!

To heal, I must find power to create a ripple in my bone matter. That power could trigger a chain reaction to fill all the material back into my bones, robbed of their matter by my mysterious illness, resulting in explosions of pain. Could I learn to alter pain's wavelength to put it to use? My bones might heal if calcium originally formed in stars drew back into my femurs.

Just as parts of the universe collapse upon itself, I imagined that matter in my bones could condense upon itself. All this rested on whether or not Lambda and I could learn how to guide energy from my pain back into my legs at precise, troubled spots. Lambda promised to help catalyze the bone matter so it could coalesce. Like ice crystals growing on a once barren bone shaft, my femurs would blossom, and my bones would heal. They would mimic that view of the lacy curtains fluttering in our bedroom window. Rippling in the breeze, those curtains swooped outward for the most part. Still, some material fell in upon itself, even as most parts billowed outward. That vision inspired me to know that, in some ways, our own bodies behave as does the Universe. It's a matter of scale. I asked myself, "Might our bodies mimic the Universe, acting as microcosms of it?"

"Now, that's a real possibility!" I gasped. I remember feeling a tingling in my spine, as one might feel at the moment that one figures out the culprit in a murder case. I ached to shout it out, but I knew that I might appear foolish if I was wrong. Since this was all just guesswork, I was not ready to commit to it yet. Still, what I imagined made sense because I belonged in a mysterious universe. You know, I had my rights! So, why not learn a bit from the creation and evolution of the universe over billions of years? Why not use that knowledge to help me heal?

As I lay there with the pain dripping upon my heart, perhaps I had found some wisdom for self-healing, through the awful Grace of God. Perhaps the Greek poet Aeschylus was the wisest man I could name. Maybe he held the keys for my healing: the best hope I could muster.

As I pondered this idea, I peered at Lambda, who grimaced at me from a lull in his sword play with Omega. He wiped some saliva from the corner of his mouth as he looked up as if to ask, "What have you imagined this time? Just give it to me directly."

"Lambda, may I ask for your help?" I asked, knowing he'd accede to anything within reason.

"Why, yes, sir," came his dutiful, self-assured reply. Lambda moved rapidly with the grace and dignity of someone special. I imagined seeing Sir Isaac Newton in the Royal Academy as he held a prism to sunbeams to form a light spectrum.

"I've grown a plan, a dubious one, to help heal my legs. I need your help."

Not hesitating one moment, Lambda replied, "But of course! I'm listening." His eyes glowed like two live embers, as if a mighty furnace burned behind his face. He also moved with great speed, as if he rode on a wave of light. Once when I watched Lambda, I had held a glass of water in front of my face to peer at him through the water. When I squinted, I saw the colors of the rainbow across his face. He appeared to radiate light, and I'd glimpsed its refraction with my makeshift prism.

I began, "Lambda, here is what I reckon I ought to do. I'm going to harness the waves of pain, just as windmills capture the force of the wind whipping across prairies. Like an electric shock pounding upon the rocky shoals of my crippled body, that energy must be harnessed. I'll use the energy as a catalyst for healing to reverse my hips' damage."

Lambda ceased tracing with his sword figure eights lying on their sides. He moved closer.

The doctors told me that my pain was from bone deterioration, triggered by my fall. I might be able to alter the energy's wavelength. Still, the energy must be focused and used carefully. That's where I need your help."

Lambda saluted. "At your service," he officiously said.

"With your agile frame and small hands, you'll be able to focus energy to precise spots on my legs where the bone has crumbled. You're skilled at rapid sword play and shifting wavelengths. I'll wager we'll be able to encourage the bones to pull matter inward that way. What do you say?" I asked, thirsting for his nod.

"But of course. When do we commence?" came his answer in precise tones, as if guided by lasers toward their target.

"Wonderful," I began. "I'll be busy capturing and reversing the energy, which I'll shoot your way. You'll apply the healing rays, like laser beams." I put on my most serious face to say, "I've never done this, and there might be trouble. You see, I'm not sure how well I can control the pain's energy. You might be hit with too much to handle. This could be dangerous. Are you willing to take that risk?" I'm sure Lambda heard me screaming, "Please say yes . . . say yes . . . !"

"Certainly," Lambda said without hesitation. "I'll be there each and every time you need me. I'll be your light in all this darkness. It will be a tiny, focused ray of hope to heal. This will work. Like a lighthouse on a rocky, windswept shore, I'll be a beacon of hope, shooting light into your legs." His eyes radiated warmth.

Mists of thanks filled my eyes. "We'll melt free from my hellish pain of icy torment!"

"The only constraint I have is one of timing," Lambda warned. "I go to bed early with the setting sun, and I grow weary in the late afternoon. My light flickers and dims. We'll need to do this work in the morning. All right?"

"Fine, we'll work by the light of each morning."

Then, Lambda said, "I have a question."

"What is it?" I blurted.

"How will we know if there is enough material left for the bones to reform? Have you taken a bone density reading yet?"

My chin headed south. "No...I have not. I'm not sure how to-"

"A-hem. A-hem!"

There stood Omega, her fingers rippling rhythmically up the sleeve of her right arm.

"Omega?" I asked. "What is it?"

Removing her fencing mask, she shook her head, releasing streams of golden hair that swished around her face. Light beams from Lambda reflected from her hazel eyes. Her eyes turned color with stronger beams of light—first green, then gray, and then hazel.

"My, my, my, oh my," echoed inward. "Will you look at that?" My lungs nudged and then demanded that I breathe. Was my breathlessness on account of her? At first I could only stammer in her presence.

Omega walked toward me with down-to-earth dignity, radiating the same humility that I saw in our neighbors as they kept on trying and working to live their trying lives. As she reached my bedside, her scent floated over me: the dampness of the earth after a spring mist, like the soil after a summer eve's rain. I reckoned seeds might sprout if she but commanded them to grow.

Lambda cleared his throat to bring me back to earth. And then I knew how we'd take our density readings. "Omega, will you shrink yourself and enter my body to read my bone density? What do you say, Omega?" She hesitated only a moment (I imagined to trumpet her displeasure at being ignored earlier.) Her words trickled off of her tongue and gurgled from her throat, the way slumbering water may bubble up from wells deep within the earth.

Then she promised, "Yes, Sean. I'll do whatever is needed."

Relieved, I laughed softly. "Thank you. But let me warn you, this is perilous!"

"Oh?" Omega gurgled.

"When you shrink into a microscopic probe, you risk being trapped by my growing bones. The gravitational force may trap you."

Without missing a beat Omega said, "Don't worry. I know what I'm doing, and you can count on me. No other friend will be more loyal. I'll be with you always, to the end!"

"Omega, may I give you a last name? You remind me of a hill of blue-bonnets, deep in the heart of Texas. I reckon you'd be at home there with your country cousins."

"What do you have in mind, Sean?"

"Well, you remind me of a picture I saw once. It was a red heifer grazing along a hill of bluebonnets, dancing on a hill. May I call you Omega Bluebonnet?"

Omega blinked rapidly seven times, and then she stammered, "Oh . . . why, yes . . . Whatever suits your fancy." (I reckoned she was partial to me, I declare!)

With our pleasantries done, we set about our plans.

First, I needed to learn how to capture my pain waves. I knew I'd never run short of pain or its energy. The trick was how to manage it. (Was I like a wooden ship caught in frozen waters, in an icy tomb? The ice crushes the ship slowly with grinding force.)

Next, we needed to alter the wavelength of my pain. Lambda and I went through trial and error for a few months. Applying controlled pressure to my hips, I sent spurts of energy to Lambda. Finally, my friend figured out how to fine-tune and redirect it. Meanwhile, Omega was reading poetry and singing songs. The stealthy Little Country Deuce stood guard at the door.

I recall the day we began with some practice shots to my hips to see if we knew what we were doing. Although Lambda guided the beams precisely toward my bones, they strayed slightly. I imagined some mysterious force wanted to bend the beams, forcing them to miss their marks slightly. Lambda redirected the beams; I spurted energy; the beams missed. Lambda adjusted, and we tried again . . . and again.

Meanwhile, spring eased into summer, and then summer coasted into fall. Lambda tired more easily, growing weary every late afternoon. He took to bed with the earlier setting of the sun. His light flickered and dimmed, fading to dark with twilight and nighttime.

Even Omega seemed worn out as fall passed into winter. Did she need to slumber through the winter? Did she need warmth to grow her ideas, to hatch solutions to help me heal? The Little Country Deuce didn't seem to mind the passing seasons. In fact, he blustered even harder. I simply couldn't understand why we kept missing our mark. Puzzling over this question, I sat on Grandmother Kearney's green upholstered furniture with raised straight lines in the fabric. The lines were straight until they bent downward near where I sat. The closer the lines were to me, the more they bent downward. They warped with my weight. The force of gravity on my body tugged on that fabric and bent it. Could gravitational force of my bones also cause the energy beams to bend? If that was what caused them to miss, he simply needed to recalibrate his shots to correct for that warping force.

"Lambda, we need to allow for the force of gravity from my bones. Aim higher to correct for that warping force on the energy beams."

Lambda made difficult calculations at lightning speed, and he reported, "I've solved the equations to correct for the force of gravity. I knew you'd ask me to make these calculations."

"How did you know?"

"Omega told me you would. She quoted a line from Henry Wadsworth Longfellow, too."

"What did Longfellow know of gravity and of light beams bending?"

"Not much. But, according to Omega, he did say, 'If you want to hit your mark, remember to aim higher.'"

"I reckon that was his way of reminding us to add a margin for victory," I said. Turning to Omega, I blushed, adding, "It was lovely of you to offer your solution. And you're right as rain. We do need to aim higher to hit our mark. Who cares why."

"Oh, let's try again, Sean," Lambda suggested.

Lambda shot the beams at the correct angles to allow for warping forces of gravitational fields enveloping my bones. We succeeded: Lambda reported directs hits. Although we solved one problem, many more lay in wait.

Our next problem meant finding a structure for my bony matter to help me heal. So, I asked Omega Bluebonnet, "Please shrink to microscopic size to inspect the structure of my healthy bones." Right away, she made her trip while the Little Country Deuce stood guard. I'll not forget her expression when she returned. She looked elated and sad at the same time. She whispered, "Sean, the structure is more complex than we could ever imagine. It rambles on and on. Every time I shrank myself to view the details more closely, I found an ever-expanding world of complicated structures. No matter where I turned, I found more and more complexity. I couldn't shrink small enough to find an end to it."

We fell silent for a spell. Our Little Country Deuce stood guard at the door to warn us of any prying eyes that might not understand all of our work. He could detect intruders far away and warn us to act normal whenever anyone approached. No one could know of our secret work, especially before we knew how to solve the problems. He remained ever wary and pricked up his ears to pick up any noise, however faint. He also sniffed the air for any sign of intruders. His skill surpassed that of a coyote sniffing and listening for intruders on a windswept prairie.

The Little Country Deuce reminded me to keep a balance between the daily world of our farm and the inner world where my friends and I struggled to find a remedy for my mysterious illness. Since the experts couldn't help me, my friends and I had set out to find help on our own.

Peering around the room, I saw both Lambda's and Omega Bluebonnet's disappointment. "What could we do?" I wondered.

I became part of the Lewis and Clark party searching for a Northwest passage. When Lewis climbed to the continental divide, he found many miles of high mountains standing in the way. I knew that Lewis must also have been both elated and sad. With a racing heart, he must have been proud to stand on the Continental Divide, but he must have also been disappointed to realize there was no Northwest Passage. I imagined my friends' expressions reflected how Lewis felt.

Sidling up to me in our hour of greatest need, the Little Country Deuce tapped me on my shoulder and whispered, "I've heard your disappointment, and I've felt your pain. Are you sure that this internal voyage, although grand and mysterious, isn't a waste of time? Maybe it's not needed," he began.

"What do you mean, 'It's not needed?' Of course it is!"

"How can you be sure?" he pursued.

"I know it's needed because I feel it. Besides, my friend Vincent and my dad told me so."

"What do they know? They tote dusty tales, outlined in shades of faded yellow and pitiful pastels. Aren't they failures?"

"No, they know a lot!"

"What do they know?"

"They know pain and grief. They've felt deeply, and that means they have not failed. They know!"

"All right, you think they know a lot. But this internal voyage, it's not needed. I know another way."

"And what way might that be?" I asked.

"I can cure you, right here, right now. You'll never hurt again, leastways not in your legs. I can also tack on as many years to your life as you see fit. You could spend those years, sans pain, with anyone you wish. Think of it, you could spend that time reading, and I'll give it to you only for the asking!"

"And what's the cost of such a bargain? Why are you telling me this now?" I was shaking.

"No cost, not really. I reckoned you'd be ready for the offer now. I know how set you are for an 'internal' journey."

"Little Country Deuce, tell me the cost."

"All you need do is to tell your other friends how powerful I am. Do that, and I'll heal you right now, no questions asked."

"And how might you do that? You don't look all that strong, and healing my bones must be a powerful tough task," I exclaimed.

"Well, it's not as tough as you might think. I have a few tricks up my sleeve, even if you can't see them. Simply tell Omega and that swaggering Lambda how wonderful I am! It's that easy, and you'll be free of this pain." Darkness rippled over the Little Country Deuce.

"Thanks for your offer, but no thanks."

"But why?"

"For starters, I'm only a simple Kansas farm boy. I doubt anyone cares to know what I've got to say about anything, least of all about you."

"I see. And . . ."

"And, there are all those poets that Dad told me about. I remember the words the Greek poet Aeschylus penned about pain."

The little Country Deuce interrupted, "What did he know about pain?"

"He said that through pain there may be a kind of learning, a growth of wisdom. So, maybe the pain isn't the point at all. Maybe the learning we find along the way is valuable. What we find along our voyage will be much more precious than any outcome, even the ones you've described." Then I added, "Besides, I've lived with searing pain for so long, I sure can take it for a while longer, don't you know!"

As I spoke, The Little Country Deuce's color faded, lightening and softening the darkness that rippled across his face.

"Then, there are Omega and Lambda to consider," I offered.

"What about them? Why think of them?" the Deuce persisted.

"Well, just take a look at their faces. They're itching and chomping at the bit to help me. I couldn't very well call it off now, even if I wanted to—because it means too much to them. It's better this way. You'll see."

With those words, the little Country Deuce faded into his world of mists and morning vapors.

After he took his leave, I lay on the bed to focus my thoughts. I felt tuckered out, incredibly tired, and I could hardly keep my eyes open. The struggle to hold us all together and to find answers to our questions (to find solutions to our hurdles in healing) had worn me slick. "I don't know how much longer I can hold on, Lambda," I sputtered as Lambda entered the room.

Lambda also looked weary. It was late fall in the late afternoon of my most inglorious and uncivil year.

"You must hold on. Sir, you keep right on holding on, as if you're clinging to a rope. Hold on until your hands are bloody from friction on the rope. But never let go, and never give up!"

"I want to sleep and to forget about everything. The doctors can't help me. Our priest won't help me. My family can't help me, either. It's all up to us: to me. And I'm too tired! I want to curl into a ball and sleep forevermore."

"Is there something I may do to help, Sean? Just name it!" Lambda sputtered. "I know I can't carry your burden. Only you can hold us all together. May I do anything to help you with your load?"

"I don't know. I don't know. All I know is how worn out I am. I can't go back to despair and pain. Yet, I don't know how to go forward.

Everybody has thrown up their arms and said to buzz off: that they can't help me. We are on our own, and I don't know what to do next. I'm so tired! I'm weary enough that I'm not frightened anymore. I hurt something powerful, and I don't care if I cry!"

Lambda peered at me as if he was eyeing a worn-out coon hound after a night of hunting gone bad. Maybe he thought I'd sprung a trap, crippling my legs. Did I appear that beaten up—or down—to him? Anyhow, Lambda looked like he wanted to kick at the dust to help persuade me to get back up. Then, his face beamed.

"Oh, I know. Remember how as a little boy you peered into the dawning of each new day? Remember how you stored up all that energy and hope? Well, in case you don't know, you have laid aside an enormous treasure. Why, your trove of pure energy is colossal! Let's tap into that energy now. You'll feel oh so much better, not too tired. Just lie back, and I'll help you. I'll direct that stored energy into your blood, and you'll feel better in no time!"

Well, Lambda did that very thing, and in a twinkling I felt like a new man! Presently, I saw how breezes rippled the ruffled lace bedroom curtains. If it hadn't been for those ripples, I would not have glanced beyond the curtains to see outside my window. There I spied a bee working to gather nectar from a flower.

Then, I thought about the pictures I'd seen of honeycombs. Hexagonal in shape for strength and for efficient use of space . . ."Say, why don't we use a hexagonal shape? We'll use six interlocking triangles. Let me show you." I grabbed a pencil and a piece of paper to commence my sketch. "The triangles must lock together to become rigid." Lambda and Omega listened as I continued to explain.

"Remember yesterday when we sat around our card table? The breeze blew up quickly, and we all held hands to hold the table up, to keep it from teetering over onto the floor. We laced our fingers together, and we pressed our bodies against the table. If we fancy interlocking triangles, it will resemble how our fingers interlocked into each other's hands. We'll form a hexagon. It's strength comes from chemical bonds shifting along each side, and that strength is like what we felt by pressing against the edges of the table, holding it together. It's shape is like that of a honeycomb." Lambda and Omega beamed my excitement. The Little Country Deuce slinked into the room.

"Whatever is good enough for the genius bees must be good enough for us!" I exclaimed triumphantly.

Well, you can't imagine how quickly dejection moved into joy as we set about making plans. Victory seemed assured. The rippling of the curtains had reminded me of other ripples in the Universe. The splendid honeycomb construction of the bees reminded me that powerful forces in the universe affect every aspect of our lives—whether or not we are aware of them. Every glimpse into the Universe brings renewed wonder. Unimaginable wonder waits for us just beyond our vision and present knowledge . . . in the ripples of a mysterious universe.

Seasons of Discovery: A Time to Remember

"A boy's will is the wind's will;
And the thoughts of youth are long, long thoughts."
-Henry Wadsworth Longfellow, from "My Lost Youth"

The next afternoon Lambda, Omega Bluebonnet, and I began employing our new solution to stabilize my healing bones while the Little Country Deuce stood guard at the door. I shot wave after wave of pain toward Lambda who swiftly redirected it according to Omega Bluebonnet's rapid-fire orders. "One degree right, two degrees up, fire, change wavelength, fire, fire, fire at will." We worked as fast as we knew how.

One hour later we'd made progress, and Omega Bluebonnet shrank for an inspection. Within minutes she returned. However, her expression told me we faced still other problems. "Well, the bone holds together for a while, but then it collapses. I don't know what's wrong." Her chin headed south. "We've hit our target with the right design, the right tools, and the correct theory. I don't know why it is failing."

Through all of our work, the Little Country Deuce paced up and down by the door. Presently, he stood still, listening earnestly. Then he sent us all into alarm. "Someone's coming! Cease all work and pretend to be reading or daydreaming. Now, hush!"

In a moment Dad walked through the door and over to my bed. "Are you all right, Sean? You're mighty quiet today."

"Yes, I'm all right, only a bit tired." Dad walked slowly back toward the door, and then he turned. "I know how much you yearn to walk again. You'll walk again some day. I feel it in my bones. You will. Try not to be impatient, though. Never let any dream become your master," he huffed in a mood of weary sadness.

"What do you mean, never let any dream become my master?"

"Don't focus all of your attention and energy on your wish to walk again."

"Why not, Dad? What's wrong with my dream?"

"Oh, there's nothing wrong with your dream—only in the way you might go about searching for it. You may be trapped in that dream, however noble it might be. Then, the dream becomes your master. That would be unseemly."

"As unseemly as whistling in the house? You know, how Grandmother Nessie dreaded that."

"Yes, at least as untoward as whistling in the house. She thought it common, you're right."

"But what about never quitting? How about your advice to work tirelessly, pray unceasingly, and reckon all depends on prayer?"

"If your wish is true, if it's meant to be, your dream will spring to life on its own. Don't grab at it, or it might float out of your reach. Let it come floating back to you. Then, you won't chase it away as it drifts your way. Wait until it's in your palm before you gently close your fingers around it. Otherwise, your very pursuit may change it, scooting it away."

"Why does life work that way?"

"There's a certain balance of action and desire in our world. There is a balance between reality and dreams. Desire to be healed, yes, but don't grow selfish and grasping. If you do, the dream will not be yours, not fully or truly."

Dad's words sounded right. I remembered reading about how scientists couldn't measure the position and velocity of a particle without changing it, too. He sounded right, but I felt irritated. In fact, I felt a flash in my throat, one of anger."

"Oh, I think I know what you mean. The other day, I tried to pull a piece of lint out of my bath water. Each time I tried to pinch it with my fingers, the water around my fingers swirled it away."

"Yes, and what did you learn from that, Sean?"

"Well, I learned to cup my hands gently beneath the lint. Then, I raised my palms slowly. The water drained from between my fingers slowly enough so that the water-logged glob of lint didn't shoot out of my cupped hand. As the last of the water trickled out, the lint came to rest."

As Dad left, I murmured, "Thanks, Dad. All right, I'll try to remember that."

Deep down I felt hot. Wagging my head, I reckoned no one was brave enough to help me figure out how to heal, and I was achingly close to an answer. Maybe I needed a little help, but I didn't see a line forming to offer it. Even though I thought I might be on my own, I did not wish to think that way. I reckoned a mist of Energy swirled all around the world, and that meant anywhere a body finds himself. No, I can't be alone! If all of us, including me, are echoes of the Universe, I can never be alone. I smiled. After all, hadn't Dad and Mom said we all part of one large Soul, part of one Great Spirit? With that pillar propping me up, I relaxed. Soon enough, I'd be puzzling again to solve the problem of my collapsing bone tissue.

The Little Country Deuce reappeared like a puff of wind, his outline growing steadily bolder as he wafted over toward me. Lambda and Omega Bluebonnet peeked out to rejoin us. They're faces sagged with weariness, and that meant trouble: distraction, crankiness, and bickering. That meant fussing and feuding enough to tucker out my patience.

"Hey, Little Country Deuce," Lambda teased. "How do you like that?" Zap! Lambda stung the Little Country Deuce with an energy beam. Zap! Again. "What do you have to say now, you pompous wind bag?" In turn, The Little Country Deuce hissed, "Lambda, you're an overrated, self-centered fuss bucket, effete and untrue."

Was that fair? Although Lambda was exacting and acted like a primadona from time to time, he was all right. Beside, he proved to be an excellent fencer, which The Little Country Deuce was not. That was not his field of expertise, and they both knew it.

Poke! Zap! Lambda plied his fencing know-how against the Little Country Deuce. "What will you fight me with, big words? Ha!" Zap!

Well, all of that riled him, sending him into gusty speeches directed at Lambda, bemoaning his poor behavior.

"Ouch! Enough of your infantile and uncouth behavior."

The Little Country Deuce thought Lambda didn't play nice, and he let him know it. He began speaking slowly enough, deliberately and with powerful focus on his wording. Then, he built his speed with each sentence until his final ones were blustery and filled with enough wind to tickle the clothes on our line. This went on all afternoon . . . until the cows came home for milking. Until-

"Stop it now!" Omega Bluebonnet choked. "Your blustery words are drying me out . . . parching my tongue. Please," her voice softened, "stop," she murmured. "I'll recite a poem now. Then, I'll tell you a story to cool us off, to slow us down, and to wet our imaginations." Her words came in a gentle rhythm, like that of the rain on a windswept summer's day, refreshing and soothing.

While she spoke, I could hear the windy words of the Little Country Deuce in the background, his temper still whipping about. "Expert, my foot. I'll teach you to sting me . . . You'll never . . ."

Omega's poems and stories took to the air to clear it, leaving a clean and crisp scent as fresh as the air smells after a gentle summer's shower.

I can still hear the soothing sound of her words as they misted onto our minds and into our hearts to calm us. That usually ended a spat, and I reckoned a few hours of peace would hold before another storm might brew.

My friends' antics sapped my strength, distracting me for a spell. Still, I knew that I had to hold us together as we cobbled a way to heal. Each of our talents were complemented and enhanced by the others. "I must hold us together!" I said.

When Omega wound down to finish a poem, The Little Country Deuce picked out a few colorful lines and repeated them gently, like murmuring winds across cattails, or rustling of dried leaves on the lawn. The way he said those words satisfied Omega and Lambda, who smiled their approval. His echoing of Omega's lines felt sweet, as if Omega Bluebonnet and he could team to send seeds of good will over a windswept prairie to grow wildflowers. I imagined those flowers might be fertilized with their loving care, scattered up hill and down dell, over gently rolling hills. I smiled, feeling The Little Country Deuce could waft Omega's ideas through the air to find a home of their own, where they would grow on fertile patches that stretched along dusty country lanes, or along fence posts that skirted slumbering meadows.

Meanwhile, Lambda laid down his foil and looked downright pleased at what he heard and at how our interlude played itself out. His warm smile sure lit up the room! Then, he hovered nearby to radiate a glow to help our fine feelings grow, the way the sun-kissed mounds of tators grew—-the ones that Mother and I planted. We'd folded those eyes into those mounds in the shape of small hills. (I declare, those tators tasted fine.) I smacked my lips at the thought of them, downright delicious!

Lambda's warm face at the end of each stormy session reminded me of the way the sun smiles down on our tiny mounds in our potato patch. Might his kindness power tators to grow? When Lambda carried on that way, I joked, "Lambda, you brought delicious flavor to our hills with seeds blown by the wind to frame the tators with wildflowers. Those seeds sprouted and grew, fueled by Omega's love."

The Country Deuce winked agreement.

When Lambda acted warmly after one of our summer spats, we knew the storm had passed. Omega's gentle words made such spats poetry that grew in our minds, teasing us all to behave. Omega's words and smile nudged just about anything to sprout, taking root to grow.

One time when I had their attention, I reckoned that I'd be cute and combine the words "hill" and "delicious" to form a nickname for Lambda. I dubbed him "Hillious" when he shone kindly. The Little Country Deuce would have none of it, blustering into my thoughts to interrupt me. He whispered his protest, demanding the word be pruned.

"What do you wish?" I asked him.

"Well, since Lambda has been short with me, stinging me and riling me, you need to shorten the word to something like Helios," he demanded with bother in his voice.

"Lambda, is that all right? Shall I nickname you Helios?"

"Well, I don't know. What was wrong with 'Lambda'?"

"All right, how about a compromise? How does the name Lambda Helios sound? Or, I could call you LH for short, since that's how the Little Country Deuce says you acted. You and I will make him feel all right, and at the same time we all know that the nickname is a compliment."

"Sounds right fine to me, Sean. You may call me Lambda Helios, and in the presence of the Little Country Deuce I'll be simply LH."

Overhearing our conversation, Omega Bluebonnet smiled as if we'd said something both amusing and meaningful. She was like that: gentle and soothing, kind and loving. Even when we had our spats, she never lost her temper. What a diplomat! She reminded me of "runners" from red raspberries or patches of sweet strawberries that could take root and grow anywhere, even in her palms. Her kindness surely had all of us in her hands, and her presence felt fine and right! By finding common ground, we'd found a way to hold the team together. And by sticking together, we enhanced each other's skills to sprout homegrown ideas and solutions to heal our hearts and minds. All of our discoveries had brought us achingly close to a way to heal. Each answer was a piece of the puzzle, hinting at a way to heal my legs.

Glancing to my right, I saw the Little Country Deuce rearing up, teasing me with an offer.

"Sean, I know you fancy reading, especially with your Dad. What would happen if . . . your Dad could no longer read with you?"

"What do you mean? Of course that won't happen."

"Well, it might if he's in another car accident. He's been in so many of them, you know. What would you do then? How would you feel if you could never read sitting on his lap again? How would you feel then, hmmmm?"

I couldn't answer, the fear authored by his words shooting down my spine, silencing me.

"I can fix it, you know. I can fix it so that both of you can live as long as you please. You can read with your dad as long as you desire. Imagine it. Even better, instead of reading stories others wrote, you could write them. Think how proud your dad will be then! And you do want him to be proud of you, don't you? Hmmmmm?"

Again, I didn't answer. The Little Country Deuce intrigued me, and I waited to hear him out.

"Here's your chance to be with your dad and to become a writer. You two could read stories that you wrote! Just think of it, and all you need to do is to tell your friends how wonderful I am. Tell them how generous and powerful I am to do this for you!"

"Again, I don't know why you're interested in what I say. What I say will take you about as far as you can spit, and that's not saying much. That's no show. Yes, I'm partial to reading with Dad—as well as making sure he's safe. But Dad's powerful smart, and he'll be more careful driving, I know that. And he'll earn his license again soon. He won't need to ride that fool bus much longer."

"How do you know that? What about wasted time, about all the missed hours for reading?"

I crossed my arms over my chest. "I know he'll come through. And he's already proud of me. Don't you know that he tells me that, through the way he stands and walks and gestures? He doesn't need to use words, seeing how words are limited anyway."

"What about writing stories? I could make you a great writer. What about that?"

Now that was more than tempting, but I wasn't about to give the Little Country Deuce an edge. "As far as that goes, I'd rather read books than write them, anyhow."

"Why?"

"Well, I already know pretty much what I think, and I don't want to bore anyone with that. What other folks think and feel is another matter all together. I'd sure like to know what others think, to know them better, to feel their joy and sorrow, to sense a connection. I reckon it's like spying the outline of a form in a fog or a mist. I don't know at first what's there, but I do know it's friendly. Whatever it is, we'll be buddies."

The Little Country Deuce turned his back to me. He peered over his shoulder. "Why is that so important? I want to know."

"All I know is that mystery bellows through the world, and all of us are in this together. We're all one, you know, although we don't always see plainly. That's why I want to read what others write, not something that I scratch out."

"But what about the fame and fortune, the glory of being a world-class writer? What of that?" The Little Country Deuce turned toward me and stamped his right foot.

"I can do without that, thank you kindly. I want only to understand and to know others. I wish only to feel this mysterious universe, to catch a glimpse of its riddles. I need only to feel my place in it as I explore it. There's so much to explore—many thoughts to be cultivated during this season of discovery . . . this is a time to remember . . . on this inner path. We'll find a way to heal."

"But how about I if I whisper the secrets of great writing to you while we explore?"

"That ability to write comes from within. It seeps out of a fog that bellows and puffs through the world. It can't be given away, and it can't be taught—not really."

"But Sean, think of what-"

"Thanks a powerful bunch for asking, but the answer is no."

The Little Country Deuce nodded. He commenced to pacing. "Okay...All right...You don't need to be a writer. Then, let me think. What else . . . ? I have it! Then, do this. Drop everything. Stop trying to hold us all together, and come. Come, fly away with me. We'll venture to places that you have not yet imagined! Oh, we'll have such a grand time. It's time, you know. It's time to ditch LH and Omega Bluebonnet. They're doing nothing but holding you back. It's time that you did something for yourself, not just working to hold us together. Come, fly away with me to a place where there's no pain, where your fondest dreams come true in the twinkling of an eye. Fly away with me, and leave your cares behind!"

"In case you haven't noticed, I can't fly. I'm still crippled, and you haven't taught me how to fly, either. Besides, I can't leave LH and Omega Bluebonnet. They need me, just as I need them."

"But we'd have such a splendid time together. You have no idea of the joys and the pleasures that lie in store for us. Come away with me, and leave all the rest behind!" The Little Country Deuce twirled in place.

"You know I can't do it. I must hold us all together. Horrid things will happen if we split apart. Simply horrid . . . I know, because Dad told me so. I know because of what happened to Uncle Jim. Dreadful things happen when people and ideas don't stay glued together . . . when they split into pieces."

The Little Country Deuce took his leave and melted into shadows.

Many more problems and improvised solutions lay in store for us in our grand journey. As I lay still to refocus, I remembered what Dad had told me. He said not to be too tied up searching for a way to walk again. He reminded me not to be overly focused on healing. A pregnant pause stretched and yawned. During that silence, I glanced out the window again. A tuft of thistledown was aiming to launch into the wind for parts unknown. Its white, striated fluffiness reminded me of how snow on our driveway caused our tires to loose traction. I reckoned that my bony matter was also slipping as it struggled to rebuild itself. Could it be that we needed some friction? Then I remembered how we laid down sand and gravel to improve our ability to steer our car. The tires would speed forward, aided by that grimy and gritty material.

"Guys," I gasped. In our work to be as precise as possible, maybe we left out the most important piece. "Could it be that we simply need some traction to help our structure remain in place? Maybe it is slipping because we have left out something for traction. What would happen if we left a tiny air pocket at the interlocking face of each triangle? Maybe that's all we need to stabilize the structure. Maybe that's all we need to hold it together!" My pulse raced. "If we use something in addition to the energy we have purified, maybe that difference will prove the key to the whole structure, to stabilize it. Out of that diversity we'll find strength," I guessed.

Well, we all figured it was worth a shot. So, we carefully crafted our hexagon with six interlocking triangles and a tiny air pocket wedged between the interface of each triangle. We directed the energy and material very carefully, and then we held our breath. Would it hold? Nothing happened. Still, seconds later, nothing happened. The hexagon held and held and held. It stood there, strong—glued together and stabilized by the air pockets which at first we'd thought we must exclude. The seemingly weakest of links turned out to be the strongest of all. The strength from that diversity meant we would triumph, our design holding firm.

Now I was sure we'd succeed. Lambda Helios, Omega Bluebonnet, the Little Country Deuce, and I comprised a *rag tag* group of country folks, struggling against all odds. We kept on living and trying as we lived our trying lives. Anyone secretly viewing our work might imagine that we would fail, that our efforts were a farce or *gag*. Our persistence raised our labors to an *art* form. Turning inward to heal, we began to understand courage. Isn't true courage working endlessly even though you probably will fail, and holding out the hope that somehow things will turn out all right anyhow?

Somehow in all of the turmoil, we found ourselves and each other. No one—especially the experts—had given us a chance to heal. Yet we did just that, each and every arduous "step" of the way. Using the ideas and the materials at hand, we had improvised and had done what must be done even through nights and days spiked with hellish pain. We turned inward to heal. Along the way, we found a way to heal, it's true. However, we also found gifts far more precious. We found persistence, which I feel is the foundation of all grand efforts. We found friendship, loyalty and courage. All of those powered hope. What we found along the way was the finest part of our odyssey.

Faithful Lambda Helios was better than his word, and he adroitly directed the energy into my bones. Like laser beams of hope, that energy shot to exactly targeted locations at the right time. Lambda Helios had catalyzed my accelerating bone growth: coalescing and layering it in hexagonal cells glued together by diversity. Did those layers mimic the universe, collapsing upon itself in certain regions, even as it drifts outward in search of itself?

Omega Bluebonnet proved to be as faithful and loyal as the earth. Only one time in the next three years did she fail to perform her daily probes. It was during the winter solstice of my eighth year. She was too tuckered out to take her readings without falling prey to the gravitational force of my bones.

Each time Omega Bluebonnet returned from her probe, it reminded me of how Noah's dove flew back to the ark. Each time she told me that the bones had not healed—that their density was far too low. Each time she returned, I was delighted to see her, although I knew I remained ill. When my bones healed, I imagined she might be captured by their gravitational force, causing her to spiral inward and cling to my bones. I lived in a hinterland of hope and pain. Ever aching to heal, I hoped that I wouldn't lose my devoted friend. Omega must not be sacrificed. She'd given too much already!

The Deuce worked with me many nights after Lambda Helios faded and while Omega Bluebonnet shrank to take her readings.

I didn't become much of a flyer, owing to how the work to heal my bones distracted me. I was preoccupied by what Omega Bluebonnet's report would show each night. That meant a lot more to me than did simple flying.

The Little Country Deuce taught me that with the proper balance, a person could fly. "Sean, do you remember the tightrope walker you saw when you were two years old at the Shriners' Circus?"

"How could I forget something that amazing?"

"Think of the way he balanced, even though gravity pulled at his body. He stayed balanced because he was falling at the same rate on each side of his body. Had he tried to focus more on either side, he would not have balanced. Instead, he would have tumbled. The secret is not in letting go, but in letting go the same degree on all sides. Then, you can use the lift of the wind to take flight, to rise above the earth, like thistledown rising into the sky."

"What does balancing have to do with flying?" I had sputtered at him in irritation.

"Balance has everything to do with flying. Just as the tightrope walker must find his balance as he falls equally on all sides, the novice flyer must find his balance—his center or focal point—before he can fly. Once he finds that place, he can use it the way a lame man uses a cane for support. Lift at that focal point, the way a high-jumper hoists himself with a tall pole to clear a high bar. By doing this, you'll be able to fly and a bunch of other magical stunts. It's not a matter of faith! It is a matter of finding your center, of handling it with care."

Days seeped into months, months drifted into seasons, and seasons melded into years as surely as juices ooze through fine cheesecloth. Our daily work dragged on unabated during these seasons of discovery: a time to remember. Lambda Helios proved a genius, excelled perhaps only by Omega Bluebonnet who voyaged daily to take my bone readings. With that knowledge, she knew where to direct Lambda Helios to shoot the energy—how much, and in what wavelength. Early each morning Omega Bluebonnet returned with new information and strategies. Her return meant that I remained crippled. But, we all knew my illness grew smaller daily. We knew that we had finally solved all of our physical obstacles.

The Little Country Deuce continued to keep watch. Then, oftentimes in the very early hours of the morning he gave me another lesson in Flying 101. "Focus, Sean, and find your center. Once you sense that, just feel it and don't think so much. If you feel your center, you will be able to fly effortlessly." I supposed that advice might apply to a host of efforts in our frenzied world. I imagined that the center he spoke about meant knowing that we are one with the Universe: a piece of it. Aren't we all reflections of it? All of us have a right to be here and heal.

I'll never forget the expression on Omega Bluebonnet's face the last evening I was to see her. I think we both knew what was due to happen. You see, Lambda Helios had made remarkable progress, accelerating my healing for months. Omega Bluebonnet had narrowly escaped being captured in my rapidly growing bones each of the prior three nights. Were my bones like salt crystals growing on a string, dangling in briny water as the water evaporates? As much as I craved healing, I could not bear to lose her.

"Omega Bluebonnet, please don't go today. Stay with me. I ache when you leave, and I'd rather stay crippled than to lose you. Please, stay." Tears seeped down my ashen face.

"I'll be with you always," Omega Bluebonnet murmured. We gazed into each other's eyes for what seemed a brief moment and an eternity. "I'll be with you always, even though now I must go. You will be healed."

"Being healed will cost both of us too much," I said. "I'd rather remain crippled if healing means losing you."

"You'll need those legs of yours for all of the work you'll do," she promised me. "Remember, Sean, I'll never really leave you. I'm as faithful as the oceans and as grounded as the earth. When you are sad, I will be sad, and my tears from heaven will fall to the Earth. When the Earth's done purifying those tears, they'll be released and gurgle up over moss-covered stones. The tears will spring up and weep over the stones. Mosses and lichens will grow there, and you will see my footprints all around those moistened stones."

Her words eased my heart.

Recognizing that I could not stop her, I said farewell. Then, I told her, "Thank you; you have no idea what you've done for me."

Slowly, Omega turned to say, "No matter what happens, I'll be with you always. You've made me proud to serve you."

"How so? I'm only a simple Kansas farm boy. How have I honored you?"

"By the way you saw me. You saw me as a lovely young girl with blond hair, hazel eyes, and moonlight in my face."

I had no idea how anyone might have seen her any other way.

"Thanks for that." Then, she turned to leave.

"Wait, Omega Bluebonnet. May I ask you a favor before you go?"

"Yes, what is it?"

"Can't we remain here for a spell? Can't we rest here to soak it all in?"

"To soak what in, Sean?"

"To soak in warm feelings and the strains of music. To see the light and to hear the music of the world; to taste its poetry, and to feel its songs."

"Well, maybe for a few minutes."

"Will you honor Lambda Helios by dancing with him?" I asked, whispering so he could not overhear us. I winked, "He's partial to you, and it would do him proud if you danced with him tonight."

Omega Bluebonnet approached. "Lambda Helios, might we dance before my next journey?"

Lambda Helios, who had been working on his equations, flashed a smile and rose to dance. He had once told me that he'd risk anything to dance with Omega Bluebonnet, just once. "I must dance with her. I must feel her fingers glide into mine . . . feel her heart beating against my chest . . . let her warmth and breath swirl with mine. I'll remember that always. Just once, I must dance with her."

"All right, but only a song or two. It's growing late, and Lambda Helios will need rest soon."

"Don't you worry about me. On this day in the Northern Hemisphere, the sun is visible longer than on any other day. This is the Summer Solstice, and I've gotten my second wind. I'm able to stay longer today."

"I see. And to what song shall we dance?" Omega Bluebonnet asked.

In answer to her question, chords of "Red River Valley" echoed from the room, the notes striking LH and Omega Bluebonnet to bounce off of them.

They rose to dance. "From this valley they say you are going. We'll miss your bright eyes and sweet smile. But remember the Red River Valley, and the cowboy who loved you so true."

I smiled as my chin sank to my chest.

"Sean, what's wrong? Your friends are dancing. Why are you sad?" asked the Little Country Deuce.

"Well, I'm happy for LH because he's powerful fond of Omega Bluebonnet, and I reckon she's partial to him, too."

"Then why the glumness?"

"She's leaving tonight, and I won't see her again. She's leaving, and I'll never get to stand up to hug her, to say good-bye. I'm still crippled, and I'll never dance with her, not once."

"Oh, that's not your fault. These things take time, you know. You'll be healed soon."

"Soon? That's too late. She'll be gone."

"I suppose you're right."

"And I tried powerful hard. We all labored to find a way to heal. I sacrificed my stories and poetry to learn what Lambda Helios knows. And for what? Now she's leaving, and I never once felt her fingers against my fingers."

"Now, now, Sean . . ."

"I never felt her warmth gliding over the dance floor. I didn't stand a chance of telling her how I feel at twilight by the light of the setting sun on the Summer Solstice. To tell her how I feel, I must dance with her in the twilight, telling her properly. To do that, I must be healed."

My chin hit my chest hard enough to bounce up and down a time or two. Out of the corner of my eye, I saw the Little Country Deuce grimace with my loss. Powerful ideas swirled in his mind, and I felt them like waves of ambrosia, echoing a solution. Before he could open his mouth, I began. You see, I didn't want to embarrass him with such a soft idea.

"LCD, although this is the Summer Solstice, it's getting late. The sun is setting, and twilight draws nigh. You've offered me several fine ideas, and now I'll accept the one you're about to offer me, even before you speak of it. LH is fading, and 'Red River Valley' has run its course. Please swish me into LH that I might stand with his legs, that I might take his place and dance with Omega Bluebonnet. He's had his chance. Do it now before he fades with the setting sun. Do it now, that I might see Omega Bluebonnet through our two pairs of eyes—aglow with love."

"You left out a detail. There's a price, Sean. You know what is, right?"

"Yes, even though I've studied LH's equations that have transformed pain into healing, even though he's taught me much, I'll agree to learn more of his secrets. I'll take up an engineering career—maybe in chemical engineering or earth sciences—whatever. I know. Yes, I know."

"And you know that means twenty to thirty years of hard labor to pay for this moment in time when you dance with Omega Bluebonnet, when I swish you into the fading light of LH, when you catch a glimmer of LH's mind and soul, when you glide your hand into Omega Bluebonnet's hand after half of a lifetime of yearning."

"Yes, the cost is worth it. I'm crazed with desire to dance with her just once. Please make it happen. Do it. Do it now!"

"But you've overcome the problems, and you'll stand again soon on your own. Is standing now worth the price? Is it? How could it be?"

"It's much more than standing. It's doing the impossible through the eyes of love. It's a healing that's as important as is restoring life to my bones. I must pay the price, or my heart will never heal. It's a yearning with strength too powerful to resist. I must dance with Omega Bluebonnet, I must—if only this one time. Please, make it happen." I reached out to touch the Little Country Deuce's right hand.

"If you ache for something so badly, can it be right? Remember what your dad warned?"

"Yes, it can, if it's love. It's a yearning in my heart that makes my stomach ache. It's both an illness and its cure. It's light and darkness, joy and despair, love and fear. It's hot and cold, young and old, fullness and hunger. It's all that rolled into one, and I must be part of it. That's my destiny. Please, before 'The Red River Valley' evaporates!" As I spoke, I squinted out of my right eye, my head slanted to the left, and I pinched my thumb and index finger together, as if I aimed to center those opposites into a still center: a oneness.

"You'd sacrifice thirty years for this chance?"

"Yes, anything. I'd give my whole life. This feeling is worth all of that and more, although that's all I have to give. If I had seven lifetimes, I'd willingly give them, too. The feeling will live on, and it will heal me. Without that feeling, I'll never really be healed. Please, before the music ends, as this evening shall never come again, and I must have a chance to remember."

LCD nodded, and the floor folded toward me as if we were anchored while the dancers swayed toward us. Peering down at my fingers, I saw LH's ring on my left index finger, and Omega Bluebonnet's fingers intertwined with the fingers of my right hand. Numbers and figures floated on the early evening breeze, most of the digits riding on three dimensional rainbow ribbons of saffron, violet, and chartreuse. Answers skittered toward me with sparkles of dust that glittered in the growing twilight . . . as if they were miniature shooting stars. Numbers pirouetted next to us, waving at us and blowing us good will. Notes of the treble and bass clef began dancing with Arabic Numerals and with Greek symbols (lined up in equations). Notes of the scales commenced reciting certain facts—like the speed of light in a vacuum, the mean distance of the Earth from the sun, and the number of known elements. The symbol for Radium (Ra) danced by and hummed. He blew a kiss at C-Sharp and then pitched toward her, half stumbling. Would he collide with her to blend into a pair? Or would he tumble across the floor, only to be pulled back to his feet by his doting partner? C-Sharp wore a white laboratory jacket and goggles which I thought had special lenses to help her see

sharply. Then, when I saw her weary eyes, I guessed those goggles protected her eyes from too-bright lights. Ra wore a business suit and sported a black beret. He spoke in a French accent. In the shadows, when his two leading edges or curlicues were shrouded, he became Po. (That's what Ra looked like without his two tails, once he had been "detailed".) Had he mutated into Po, or was it only the new way I spied him there in the shadows? Can people change merely because we see them differently? (How about something as mean and ornery as thistles? Might they prove useful, too? Maybe . . .)

He called C-Sharp Marie, and she muttered, "Now, Pierre, do be careful. You're distracted. Please, you must remember to be careful when you're out. Do watch where you're going, or you may be hurt. You might be trampled."

Hugging, they pitched around the dance floor, blending into one, even as light leaking from the chandelier edged its way between their faces. Pierre muttered sweet nothings into Marie's ears, while she (C-Sharp) hummed of amazing scientific discoveries awaiting them. As they kissed, the light flickered and went dark, blocked by their embrace. Rays seeped out along the outlines of their forms, as if searching for a way to lighten a too-dark world. Might that kindly couple discover a way to treat diseases, to give people hope? Might they find a way to treat cancer?

The next song sounded familiar, one by Billie Holiday. "I'll be seeing you, in all the old familiar places, that this heart of mine embraces, all day through . . ."

Then, gazing up at Omega Bluebonnet, I saw light from the chandelier sparkle a reflection in her eyes—not of my eyes, but of her eyes in her eyes! First they were hazel, then gray, then blue. First they had been her eyes, then they were my eyes of blue. As she began to explain Professor Einstein's General and Specific Theories, I began to answer. To my surprise, I recited a love sonnet by Robert Browning, while she carried on with her scientific equations. Formulas swirled from her lips and danced in mists. Then, I heard myself—or was it me—whispering Longfellow's words, "A boy's will is the wind's will, and the thoughts of youth are long, long thoughts." Did LCD know what I was asking, what I was hoping for in that night of healing?

As Omega Bluebonnet commenced to recite another equation, and as I began to start another poem, we reached up to touch each other's lips. "No, not now. Let it rest," we told each other. Did she see pieces of me—of my eyes—reflected in my eyes?

The music droned on. I recalled the small seafood cafe across the way from Disneyland, that shimmering park slumbering in the night air. I remembered the children's carousel there with the music sounding on evening breezes. I also pictured our swing set, sticky on top, that had started our mysterious voyage. I heard the sound of baying bloodhounds that had just treed a coon in an ancient chestnut. That tree was mostly chopped through, and it teetered in the breeze before tumbling down (provided a healthy gust of wind prevails), just as the way times sway gently before crashing into a new era. Then I remembered the deep spot in our creek where an ancient cottonwood rests at an angle, a thicket of gooseberries camped on its eastern flank. I remembered Dad's advice,

"To toss a worn stone into the pool and wish for answers born on the Kansas winds." Might I find an inkling of my place in a mysterious world? How many wishes, how many dreams had I seen rippled after I tossed a worn stone into the deep spot of the pool? How many grains of sand and pieces of silt had been caressed and then moved by those ripples, a mere reflection of the stone's motion?

Presently, a wisp of the Little Country Deuce passed nigh as I danced in LH's guise, as we reflected Omega Bluebonnet, who in turn reflected LH and me.

"Please, let this moment last," I importuned to no one in particular. "And a boy's will is the wind's will, and the thoughts of youth are long, loooonnnggg thoughts . . ."

He knew what I was asking. A wisp of LCD caught my eye in a fleeting glance. LCD smiled, knowing how desperately we needed to slow down time, to make the moment eternal, this one shining moment in time. With a nod and a wink, he began to swirl around Omega, LH and me. He blew extra hard. He whirled, and we twirled faster and faster. Why, we began to spin much more quickly than any children's fool carousel—in that moment of sparkles, of music and of dance, in that evening of reflections and of healing.

More and more swiftly, round and round we twirled. And time began to slow as our speed mounted. The room stretched and yawned, its size growing. Lightheaded and giddy, I felt as if we were swirling off of the dance floor and into a lightness. Pressed closely together, I could feel Omega Bluebonnet on my chest, the beating of her heart slowing. Each of her heartbeats grew weary, increasing the interval between them. As a sweet feeling of loveliness twitched over us, my breathing nearly stopped. I felt no pain and no need. Peace lived! (Had our union swirled into the guise of a small dirt devil with peace and life echoing in its center?)

Omega Bluebonnet smelled of lilacs and honey roses, as had Grandfather's garden. My mouth watered as I thought of peanut butter and honey sandwiches folded over on one slice of whole wheat bread.

Dare I kiss her? Magnetic forces drew my lips to her, as if they were iron shards. Leaning in, I felt her cherry lips on mine, and I floated in her mist. Were we riding a wave of light, or we part of one? Are we all reflections of energy rippling through the cosmos, aching to know itself?

Light flooded my mind, and then it happened. I felt a oneness, a purity, an Intelligence that no numbers or equations can mimic. Not even music, poetry, dance, painting, sculptor or any other art form approaches it. For in describing it, that loveliness changes and is not Itself. Mere words debase it, inflect it, diminish its splendor. But here is a faint echo of what I felt at that moment, as time slowed, and as our room stretched in length, width and height.

The moment was eternal, and eternity was the moment.
The location lived without bounds, and boundaries had no location.
Without end in dimension—no length, width, height, or breadth;
Without start or finish, no beginning and certainly no end.
The infinite universe was this solitary, simple location—everywhere;
And this location was the infinite universe, definitely somewhere.
The moment and that misty place simply were there;
Part of that which is, that which is there and everywhere.
The time was now and then and, suddenly, ALWAYS;
All that is, past and present, here and everywhere, simply being.

Slowly, our spinning subsided. The room shrank, and our heartbeats and breath sped up to a normal pace. When I gazed into Omega Bluebonnet's eyes, they looked hazel once again. A sparkle from the chandelier no longer reflected her eyes in her eyes. Instead, I saw my eyes reflected in hers, and I heard myself reciting atomic weights of various elements.

Meanwhile, Omega Bluebonnet hummed a tune and then recited a poem by Emily Dickinson (something about how pain creates another reality all its own). The next thing I knew, I was peering at Lambda Helios and Omega Bluebonnet as they finished dancing. The notes of the song sounded normal, too, not slowed down to suspend in infinity. "I'll be seeing you in every summer's day, in everything that's light and gay, I'll always think of you that way. I'll find you in the morning light, and when the day is through. I'll be looking at the moon, but I'll be seeing you."

The light from the chandelier stopped spinning. The music ended, and Ra stopped dancing with C-Sharp. Poof—they vanished. Wham—I knew that I sat once again on my bed next to LCD. Omega Bluebonnet gazed lovingly into LH's eyes as she let his hand go, one finger at a time. For a moment she suspended his index finger on the tip of hers. Then, she exhaled, let his index finger drop, turned, and took her leave.

She commenced to glow as she began to shrink. Misty curtains rippled as if she passed into another realm, smack through an eerie shroud of vapors. Then, I wondered if that scene was something like the one our ancestors viewed when ships left Ireland, the salt mists rising from the ocean to cloak a farewell glimpse of their loved ones.

After Omega Bluebonnet disappeared, The Little Country Deuce stammered, "I can save her. I can save Omega Bluebonnet. Just say the word. Unless I help you, she'll be trapped tonight!"

"I've already implored her not to sacrifice herself. I told her that I'd rather stay crippled than to lose her. She'll do what's right. I have confidence in her."

"What if she decides to sacrifice herself that you might walk again? What then?"

"I don't want her to, but if she decides that, there is nothing I can do about it. Just as I can't force anything against its well to drift my way, just as my snatching at it would change it, I also can't force Omega Bluebonnet to save herself. She must decide. It's her life."

"You can feel what she'll do. She's toast! I can save her. You'd like that, wouldn't you?" the Little Country Deuce urged.

"It's not my decision. Only Omega Bluebonnet can choose what she will do with her free will. If you tried to save her, it wouldn't be Omega Bluebonnet anymore. By intervening, you'd change her. It wouldn't be right, and that's a kind of sin, I reckon."

Lambda Helios, the Little Country Deuce, and I waited anxiously to know what might happen. The sun was nearly gone, and LH dimmed and flickered. He would need to rest soon.

Mystery Sounding
Inward, Echoing There

Then—in my childhood—in the dawn
Of a most stormy life—was drawn
From ev'ry depth of good and ill
The mystery which binds me still!
—(excerpt from *ALONE* by Edgar Alan Poe)

"Sean, I'm picking up Omega Bluebonnet hovering over your bones," LH said. Even though he was fading, he'd agreed to monitor Omega's descent.

"What is it? Please tell me," I said.

"I'm picking up separation, sir. Omega's splitting into two pieces. She's replicating."

"Nooooo! Omega, no," I gasped.

"Separation complete. She's going in."

"As slim of a chance there was when she was whole, if she's split into two pieces, she'll be trapped! LH, please shoot a field around my bones to stop her!"

"All right. Calibrating. Calculating. Stand by . . . away." Two pulses of energy thrusted to form a shield to block the advancing Omega who moved toward a death spiral.

"Report, LH, report!"

"Processing, processing. Yes, it's holding. No, wait a moment. She's breaking through. Omega Bluebonnet knows all of our passwords and codes, all of our secrets. She'll pass through momentarily."

"Random array—Monte Carlo simulation to create passwords. Go, now! Do it, do it now! Change passwords every three seconds. No, vary time intervals between password generations. Ready, set, go! Change now, and then again. Hold, hold, don't change! Now change, again and again!"

"Processing, changing, altering. The fields are holding. No, hold on, they're failing. She's found a way, even without the proper password. Fields warping, failing, failing. Fields folded!"

"Advise, advise, what to do? Report!" I rapidly twirled my forelocks.

"Warning, warning, impact estimated in ninety seconds. She's hunkering down for a landing. She's coming in. Incoming, incoming. Warning, warning!"

"Warning shots! Fire warning shots. Do it now!" I ordered.

LH hesitated.

"Come on Lambda . . . It's the only way I know to save her. We must stop her. She must not be lost."

In less time than it takes to blink, LH got off two warning shots. He'd calibrated their speed and trajectory to graze Omega Bluebonnet.

"Report, status. Report!"

"Omega is slowing, slowing, turning. No, she's taking final readings. She plans to merge there in order to become one with your bones." Anxiously peering around the room, I spied the Little Country Deuce smirking.

Instinctively, I shouted, "Fire a near miss, or hit, across Omega's surface, scorching her skin. We must show her we mean business. Do it, do it now," I gulped. Might we really harm her?

The Little Country Deuce shook his head and rolled his eyes.

"Shots away," LH barked. Impact, impact. She's slowed and stunned. Perfect strikes . . . grazed her skin. She's not hurt . . . only stunned. She's slowed."

"Is she turning back? Please say she is."

"Processing, processing. Wait a minute. Where we grazed her skin, untold numbers of fine threads are forming. Still more are coming, like thistledown tuft, many thousands of times more in number."

"What's she doing?"

"Sean, sir . . . I'm fading. Can't continue much . . . longer. Can't stay lit . . . much-" Just then, LH flickered and vanished. Night had fallen, and LH had gone with the setting sun on the Summer Solstice.

"No!" I sobbed. My world grew dark and silent.

"Of course!" blustered the Little Country Deuce. "What else did you think she'd do? Don't you know that whatever you do to stop her only helps her designs?"

"All right, but what to do? You, what help have you been? You said you could save her. You, with such cunning, such intelligence! Then, save her. Save her now, I command you!"

"I can't," he mumbled. The Little Country Deuce lowered his eyes.

"You swaggering thing? Why not? What's your excuse?"

The Little Country Deuce snapped to, "It's too late. Besides, as you said, we can't force her to do anything. Just as we could not force something drifting our way to stop in our hands, just as trying to snatch it will change it and force it away, we also can't stop her."

"But we have the formula for healing. She needn't throw away her life."

"You need more than that! Your bones must be stronger than they were before the accident. Omega is seeing to it."

"How will she make them stronger with mere threads of thistle-down?"

"She'll knit that into your bones—and more. She'll give you intuition, an ability to feel deeply so that when you're healed, you won't be a target for folks who don't listen to their conscience. You will know their intentions even before they open their mouth. You'll be able to read them and know more about them than they know themselves."

"But I already read people—by watching them, by studying their face and body movement, by gauging their tones."

"You and your puny reading of body language. Child's play—utter child's play!"

"What do you mean? It's served me well."

"You have so very much to learn. You must reach far beyond watching gestures and expressions. You must know a person's motivations and deepest feelings. You must feel their pain in your bones. Become them, and know more about them than they know themselves!"

I cocked my head and squinted my right eye.

"Sean, really . . . a person who reads others knows how to become the person observed." The Little Country Deuce cupped his right hand into a loose fist and slogged it through the air, as if he probed someone's innards. He twisted it about, motioning to me that I could retrieve ideas and dark secrets a person might not even know himself.

"You'll trade your youth and innocence for this intuition. This will shield you form harm."

"Why did Omega Bluebonnet decide to give me this? Oh, Omega Bluebonnet . . ."

"She was touched by the way you saw her: as young and beautiful."

"But isn't she? How could anyone see her any other way?"

"People usually see her as a hag, as an ancient and tottering woman who knits fate as easily as you and I breathe. That's the way that nearly all see her."

"And she's knitting intuition into my bones? But she will be lost by doing so, won't she?"

"I can see you have much to learn. That's not Omega Bluebonnet. Well, it is and is not her."

"You're speaking in riddles. Then who is it? What is binding together my bones? Who?"

"It's not Omega, and yet it is. It's her reflection. Your bones are being knitted together by a reflection of our mysterious universe."

"What?"

"It's mystery sounding inward and echoing there!"

"Mystery and intuition are binding together my bones? The reflection of a mysterious universe is sounding inward, echoing there, to bind up my bones? You mean I'm stuck with that for the rest of my life?"

"Yes, mystery will hum there, binding your bones together. You'll feel the intuition from all that mystery living there."

"Really?"

"Yes, and you're powerful lucky, you know.

LCD's words rang true, as true as truth itself. Although I never saw Omega's face again, I did see her handiwork on the ground and in still, small pools that had collected her tears. Omega didn't return to me, like Noah's dove, which one day did not return to the ark. Finding high and dry land, the dove stayed away; similarly, when Omega found high, dry bones, she did not reappear. However, unlike Noah's dove, Omega had not really left me. Entombed in my bones, she became part of my body's very under girding. I liked to think that it really was Omega, not her echo.

"How ironic," I thought. The very moment that I stopped asking to be healed, when I knew how much I needed Omega Bluebonnet, the very moment that I let loose of my iron-fisted grasp I had on my dream to walk again, I healed! In letting go, I saw my dream come true, and in the giving up, I healed. Dad had been right. No matter how noble a dream must be, I must learn not to become too focused on it. The gentle pursuit of it will not chase away the dream, not push it out of my reach. I must learn to cup my hands gently under it so that I do not disturb it. Then, when it wafts into my palm, I'll slowly press my fingers around it. Then I won't change it by trying to grasp it. It will be my dream and part of me as I am part of it—as I am part of a Mysterious Universe. I fancy that I reflect a tiny portion of Its Wisdom.

The next morning, Lambda Helios and the Little Country Deuce reported that their work was done. They needed to move on to help other little boys and girls who struggle to find their way.

"Never forget, that you're never really alone, Sean," LH and LCD reminded me. "You always have your special friends. The entire universe is there to help you," LCD said. "You're part of it, and all of it is it filled with a puffs of energy, of Intelligence. You are never alone, because everything is all part of the same, big existence. All things are one," they assured me. My parents taught me that all things won't merge into one because that's already happened. Yet, a hazed and cloudy vision makes us think they're separate. It's as if we're focused on one tiny stone in a colossal mosaic, and we don't see the big picture. It's as if we're looking at one small ripple in the water to try to see the reflection of a mountainside.

"When I feel alone, it's only my dim vision that makes me feel that way. It's an illusion, just as false as is a mirage in a desert."

Lambda Helios assured me, "You'll see my face shining through clouds after spring showers, my eyes brightening the dawn with colors of the rainbow: flashes of magenta and salmon framed in saffron." I knew I'd be reminded of LH, of glowing energy.

The Little Country Deuce bade me good-bye, saying, "You'll see my hands pawing at leaves in chestnut trees, my fingers pulling at flowers and weeds as I waft their seeds on prairie winds. I'll tote those seeds over the windswept prairie with my windy hands, too fine to be seen. My fingers are hidden from view, stealthy so that clearly your wonder will mend."

As I considered my loyal friends and their sacrifices, I imagined that our earthly bodies heal in a way that may echo the universe, grand and miraculous. Even the disease I battled might reflect some spot of the mighty cosmos, uncertain and brimming with mystery, unknown in origin and in resolution, just as the doctors had no way to explain my illness or the way I healed.

This time, I expected my bones would be the last part of me to fail, not the first. This time I figured my body would behave the way it does for others nearly all of the time. I guessed my mysterious illness was a reflection of some strange and unexplained actions in the universe which are too rare and too fuzzy to see clearly or to understand fully. I let it remain a mystery. I learned as a child that sometimes it's best to let certain things just be. It's better that way. Some mysteries are so deep that no answer can honor them properly. The reverence they evoke IS!

Omega Bluebonnet's reflection—her echo—endures inside of me. She'll remain with me after I die. I knew it then. I know it now. I hear her words still, words that ring out crisply, "I will be with you always!"

Starlight, Star Bright, the Color White

We kids reserved summer evenings for a game that's best played under a starlit sky. The game whisked us all onto a fanciful land where cares flitted away, as do mists on a summer's morn. Heat-stressed feelings slipped from our faces. In our play land, we misted into another world. Although we wrangled with ghosts there, we staggered away unhurt.

The game is "Star Light, Star Bright." It commences when a pack of voyagers bravely gathers around an ancient walnut tree to choose a ghost. While the ghost darts into the darkened yard, shrouded in a luxurious veil of invisibility, the other players close their eyes and count to thirty. The ghost creeps along a tree line or behind a row of bushes, and then he lies in wait for those who dare to invade his realm. The interlopers march from the walnut tree home base, and they trudge uneasily around the house. They chant, "Star light, star bright, who's the first ghost we'll see tonight?"

Although the ghost hears every word, he waits for when his victims are most vulnerable. Then, he sprints from his hiding place to tag them, turning them into ghosts. Who dares invade his eerie realm, anyhow? The race is on. Anyone who makes it around the house and back to the walnut tree without being tagged "lives" to the next nerve-racking round.

As the band of survivors shrinks with ghouls picking them off more easily, excitement mounts. The non-ghosts thrash to make it back home alive.

The game ends when the sole survivor makes one last, heroic journey. From where I sat (owing to how I was crippled, in case you've forgotten), I heard the faint peeping of Mark's voice, "Star light, star bright, who's the first ghost I'll . . ." before he dashed into the night and behind our house.

"Get him . . . there . . . next to the bushes. Tag him. Go, go, go!"

Mark hid behind a bush. His wispy words might have helped him drift into a safe place, shrouded in darkness, but not this time. Spotted, he tried to outrun them all. Would he make it back? Maybe yes, but probably not. He quivered alone, facing all of the ghosts on his homeward voyage. But, alas, they caught him. That made him the first ghost in the next round— his chance to spook his tormentors.

The victim becomes the victimizer. "I'll fix you all this time," Mark growled. Although an outcast, as the new ghost Mark held power over the other players.

Watching on the lawn, I felt the still darkness and unknown of night cast a spell over me. My heart raced, as if I rode a roller coaster. The game reminded me of how I held my breath for a tottering tight rope walker I'd seen in a dusty Big Top of a circus when I was a small boy. The walker balanced on a thin rope stretched over the crowd. Please, let him make it to the other end of the wire. He must tag home without falling, I pleaded.

I wondered how often Dad and Uncle Jim faced "starlight, star bright" creepiness. Most of the time, they were all right. Sometimes they darted to safety, but sometimes they were "tagged".

I remembered how I felt when I heard eerie sounds "go bump" in the night, sounds which were often nothing more than raccoons pawing through our trash. "Heck, if that's my boogie man, I'm in fine shape," I reassured myself, my right hand patting my left one. Maybe being crippled was all right, seeing how I'd invented my make-believe voyages.

The next group of players commenced their trek around the house. They knew for sure that Mark would spring out to tag them. They banded together for fear of becoming the next "casualty", I thought. How important is it to belong to a group, especially one under siege? Julie fidgeted her right hand into Ann's left paw. Jean patted Mary on the back. "Come on, he's not over here. We're safe . . . for now," she gulped.

I'll bet round two thrilled Mark, seeing as how he could pick off anyone he pleased. "They had their way with me, and now it's payback time," he sputtered. Mary, Jean, and Ann stumbled into the darkness as they mumbled, "Star Light, Star Bright-" each one wrestling with the fright of being "murdered" at the touch of a ghoul's hand.

As I watched the game, I remembered an old man who lived about one mile west of our farm. A widower for more than twenty years, he lived alone and didn't show himself. Why, I wouldn't have known him had he walked past our house.

"He ventures outside only on moonless nights to gather eggs and to gnaw at vegetables," townsfolk gossiped. He doesn't use a lamp, seeing as how that would outline his form in the garden. I don't know who helped him keep up his farm because it needed a lot of daytime care. Nobody admitted sighting him during daylight hours.

"He needs to be by himself," the ladies in our town mercantile mumbled, their hands clasped together tightly, their knuckles whitened. But I guessed he must feel mighty lonesome. Did he see anyone?

One summer, a late-model Buick with Oklahoma tags pouted in his driveway for a week. Our grocer Mr. Hamlet told Mother, "Mr. Fields' cousin drove up clean from Oklahoma City to visit. He stayed a whole week." I suppose his cousin stayed put in the house with him all week, seeing as it looked like the car never budged. One morning the car vanished, never to be spotted again.

A rumor spread. "Mr. Fields slit his cousin's throat and lapped up his blood. Then, all that hotness drove him outdoors. He floored his cousin's Buick—his dead cousin inside—and shot it into a pond. Mr. Fields jumped out and rolled at the last second while he watched the car gurgle to its death."

While that was the word in town, I figured the truth was much less sinister. I imagined his cousin left when Mr. Fields told him he longed for his peace.

Did Mr. Fields also miss his wife who had died before I was born? I suspected he did. Can a man miss his wife enough (even after twenty years) to haunt him with her memory?

While I figured that was the case with Mr. Fields, some of the towns-folk quipped, "Mr. Fields isn't all right. He's not all there. Stay away, or . . ."

Stay away, or what? I gave him more credit than that. For starters, although most people don't like being alone all the time, maybe that suited Mr. Fields. Why? Well, if he saw other people, he might think about his wife. But he didn't want to do that, seeing as how that made him feel powerfully sad.

I remember asking Dad why he thought Mr. Fields didn't want anything to do with folks.

"He doesn't fancy company, and that's nobody's business but his own," Dad said.

"But why does he need to be alone?"

"Some people grieve that way. I imagine Mr. Fields would be working outside every day if his wife hadn't died. Most people like company, and I think that's the way humans are made."

"But not Mr. Fields, not now?"

"Yep, not now. Let him be, okay?"

"Maybe Mr. Fields thinks that no one wants to be his friend."

"Whatever his reasons are, they're his and his alone." If Mr. Fields wants to stay in his house, that shouldn't make you wonder what for. You tell the other kids to leave him be, hear?"

"Yes, sir."

"Be patient. God's tested him in a mighty way," Dad concluded.

Well, I thought Mr. Fields must be sad. Don't sad people need to be alone for a considerable spell?

Still wondering about Mr. Fields, I sat with Dad on our front porch. We gazed at a meadow that stretched on the west side of the south road to town. A bunch of thistles lined the road, skirting the meadow.

Dad said, "Take those lonely-looking thistles. They scouted a spot where nothing else cared to grow. I imagine they are satisfied all alone."

"They look happy."

"Do you know why nothing else is growing there?" Dad asked.

"Well, . . . no. Can anything else live there?"

"I'm asking the questions."

I saluted, "Yes, sir!" As I giggled.

"You're partly right. Farmers burn the land to clear its weeds each fall, and that stresses the natural order of things. Fire, disease, and adversity—you name it—change the natural order. If it wasn't for fire, plowing, disease, overgrazing, and such . . . prairies would sway in tall grasses. We'd see precious few thistles."

"Oh."

"The thistles got their chance once something stressed the ground. The thistles got their chance to move in, to put down their stalwart roots. Yes, they're there partly because nothing else could grow there. Nothing else could grow there because something happened to disturb the prairie. How do you feel about that?"

"You told me as much once before. Remember, when you spoke of Uncle Jim?"

"Oh, yes. Well, now that you've had time to think about it, how do you feel knowing that when a disturbance comes, certain plants thrive where tall grasses no longer live?"

"Hmmm. I think that's sad in a way, but happy in other ways."

"How so?"

"Well, it's sad that the tall grasses left because I think they're lovely."

"I reckoned you'd say as much."

"It's sad because tall grasses are home for grasshoppers and chiggers, lightning bugs and ants. Western meadowlarks and prairie chickens nest there, too."

"Right."

"If the bugs eat the seeds, and the chickens eat the bugs, everything has a place. There's a balance of life in grasses," I purred. I began thinking about a circus tightrope walker once again.

"Yes, the prairie is in balance . . . that is, until something happens."

"Right, and I know that the buffalo needed the grasses for food."

"True. But then, the hunters nearly did them in. That threw the prairie out of balance."

"Yes, and then came fires and a bunch of suffering. The ground was bothered, and now most of the tall grasses are gone: plowed up to make room for other plants and animals."

"And you feel sad about that?"

"Yep. I feel sad because it is sad. But I'm also glad to see that some plants made sense of it all. They found a new home."

"Thistles came to live where the grasses once swayed."

"I'm happy about that. Thistles, stalwart as you say, found that ground. They clung to life where nothing else lives."

"Why are you pleased to see that?"

"That shows character and strength."

"And there's a kind of quiet strength and wisdom earned. It's earned only one way."

"What way is that, Dad?"

"Strength and wisdom are earned by trial and suffering. Real character is forged in the blast furnace of adversity—no other way!"

"But that can hurt a bunch."

"Yes, and the secret is to survive. One must live in order to grow wise."

"Yes, sir."

"Yep. And how about Mr. Fields. Don't you think he felt disturbed when he lost his wife?"

"Yes."

"Do you think many other folks could've lived through that?"

"Maybe not."

"And so what if he lives alone on a patch of ground that others can't tend or stand. It's his right. He's trying his best. What's wrong with that?"

"Nothing's wrong with it. I reckon that Mr. Fields is courageous."

"Indeed. If the Mr. Fields of the world folded, who would tend to those disturbed patches of ground where nothing else might grow? If folks like him left, the world would be filled with barren patches. Those empty spaces remain where giant hearts of common people went missing, in those dry and dusty places where no one else found a home, lonely as it might be."

"All right, I'll tell the other kids to leave Mr. Fields alone . . . let him live in peace on his dried-up, beaten down patch of ground."

"Try to remember that, and never forget the 'Mr. Fields' of the world."

"Yes, sir."

"There are a powerful large number, seeing as how this world is haunted by folks who have dealt with loss. They've been beaten up by disease and gnawed at by pain and death."

"Yes, sir."

"If the Mr. Fields of the world don't survive, I reckon the world would be one empty place."

"How so? Not everyone has lost their best friend."

"Maybe not. But, I figure that everyone struggles at some time or other. If they don't, they might be flitting around with a smile on their face and with nothing worthwhile inside."

"You mean like a jackass eating briars?"

"Yep. The Mr. Fields of the world are overflowing with kind feelings, but unhappiness has blocked them."

"Yes, sir."

"And you'll let them be in peace, hear?"

"Yes, in peace."

Just then, a chill shot down my spine. The glint of the moon on the shirt of a runner made him faintly visible in eerie darkness. Seeing him tagged, I thought of a ghoulish story that Mr. Zettle (a boarder years earlier) told us. He spoke of a morgue with a crazed zombie who drove a hearse belching noxious vapors. That zombie gunned the hearse to track down his victims before he turned them into zombies . . . cursed, the same as he was.

Who laid the curse on him? I wondered. Why? How many innocents were turned zombie? Did any get . . . ?

Wham! Someone struck me from behind, sending me sprawling.

My breath knocked out of me, I struggled to catch it while I braced for mind-numbing pain. Vicki Sinclair began apologizing. "Are you all right? I'm sorry. I didn't see you lying there." She wore a pleated flannel skirt and a luminous white blouse: a uniform commonly worn by girls in parochial schools. Her blouse reflected light, and it nearly glistened in our darkened yard. I thought she looked like a neon bill board on legs.

Janice told her, "It's Sean's fault. He ought to watch out. Besides, he'll be fine."

Then, my sister Mary scolded me for living. "Why were you in her way? You know we always run through here." Tuning them out, I wondered how I'd handle the pain to come from my collision. I'd thrown pressure onto my legs, and that meant pain. Although I imagined that my legs had healed after a bunch of adventures inward with my imaginary friends (Lambda Helios, Omega Bluebonnet, and the Little Country Deuce), I didn't aim to jinx myself by counting on my chickens before they hatched. While I suspected I was healed, I could not count on it.

I waited for waves of pain to hit my body, like a tidal wave pounding a skiff, the typhoon aching to snap it into pieces. So, I lay on my back and stared into the starry night. "Gunslingers in the old West bit down on a stick or even a bullet to help with the pain," I mumbled. Where was my bullet?

As I lay on the moist lawn to manage what might come next, I gazed into the night sky. How dazzling the stars looked. Each glimmered with a beauty that I hadn't noticed earlier. Fireflies flitted around me, and they hovered in the balmy breezes. Hadn't I seen their glow the evening I fell from our swing set, when I figured that I'd entered another realm? The fireflies added to the spectacle, framing it with an otherworldly feeling of serenity.

No pain shot down my legs, and I guessed I was dreaming. Why was the night sky hypnotizing me . . . marooning me in loveliness?

"Now, hold it. What's happening?" I mumbled.

A coziness oozed inside me. Curious and comforting, it didn't feel like the warmth in front of a fire. No, this came from the inside out, not from the outside in. Was this glow like what adults felt when they swigged whiskey? Was I drunk from a bump on my head?

The feeling was like nothing I knew—excepting the night that Omega

Bluebonnet, LH, LCD and I had danced. It consumed me, and I wondered if I was being drawn into it the way a stick is sucked into a whirlpool. At one with the feeling, tenderness oozed from lights, at once both dim and bright. Had I become part of it? The feeling grew, and soon I rode a wave of light. Was that the way the universe felt as it expanded from a singularity?

Then, I became part of that wave, and all else faded: Vicki Sinclair, her white blouse, and all. The light wave hummed, filling my "craw" with orange and yellow glows. That felt snug, and I heard bars of "Moon River" as sung by Audrey Hepburn.

As I rode that wave of light, I sensed that I was part of it, and energy surged through me. It vibrated inside of me, the humming growing. It blossomed to find a color of its own—crimson with amber edges. I smelled sun-ripened cherries, and then the aroma grew richer. Was it Grandmother's kitchen during the holidays, the smell of baked apples leaking from her stove?

Words can't describe what I felt. The feeling simply lived, and that's all I know. Peace overflowed, and I felt I was a piece of a mysterious universe. I felt connected to something with unknown power and Intelligence, to that which IS.

The moment passed, and I knew my surroundings. I knew—or thought I knew—that my legs were fine. Had I healed? Since my crippled legs didn't ache after the collision, I guessed I might be healed. After all, Omega Bluebonnet had done her work well.

One of my sisters squawked to Vicki Sinclair, "No, don't feel bad. Sean's forever getting himself messed up in something. He fancies his Tiny Tim routine, then." Was I hearing a poorly-scripted movie?

"Could this really be happening? Am I really healed? Have my prayers from the past four years been answered?" I scarcely dared to believe it. I thought, Okay pain, let me have it. Don't hold back 'cause I mean to be over with this. Still, waves of pain didn't come calling.

Was I healed? I had to be. But seeing how miracles need a lot of proof these days, I decided to test if I'd recovered by pushing down gently on my feet. Nothing happened: no wave of pain, no electric shot of hell.

The light feelings flooding me grew strong enough that I had to bite my lip to contain them. This was a night to remember, one of mystery and of my miracle, one for which I had been hoping and praying for half of a life time. I luxuriated in it. While happiness burst out of me that summer's eve, I decided not to let on right away.

Wallowing in fortune, I let my eyes fix on a darting vision. It was a teenage girl scampering about the yard. Her luminous white blouse accented her spectral appearance. While the top half of her radiated whiteness, her bottom half was shrouded in darkness. Didn't she remind me a disembodied torso freely floating over the lawn? She searched for her bottom half.

Was it a ghost? No, it was Vicki Sinclair wearing her fluorescent white blouse. It was Vicki Sinclair who had collided with me in her mad dash to the walnut tree home base. It was she who had apologized for leveling me, who had nearly knocked me cold. But I was grateful that she appeared. You see, it was the same Vicki Sinclair who served as a conduit to my knowledge of healing that evening—my special night of miracles—the night when I knew my brokenness healed.

I wanted to tell her what happened because I needed to share my good fortune. "Hold on," I told myself. "She might laugh at me and tell my sisters, who would do the same." If this was a miracle, it was probably too much for a nine-year-old boy to handle. "No, I need to hold it within for a spell in silence. I need to let its sweetness age to know that it's permanent. I must know for certain that I'm healed. I must keep it secret for a spell."

Deciding to hold my secret, I considered a picture in our *Blue Book of Knowledge*. It was a drawing of Sir Isaac Newton as he held a prism in the Royal Academy to refract a beam of light to form a spectrum. He showed us that white light is a mixture of colors with different energies. In my world, white light also held sounds and aromas. Each color of the rainbow felt differently on my skin, and each one reminded me of different treats that Grandmother baked in her kitchen. The yellow light felt and tasted like peach cobbler, while the red light smelled like raspberry pies. Just as light is mixture of many colors, I knew that my life would be a swirl of colors, too. I sensed that life like light is a blending of many parts, and that's a bunch to think about for any nine-year-old boy!

I knew that the color white was a mixture masked by its simple appearance. Likewise, life is complicated. Even healed, I knew that I'd face many challenges. Those might distract me, and I'd no longer be excused by my illness. (As much as was expected of me as a crippled child, more would be expected of me since I'd healed.)

On the spot, I promised I'd surround myself with friends. "Even though I respect Mr. Fields, I don't want to end up like him, a hermit," I told myself. "I'll live on my patch of ground and welcome others in, even if they laugh at the soil that's too poor for them. I'll convince them otherwise. There's fertile ground here, even if it may look barren and scant."

My pledge after my miracle had really shaken me, and I felt a few salty tears trickle down my cheeks. Moisture crept near my mouth. For a boy or a man to cry in the Kansas of my youth was the worst possible offense. Although I didn't believe that, our priest and nuns had told us so, and the adults clinged to that idea. Blotting out the silliness, I didn't need any heavy feelings to spoil my night of lights and of the color white. I wanted to remember only my night of miracles. So, I crept into the shadows to avoid detection and ridicule.

I even knew the answer to the question, "Star light, star bright, who's the first ghost we'll see tonight?" The answer was me, the ghost of my past. It was the first and only ghost I saw that night, although I felt that I'd spend decades laboring to understand all the richness of its meaning.

Back Against the Wall

A month after my starlit night, no pain throbbed in my legs. When Dr. Hoffman showed Mother my quarterly x-rays, he told her my bones were whole. Even so, I must have flinched a bit the following afternoon when I tried to stand for a second. I paused to peer around the room, just as a swimmer might stall before plunging off of a pier and into icy waves lapping at its encrusted timbers. Someone might yell, "The water's fine; come on in!" Yet, since those waters had seared my flesh the last time I'd plunged in, naturally I hesitated.

They all stood there watching me: Dad, Mother, Janice, Ann, Paul, Mary, Mark, Jean, Julie, Leo, Greg, Grandmother, Grandfather, and Sister Henrietta. I reckoned that Dr. Hoffman would have been present had he not embarrassed himself the prior day.

"What do you mean by mixing up these files?" Doctor Hoffman shouted at his office manager. "How the hell could you be that stupid? Do you want to see me sued?"

"Sued?"

"Yes, I could lose my practice!" he snarled, like a rabid wolf ready to attack.

"But Doctor, I didn't mix up the files," the office assistant insisted.
"Of course they're not! Look at them!"

Dr. Hoffman placed the x-rays under metal clips. He flipped on the light behind them.

"Sean's the only child we x-rayed today—the only person we x-rayed, period," the office assistant said. Then, she tipped her head toward me as if to say, "Watch yourself! There's a kid in the room."

Dr. Hoffman looked at me with lifted eyebrows. "Think these are yours?" he asked.

I nodded, aiming to hold back my "Didn't-I-tell-you-so" grin.

"That can't be, Mrs. Stoddard. It just cannot be. Look at them! I don't believe it!" Had he missed a hint of the disease? Dr. Hoffman traced the image of my bones with his light pen. Maybe he felt that tracing over the bone images might change them—back to what he expected. He looked at me again. And, once again, I nodded.

"All right, then. I need to test his reflexes and run some other tests," he finally mumbled. "Call in Mrs. Redmond. She's a nurse, and she won't be able to explain Sean's recovery anymore than I can. It's nothing short of a miracle."

I knew that would please Sister Henrietta. She'd wagered on a miracle for some years by then.

The next day when we gave Sister Henrietta the news, you can't imagine the joy she let loose. First she jumped to her feet and let out a holler that might have raised Lazarus from the dead. "It's a miracle, it's a miracle!" she screamed, as tears of joy seeped from her face. "I've got to tell Father and the Bishop. To think, after only a few weeks! It's a wonder, a miracle!" she whooped again, shaking her head violently. By this time she had flicked enough tears around the room to compete with a hound shaking water from his coat when he's caught in a summer's shower.

Sister must have carried on like that for a full five minutes, pausing only to reach over and to pat my hand to congratulate us both. She kept sweeping her right arm over the front of her habit as if to pat herself on the chest. Congratulations also helped her breathing. Sister Henrietta was an asthmatic, and I wondered if the news could trigger another episode.

Stealing a glance around the room filled with relatives and my tutor Sister Henrietta, I slowed down to gaze into the eyes of each person there.

My siblings, parents, and Sister Henrietta stood frozen as they watched me sitting there with my back against the wall. I had sat there awhile as I began to apply pressure to my legs to push up slowly and to stand for a few seconds. Panting to gather strength in order to stand briefly, I felt a chill surge down my spine. After all, standing had been a stranger to me for half a lifetime. I needed to coax my mind and my body to believe that I could stand again, and I needed to remember the faces of anxious watchers as I rose.

I had believed that I would heal again when no one else dared to join me in my fantasy. I had overheard people jesting about the crippled child who just kept smiling through it all. "What is he thinking, and don't you feel sorry for that poor thing," echoed in my ears, but I tuned out all of that bother. If I listened to that bunk even for a moment, I guessed that I might begin to think that way, too. Then, my miracle couldn't happen. No, I'd walk again only if I kept hope alive by stripping doubt out of the picture. Dr. Hoffman said I'd take a few steps within a month.

Although thrilling, his words sounded unreal. Imagine, he had uttered that glorious phrase—"take your first few steps." I must learn to walk again after all of those years of frantic inactivity. Learning to walk at 9 months, I needed to relearn that at 9 years. Although it sounded too grand to be real, after a few days I knew it wasn't a dream. On the way home from the doctor's office that afternoon, I smiled at the sunset oozing over the Kansas prairie, its dust refracting colors. "My prayers have been answered, and I will walk again," I gasped. I imagined my dream to walk again had taken root as surely as a thistle which found a home, its thistledown wafting over the rolling prairie before alighting on soil rejected by other seeds. I'd triumph through sheer faith and persistence. Without them I'd never have healed, and my dream to walk again would would never have taken root.

Others had chimed in to say that their prayers had been answered, too. Many had prayed for me, including the sisters at The Queen of the Holy Rosary convent in Wea. Sister Henrietta taught at the Queen of the Holy Rosary School in Wea where my siblings attended. She'd been assigned to oversee my home studies. That meant weekly tutoring on Wednesdays (about an hour a session).

Well, after her first four visits, Sister Henrietta declared that I'd completed an entire year's worth of work: the first grade. Then, after only seven more visits, she said I'd conquered the second grade as well. "Mrs. Redmond, I'm not sure when the work will catch up with Sean, if it ever does. But, I've planned many projects."

"Thank you, Sister." Mother said.

"Don't forget, we stock a treasure trove of books in our convent. I'll let him read as many of those books as he wishes, and that will keep him busy for awhile." I suppose I'd finished my work that fast to spare more time for reading.

"We'll also work on religious studies, and I'll prepare him for First Holy Communion and Confession. Sometimes, we'll simply pray." Mother crinkled up the sides of her mouth, and I wondered if Sister's list seemed all right to her.

After several months passed, Sister Henrietta reported, "Sean, I've told my Wea class about you. I've used your story as an example."

"Oh, no. What did you tell them, Sister?" I didn't want people to make a fuss over me. All I really wanted was to walk again and to be normal. How could I explore my world if people stopped me, distracting me? That would never do. If I couldn't explore, how could I possibly find my place in the world? That thought terrified me, and it would never do.

"Well, I told them that you are crippled and that you know how to read. I said you're reading at a high school level . . . that you are reading my high school books."

I swallowed hard at her words. Didn't she know that I didn't wish to be different from the other children?

"Sean, I told my students to look at you as an example. When you apply yourself, you can do whatever you want to do in life."

Her class took the news well, and I became something of a celebrity. I knew this every Sunday when kids my age waved and smiled at me as my brothers or dad carried me to our pew. Embarrassed, I decided that a life of celebrity must be one large bother.

Sister also told her class, "He's an invalid, and he whiles away his hours in daydreams. I've caught him at it during lessons. Each time, I say, 'Sean, are you daydreaming again?' Then, he says, 'maybe so', and repeats the last few lines that I read to him."

"I suppose someone asked what you did to make me pay attention, right?"

"They all asked me that," Sister Henrietta laughed.

"What did you tell all those children?"

"I told them, 'Class, when he gazes up at me, his eyes of sapphire remind me of waves lapping at a Grecian isle. Those waves brim with hope, and I don't have the heart to discourage him. He's progressing well, and I'm patient with him.'"

Her words hit me hard, and I wanted to wilt. How could she embarrass me that much? I needed to pull her off the praise. "Did any child ask if I needed anything?"

"Yes, one little girls asked, 'Is there something we may do for him, Sister?'"

I'd hoped someone might ask that.

"Yes, there's something we may do. Let's pray for Sean to heal so that he'll be able to join us here at school."

News of their prayers and of Sister's progress reports trickled back to me from siblings and from the weekly visits to our church. I learned that the rest of the sisters at the Queen of the Holy Rosary Convent remembered me also in their evening prayers.

Then, one day Sister Henrietta told me her best friend, Sister Marie William was traveling to Lourdes, France in the summer. "I'll tote a bottle of holy water from Lourdes for you to give to Sean," Sister Marie William said.

With that news, the late spring of my first year with Sister Henrietta ended, and Sister Marie William began her pilgrimage.

That autumn when Sister Henrietta returned to tutor me, she brought her promised bottle of holy water from Lourdes, France. A girl named Bernadette had seen an apparition, the Blessed Virgin Mother, who asked her to pray for world peace. When the locals had asked Bernadette to make the vision appear to them, nothing happened. Instead, she asked a local farmer to dig a well so that healing waters could gush out of the ground. Countless visitors had taken those waters, and many folks had been healed.

Sister Henrietta had received strict instructions for the water's use. "Tell him to use a teaspoon a day applied to each hip. Then he should say 5 Hail Marys and 1 Our Father. That is sure to do the trick. The Blessed Mother will help Sean to walk again, don't you know."

By that time, I was willing to try anything to walk again. Besides, her bottle intrigued me. It smelled musty with traces of rust crinkled on the inside rim of its dented and scratched lid, lined with a piece of waxed paper. (Learning to make do with hand-me downs and leftovers, I found the bottle intriguing.)

I was also fascinated knowing it had journeyed clear across the Atlantic Ocean from France where some of our distant ancestors had lived nine hundred years ago. They joined William the Conqueror to invade England. Somehow, to touch that water helped me connect with my glamorous ancestors. "What had they thought in their lives, and what dreams had they wished all those years ago?" I wondered. Touching that bottle of holy water touched off many questions. Stories and plays swirled, especially ones that featured my ancient ancestors. What had they done in those times, in a misty realm that echoed through time?

The bottle felt warm. That made me feel safe, and my throat felt all cottony when I saw how Sister Henrietta cared. Her loyalty sent me into a reverie about a mother hen that tucked her chicks under her wings to keep them warm. I imagined that Sister Henrietta had toted that jar under her arm to help warm me and to raise my hopes to walk again. The thought stirred a glowing ember in my heart, raising me. "Why not?" I'd thought. "Finding someone who cares like this feels right nice."

For the first few weeks after she brought the holy water, Sister Henrietta scampered up the sidewalk every Wednesday and collapsed into her favorite chair in the living room where we studied. She always gasped the same question, "Has it worked? Can you tell?"

Each time, I felt a bit sad to tell her, "No, nothing yet." I also felt badly because I knew something had happened about one week before my first encounter with the holy water. That starlit night as I sat on our lawn, it was clear I had healed. Since I was scheduled for my checkup in two weeks, I stalled Sister until my x-rays could prove I was all right.

Sister Henrietta stood front and center. My family wrapped itself around the living room. I was about to begin to exercise my shriveled leg muscles, and I had a crowd sending me off.

My back rested against the wall. The drama unfolded slowly as I worked to move my withered leg muscles, easing them into use for a few seconds. Doctor Hoffman had told me, "Your bones are healed, and there is no trace of the disease. You'll be able to start exercising to build strength in your leg muscles, which have wasted away all of these years. Begin by leaning your back against the wall, and stand for a second or two. Then, increase the time daily over the next month until you are able to stand for one minute. After that, you will be strong enough to take your first few steps."

Dad looked right into me. Did he reckon a miracle—a cure—came from nowhere? Had he longed for the same kind of cure for his brother who died in a state hospital? Then, Dad's words came back to me. "We can only do the best we can do." I thought about how he leaned gently into the wind, as he hoped to accomplish some good. Well, I confess I grew anxious as "I" leaned forward. "I'll do the best I can leaning into challenges," I mused.

Then, up I went, hovering for a moment like a tuft of thistledown wafting in the summer breeze. Two living room windows overlooked our east lawn. A tuft of thistledown drifted by them. Had the down come to watch me? Had it floated by to cheer me on? Its color was downy white, nearly the same color and texture that my hair had been when I became crippled. My hair had grown a bit darker and coarser with age—all of my nine years. "Does hair grow coarser and darker with age like a hide that is tanned into leather, as if the trials of life scar it to thicken it?" I wondered. I know that Grandfather might agree, but he would add that as you pass your middle-age years, hair often becomes lighter and finer again as it aims to come full cycle. (There they were again: those cycles.)

I hovered for a moment longer to prove that standing was no fluke. I looked (as if in slow motion) at everyone peering at me. Then, applause broke out, and I plopped down.

Some of my siblings laughed. "Sean, you looked goofy," they teased. "You looked like a freak," they promised, "what, with your spindly legs and all."

Grandmother beamed. Was that a tear or two I spied on her cheeks? I had never seen her cry in her life. What an honor for her tears to leak on the day that I stood once again, my back to the wall.

"Don't you listen to the kids for a second. You looked free. When you

bobbed up and down, your white-blond hair looked like thistledown wafting over the prairie. Why, it looked like thistledown rising!" My dream had been to stand and to walk again, and my dream had drifted with imagination borne on downy tufts of thistledown in flight over windswept prairies. It was only natural that as my dream drew near, I looked a bit like the thistledown that bore my fondest wishes. Grandmother was talking about me, and Lordie . . . I was healed.

Sister Henrietta grinned graciously. Then she began to cough and wheeze.

"Sister, are you all right?" I asked.

"Yes, just a bit excited, dear."

"Sister, I can tell you are not healed of your asthma. I'm sorry."

"Now, don't you fret, dear. It takes awhile, that's all. It took years for you to heal. The Good Lord uses His own timetable. Don't you worry, honey," she hugged me. I remember thinking that maybe the bees could help her find a way to heal, to see it. Maybe falling snow, softly and peacefully on our driveway, might inspire thoughts of traction and friction she could use to heal, as they had for me. Could Omega Bluebonnet help heal her lungs? She might, seeing as how she bound up my legs with marvelous weavings. Tinsels of thistledown served as magical threads.

Then, out came her plea, "Oh, please let loose of your water. I need to dab it on my chest! You don't mind, now do you, honey? Spare the water and spoil the miracle, I must say," Sister giggled, darting for my bottle like a duck on a June bug. "Your water must be the real deal. The water that Sister Marie William brought to me must have been mixed up with ordinary tap water in the confusion. My water must not have been properly blessed."

Well, you can't imagine how quickly Sister Henrietta snatched my bottle of water. Out it went, and she commenced to dab it all over her chest. Blessings gushed from Sister Henrietta's mouth. She became liberal with the quantity as she gleefully splashed the remaining water all over her body. Before you could say, "Jack Robinson," she drained the entire bottle. Was she carrying on like a monstrously large black bird splashing about in a bird bath? As she decorously patted the water over her chest, she appeared to be a blackbird indeed, preening her feathers. I'd never seen a happier bird. Then, Sister began to hug me. "Oh, Sean, thank you for sharing your water. I know that I'll be healed. Bless you."

I twitched in my seat, and I hoped she was right.

Then, I asked, "Sister, do you know much about gravity, bees and snow? Those ideas had all helped me heal. What about Star light, Star bright? Do you know how to play that? And what about Greek symbols, especially the last one in their alphabet?"

Puzzled by my questions, she said, "No. Oh, well maybe. Now, honestly, Sean—you and your questions. What do they have to do with anything?"

I don't know if my miracle had something to do with that holy water from Lourdes. Even though I felt I had been healed shortly before I received it, who is to say that such a slight miss in timing—one week after half a lifetime of waiting—counts for much. Do miracles sometimes creep inside a body, bound in a package deal?

Maybe the idea of my cure needed time to warm up in my mind. Maybe the Blessed Virgin Mother had given me some time to prepare for the waters, which would cap it all for me as Sister Henrietta carefully uncapped that bottle of holy water. I can't say for sure whether or not a week is large in the grand scheme of things.

Besides, I didn't have the heart to tell Sister that I thought I had been healed shortly before I received the holy water. I could not do that to her.

Thereby began my voyage. I knew that my brothers and sisters would not be laughing inside of a few months. I'd recover fully. The doctors told me that I'd feel no lasting effects except for a tendency toward arthritis in my hips much later in life. Otherwise, no physical effects would trouble me at all.

Within two months, I walked again, and within one year I attended school. The doctors insisted that I stay home one more year, ensuring my legs did not break down again.

Still, I knew that I would struggle with all of the spiritual and emotional trauma. I knew one day I would need to write about it—once I could put it into perspective. I needed to remember it all to write about it one day. But I also knew that would be many years after I braced myself, my back against the wall.

'A' Hunting We Will Go

The dusky night rides down the sky,
And ushers in the morn.
The hounds all join in glorious cry;
The huntsman winds his horn,
And a-hunting we will go.
—From *The Three Jovial Huntsmen*

My oldest brother, sixteen-year-old Paul, fancied himself a hunter. Pouring over dog-eared catalogues from crusty mail-order houses, he dreamt of which gun to own. Long thoughts of desire for the guns pictured on crinkled catalogue pages were not shortened by the paltry sum of money he'd saved. With a meager stash swelling in the belly of his piggy bank, Paul kept right on dreaming. He knew he'd have his gun.

After a season of odd chores for neighbors and a loan from Dad, Paul had his way. Firmly etched in my mind is that Saturday morning Paul and Dad tromped over the lawn toward the True Value Hardware Store on the south side of the our county seat square. They fetched Paul's Daisy air-pump BB gun there. Our county seat square anchored the stores lining four cobblestone lanes, rounded and worn by tires that hummed over them. The courthouse, circa 1890, stood confidently in its coat of kiln-fired red bricks, its foundation of native limestone.

Even before Dad and Paul left the True Value hardware store, Paul began to pump his prize, pawing it the way some folks rub a charm for good luck. I watched as he marched in the general direction of our car, his progress interrupted by a few sideways steps as he lurched to one side. He braced himself. Paul hunched over his gun, and he stroked it as he crouched over the red bricks lining the sidewalk. He loaded his air rifle with BBs.

Half-grimacing and half-smiling, Paul looked excited enough to heave.

347

Paul pumped it with air to its limit, and he bellowed, "Come on everybody! Time to head home!"

"It's target practice time!" Paul shouted as we unloaded groceries from our white Pontiac station wagon that dusty afternoon. Paul fetched three tin cans from a gunnysack waiting for our next trip to the dump. Then, he raced toward the barbed wire fence lining the east side of our barnyard. There, he capped three of our weathered fence posts with those fool tin cans. Aiming, he pulled the trigger. A burst of air and a "pitiful" silence followed.

After missing all three cans, Paul decided to use a gallon metal pail. Missing that target as well, he aimed for a larger and higher target: the tin roof of our chicken shed. I told him, "I don't believe the shed roof is alive, or that it ever will be. I'm sure it wouldn't taste fine, no matter how much elbow grease you apply to cook it up."

"There you go again," Paul answered. "Diarrhea of the mouth, I'd say. I'm only gauging its muzzle velocity. I need to know how long it takes for a BB to fly to the shed."

As I watched Paul shoot at our shed, I didn't know I was watching a boy inching toward manhood. He might need to manage a piece of his world his own way.

Breathing heavily, Paul rhythmically pumped his air gun. A puzzled look of frenzied relief blossomed on his face. I knew better than to interrupt him. Did Paul need to wrest some power, enough to impact his world, just as surely as the BBs pinged the metal roof of our hen house? He needed to go hunting. "Just watch me. Why, I'll bring down a bird—any bird—wait and see," he boasted.

Well, we waited and sure enough we saw. Paul downed a sparrow, which is hardly enough to eat, unless you're a cat. He cornered the bird in our tool shed where it had taken refuge on our rafters. My stomach turned as I imagined the terror that poor thing must have felt. There Paul pounded it with BBs until it crumpled into a pitiful, writhing lump. The corpse bore multiple wounds around its neck and torso, and a few

348

crimson drops colored its tiny feathers. I felt sorry for both the sparrow and for Paul.

"The air gun did the trick!" Paul exclaimed. I knew he wasn't proud of his deed because after he displayed his bird, he lowered his head and moped out of the barn. Did he let us see his sparrow to prove his power? He lost his steam when he paused to blow his nose with a Kleenex, which he then used to wrap the body. Did blowing his nose let out the bad air that powered his attack?

Thoughts of that tiny sparrow haunted me. Was Paul more in love with the "idea" of hunting than with hunting itself? I reckon so, because he never again showed us any small animals done in by BBs. His hunting career started and ended that very day.

Not much interested me in hunting, although I was snagged by the path BBs took when fired from that Daisy air-pump rifle. Paul's target practice with the corrugated tin roof of our chicken house is to blame. At first I couldn't say what fascinated me. Perhaps it was the idea that Paul authored those magical flights. Or was it that I could roughly predict which way the BBs would fly?

Was the skill to work out flight paths of BBs some measure of control? For example, if I plotted a BB's curved flight path, did that mean I aimed to take charge somehow? Would that make me feel better, as if I controlled a piece of my world? Do we all need to manage pieces of our world?

That evening as I lay in bed, I stretched in comfort with long thoughts. A thunder storm rumbled in the distance. I relished counting the seconds between the flash of lightning bolts and the thunder's lugubrious reply. My dad had explained, "The light from lightning travels very fast—much faster than sound waves we hear as thunder."

"How fast is that?"

"Faster than planes fly."

"How can that be? I mean, planes move much faster than trains, and trains move fast enough to zoom across Kansas in one night. By morning a body's in Colorado."

"Yes, that's fast. But a plane moves faster than that, and sound travels faster than planes."

"And lightning moves faster than sound?"

"Yes."

"Even faster than a rocket ship?"

"Yes, even faster than a rocket ship. Depending upon how far away the lightning strikes, the thunder's delay stretches or shrinks. Strikes nearby make short delays, while the strikes far distant in the valley take longer. A lengthening thunder report shows how much slower sound travels than light."

I remembered the time it took Paul's BBs to collide with our hen house roof: some two seconds after he fired his air rifle. That delay included the time for the BB's faint ping to reach my ears, as well as the time for me to register it.

Dad had told me, "Sean, lightning travels very fast—why, you can't imagine it."

With his words, I asked, "Is it instantaneous?" I'd learned that word in a Sunday school class when Sister Henrietta declared, "God is everywhere and moves instantaneously." Of course, that didn't make much sense to me. "Sister, if God's everywhere, what need is there to move?"

Sister wasn't pleased by my question.

"No, the lightning's speed isn't instantaneous," Dad explained. "However, its speed is so great that we can't really conceive of it. For example, it travels at the same speed as light, which takes about a second and a half to travel from the moon to the Earth."

That was about equal to the time it took for Paul's BBs to strike the chicken shed roof. Might there be a little boy shooting light beams from the moon to the Earth to hear the delighted ping of laughter from children? I was one of those children, but I doubted any child standing astride the moon might shoot light from a gun anywhere near our farm. In fact, I suspected that no one lived on the moon.

Once I asked Dad about even more distant bodies. "Well, just how long does it take light to travel from the sun to the Earth?" Dad hesitated a moment. "Well, just about eight minutes. Really, it's eight minutes and twenty seconds."

"Does that means that the sun is roughly four hundred times farther from the Earth than the moon is?" My tone was more of a conclusion than a question, seeing as how I'd worked my way into one of those moods when I'd sputter answers that fast. (Heck, I needed to wait to hear the answers myself, not knowing how I got them.) When Dad grimaced, I paused a second to recalculate.

"Yes, that's just about right," Dad mumbled before he swiftly left the room. Did Dad sense I'd soon commence with tougher questions, as I was prone to do? He escaped me.

Well, that day I didn't need to ask more questions. I simply wanted time alone to ponder all the stars in trillions of galaxies untold billions of years old. I wanted to feel the fact that the sun and its planets are only one no-account solar system in one measly outpost of the Milky Way Galaxy, and how the Milky Way Galaxy is one average galaxy amongst billions of more impressive ones. Boy, if the Milky Way Galaxy was a grain of sand, the known galaxies might fill the seashores of the world many times over. Why, if each galaxy was a dandelion head, those flowers might cover the world more times over than a body could count before losing track from boredom. All this I knew from Janice's science book, which I happened to be reading.

No one knew how many suns and planets like ours hurtled throughout the universe. Did our solar system and humans amount to much more than a few grains of cosmic dust in all that grandeur? Well, yes and no—that is, maybe. We may be tiny, our world small as compared to the cosmos. But, I reckoned we need only to find our place. That's all. Besides, the rest is too much to think about all in one show.

I also knew that a certain Professor Einstein claimed that nothing in our universe traveled faster than light in a vacuum. Nope, only light in a vacuum could move fast enough to shine from the sun to the Earth in eight minutes and twenty seconds. Can you imagine how long it takes to reach us from stars in other galaxies—like Andromeda, for instance? The vastness of the galaxies and of the universe loomed inconceivably immense to me, even in my wild imaginings.

"And, oh my gosh, what about the light from each star? Here it claims there are billions of galaxies and perhaps an endless number of stars." That thought puzzled me, and I giggled, "If that's true, then the night sky ought to be drenched with light."

Overhearing my objections as Janice searched for her schoolbook, she retorted, "But the light from all those stars hasn't reached us yet. That's why the night sky is dark."

"Oh, but if nothing in our universe travels as fast as light in a vacuum, then why hasn't the light reached us yet?"

She had no answer. Then, in about two seconds, I imagined one. My answer spread over my scrunched-up face. Then, I smiled, speaking before I knew what I would say.

"Oh, I know. That's easy. It's because not all of the stars were born at the same time."

"What? What nonsense are you spouting?"

"Well, some stars were born billions of years ago, along with the universe, as it expanded. Other stars are babies, perhaps only a few hundred million years old."

"Mere toddlers, I reckon."

"Yes, quite young. The light from those babies hasn't reached the Earth because they started so far from us—after the universe stretched for billions of years. Maybe their light will reach us someday. Maybe not. We might see those newcomers one day. But then again–"

"What nonsense. How can you be so dense? How can stars be born? Not possible." She often voiced such reluctance about my ideas.

I didn't answer. It felt right, and I didn't breathe a word. Something about my answer troubled me, though. The trouble rested in the fact that the "Big Bang" had marked the beginning of the universe's expansion. It continues some seventeen billion years later. "Maybe the light from those new stars will never reach us. What if the expansion is so rapid that their light won't catch up to us? It can't travel all that distance that the universe stretched from the Big Bang until when the new stars were born. Maybe those stars formed late enough and far enough away that their light will never make up for all that time and distance. A tinge of sadness shot through me. I ached to see their light.

"Well, maybe so," Janice grimaced as she left the room.

I cleared more rooms that way.

The ideas I played with felt delicious. Such ideas I hunted on my voyages of discovery left a wondrous feeling of control inside of me. I knew that I was only observing the mystery of it all. First a grin, and then a broad smile spread across my face. Such thoughts soothed me, and I felt not myself for a moment.

"What are your grinning about now?" Janice snapped as she stomped back into the room. I didn't answer.

I suppose I hunted and pawed at ideas the way some folks hunt for game. Thinking often left me spinning my tangled forelocks, my head tilted to one side, my right eye squinted. I didn't know myself, and I surely knew no time.

"Sean, Daydreaming's over. Time for chores," Dad's voice wafted on evening breezes.

"Time to stop *thinking* and start *working*," I murmured in disgust.

I must admit that I often kept right on daydreaming even as I went through the motions of my evening chores. If I ever did chores without such wondering, I guess that I must have been sick or something.

"What a marvelous universe it is: such mystery," I stammered as I rose to my feet, "So many worlds to explore," as I wended my way toward the milk barn.

Just then the ping of a wayward BB striking our hen house tin roof caught my ear. Paul was at it again.

$\mathcal{D}$reaming of Red

I recall where every piece of furniture sat in my grandparents' living room. Grandmother's vacuum and its swish marks made fresh daily on her carpet meant clean with a capital "C". I never spotted a speck of dirt or dust there, although my grandparents endured the same kind of dust showers as we did, blown daily by stubborn Kansas winds. (As a small boy, I guessed that Grandmother's living room was too "neat" and "orderly" to be real.) It invited rest with its firm yet comfortable furniture: couches with matching raised green upholstery, easy chairs, and footstools. Whenever adults began to speak, I welted into daydreams and into her couch. Tracing my thumb and index finger along the raised lines of its fabric, I noticed how it stretched downward under my weight. I'd heard that space and time warp when massive bodies drift by to visit, and I knew that the same holds true for little boys on couches. Might people also bend downward under weighty thoughts?

One Christmas Grandfather got a wild hair and splurged on a leather recliner with built-in massage from Troutman's Home and Furnishings Store on Main Street. Grandfather's lower back ached from considerable gardening, and Mr. Troutman aimed to help. He showed Grandfather a chair with vibration controls under a hinged lid at its right arm. After that, neighbors came calling with any excuse simply to plop onto it, their groans luxuriously full.

Their Motorola television rested in its cabinet against the wall next to the window where the Venetian blinds hung. Although TV sets were common by the early 1960s, his thirty inch tube was finer than most. He owned one of Osawatomie's first color televisions, and it was a treat! If Mother left me at their home while she ran errands, Grandfather ruled, "Sean, you may watch television for one hour."

I fancied its every colored image, more interesting than the drab black and white pictures in mottled shades of gray. Did that color TV set mean I would never again need to add color to black and white pictures? Hardly! The reds, blues, and greens didn't compare with what "I" imagined. Naturally, I colored over those clumsy images. After all, I had been dreaming in living color for as long as I could recall.

If Mother came to visit with some of my brothers and sisters, we usually lined up on the living room furniture, each of us plopped down in a semi-assigned spot. We switched on the television only for news or for special programs. Otherwise, the set held its tongue while Mother and our grandparents exercised theirs. Adults rambled on about many subjects, and I felt fidgety enough to be tied. Why, I could simply spit! Get to the point. Why open one's mouth unless a body has a firm idea in mind and the will to say it?

But, just as one topic played itself out, another one cropped up to stretch the talks and my patience. Each subject glided into the next one with stunning ease. Heck, I needed something else to do, and I played to distraction, crafting games out of . . . out of . . . burping, for example.

Now, burping is an honorable sport, provided it's done properly. I imagined burping in slow motion, backwards and forwards, the sound suspiciously similar in whichever direction I pleased. Then, I threw in a great, wrenching yawn for good measure.

News of neighbors and friends surfaced, ones whom my grandparents had known since the 1920s. I suppose that was important, although they were strangers to me. People whom Mother had known since childhood were reported to enjoy anniversaries, birthdays, and weddings. All became newsworthy! Living in a small town meant folks thought twice about doing anything foolish, seeing as how nearly everyone would know about it by supper time. Some called that being nosey. Others said it meant we all took an interest in our neighbors. We cared about them. Maybe our idea of news was gossip with a dash of concern swirled in.

My eyes glazed over, and I began to trace out the raised lines in the couch's green fabric. Those lines reassured me, reliable and predictable as I glided my fingers along each parallel line. As I did this, I usually wondered about Dad and our farm, of bankruptcy and failure, or car wrecks and illness. Folks were expected to handle their problems as best they could. If the town caught wind of a body's dirty laundry, shame lived. Charity was an outright insult, and so we all did the best we could do.

One day I imagined, "If the furniture and its lines on the raised fabric are predictable and logical, why can't life be that way . . . predictable and logical?

I slipped from one piece of furniture to the next. (Had they changed since the last time I made my rounds? Nope.) First came the couch, and next came the matching chairs and ottoman. The leather recliner followed, and it magically wiggled metal rods up and down Grandfather's back to massage away aches.

A panel under its hinged arm held control knobs and switches which Grandfather turned and flicked to stir the chair to life. (Of course, we kids were forbidden to touch any of them.) Oh sure, I'd waited patiently—well, maybe not too patiently—for my chance at that control panel. When Grandfather finally let me work the knobs and switches, I set the chair to massage my back. Wow! It crinkled a grin over my face. A sense of power over the chair thrilled me, and I cupped my hands underneath my legs to keep from snatching at those fool controls. I had ached to feel comfort, and I knew I could handle the controls had I been allowed to touch them. Sadly, Mother had promised Grandfather that we kids would leave the chair alone, and I obliged.

Even though I kept my word, I asked myself why it mattered who ran the controls. If I moved the same knobs and switches in the same order as Grandfather did, what harm could come? Maybe adults didn't think I knew what to do if something went wrong, like if I threw the chair on its side from unheard of speed, or if I shorted it out by working three controls at once. Who knows? I giggled since any self-respecting kid is liable to work controls far better than distracted adults can.

Usually I ended up stretched out on the floor next to that recliner. I lay on my side as I stared at the ceiling or at the vents in the carpeted floor. Our grandparents had installed central air, and those vents enchanted me when they spewed out cooled air. Their pet terrier marched in from the kitchen, and he plopped down with a thud, stretching his belly over cooling comfort. Even though he could lie on the vent, I couldn't even touch it. Would I pull the lever and shut off the air flow . . . backing up the air and causing the air conditioner to pop (like an overfilled balloon)?

Likewise, I couldn't touch the draw cord on the Venetian blind or curtains. Did grown-ups think I'd snatch it clean off its rod? That fool rod might klunk me on the head, and I'd black out: dead by morning. Or, did they reckon I'd craft a lasso from the draw string, snag the TV, and crash it into a fiery rubble? Tough to say . . .

Growing weary of asking "why", I slipped into my dreamland. I entered my favorite television movies like "The Wonderful Wizard of Oz", or serials like "The Adventures of Johnny Quest." (Do you recall the episode when the spidery-looking robots shot laser beams, or the one with the Komodo Dragons leashed by someone looking like a summa wrestler?)

While on the floor, I usually checked under the leather recliner for coins. With a keen eye to find any stragglers, I reckoned the coins panted for me to find them. They waited to be rescued, glistening their misty relief as I held them up to the table lamp.

Once I had spotted a half dollar, two quarters, four dimes, and a few nickels. They rested precisely below where Grandfather's pockets would be as he pushed back. Imagine what they could buy: toys, candy, comic books, and marbles! But, I knew what I had to do. Clutching the coins in my sweaty right hand, I sauntered to Grandfather. My head bowed, I stood still for the most part. My left foot pawed at the carpet to trace arcs rhythmically.

I blurted, "Grandfather, I found these under the reclining chair."

Before I could continue, Grandfather asked, "What, Sean? Where did you get all of that loot?"

Knowing adults sometimes don't listen too well, I repeated my answer. "I found these under the chair. The coins must have fallen out of your trouser pockets."

Grandfather pocketed all of the change except for a shiny dime. "This dime prefers a new home, I reckon." (A portrait of Franklin D. Roosevelt glinted at me. I'd grown partial to the President after hearing about his struggles with crippled legs.)

Thrusting that dime into the palm of my right hand, Grandfather declared, "Thanks, Sean. Here's something for your trouble." To own that ten cent piece felt important, and his thanks felt even better.

Those feelings made me stretch an inch as I marched around the room. I grinned at the thought of that shiny dime in my pants' right pocket. Doing what's right made me feel grown . . . and free. After all, only children goofed up now and again, and I'd heard that adults rarely make mistakes. Was that true? Feeling independent was the best show of all: free to decide what to do.

All that hunting was hard work, and it made me thirsty. Traipsing into the kitchen, I asked Grandmother for a drink of water. "You're a big boy now. Get it yourself," she declared as she pointed to a light-blue metal tumbler. She'd turned it upside down near the faucet.

The cold water faucet filled the cup with my grandparents' strangely smelling liquid. This was no water that I had known on the farm. This water came from the Marias des Cygnes River which flowed near their home. (The river had been named by the French for all of the swans that floated down it.) Heavily chlorinated and filtered at the water works, that water was unlike the cistern water I knew at the farm. It wasn't foul tasting, only strange, as if it wanted to be foul but couldn't quite find the way.

One late Tuesday afternoon we all visited Grandmother and Grandfather. The clock sitting on the wooden ledge in the living room chimed seven o'clock, saying the afternoon was long gone. "The Red Skelton Hour" was set to air then. Could we watch it? Red's characters tickled my sides, and they felt true. His show charmed me, and I hoped to be as quick-witted as the fun-loving clowns he played. Some looked foolish, but I guessed they were wise. Klem Kadittlehopper worked my jaws in broad grins, especially when he leaped in a high arc from one foot to the other while the silly cow bell clanged. Klem toted a bouquet of flowers in his right hand, and I wondered if he'd be smiling if his bouquet was only a bunch of ornery thistles. Why, I'll wager that Klem wouldn't care much for them, either.

When Red played both the role of a young boy and an old man fishing in a boat, I couldn't contain myself. But then I wondered if that meant his mind had split into pieces, as had Uncle Jim's mind. Maybe that wasn't funny after all, but it sure felt silly when I watched. Freddie the Freeloader managed to chase away thoughts of Uncle Jim.

"Red Skeleton's a ham, and a damn foolish one at that," Grandmother Kearney announced.

"Red *Skelton*, Grandmother," I was forever correcting his name for someone. But, I didn't feel too poorly when she let me know her opinion. She saw Red only as far as his silly antics and jokes, most of which tickled him enough to laugh at himself. Grandmother may have thought he was a lowbrow, but can a lowbrow fool laugh at himself? It takes a wise person to do that.

"He has no talent," Grandfather declared.

"He's awesome! He knows a lot about life!" I objected.

The next thing I knew, Grandfather wagged his head and retreated into the kitchen for a glass of water. Had I been wrong to stand up for Red? I didn't mind as long as I could watch his show.

Whether he was acting the part of a poor, drunken clown or a senile fool, his pantomimes showed someone who searched for answers . . . someone who coped with life in all of its flaws and foibles. The absurdity of life with all of its unknowns snatched at me. I reasoned that life might be something like what Red showed us.

While I watched Red, the clown I saw as a little boy crept back to laugh at me. The other children laughed while I merely smiled. Why? I sensed his world of light and meaning under all of his silliness. But the other kids laughed because "he's funny". What was underneath his mask that few saw? Maybe he hid his true light. Do some of us shield who we are from the ones we love most? Maybe that's what my grandparents did when they spouted low opinions of Red.

Glancing down at the furniture, I thought Red might laugh when he saw the predictable lines of Grandmother's raised fabric furniture. Even the color of the furniture was wrong—a verdant green, not like the funny red color of the hair many clowns fancy.

Would tufts of thistledown act a lot like Red if they became humans? Maybe. Shucks, maybe thistles weren't so bad after all, not if they acted like Red, improvising to do the best they knew how.

Closing his show, Red always said, "Good night, and may God bless." His show alone was blessing enough.

A Summer Social Farewell

Festive booths punctuated the lawn east of The Queen of the Holy Rosary Church. Iced soda pop floated in aluminum tubs, country fried chicken nipped at noses and taste buds, cake frosting glistened at the bake sale tables, and parishioners whirred with activity. Wea parish was finally in the midst of its annual July Summer Social, a fundraiser for our church and school. Why "finally"? Because talk of the social usually commenced way back around Memorial Day which, for me, made the Social as far away as Lake Michigan. But, gradually, I saw our Summer Social ship inch upward from the horizon, only the tip of its mast at first visible. Before long, I could see all of the mast and a bit of its hull. Our excitement rose with the growing sight of the hull. And that went for a bunch of people—not for me alone.

One young boy springs to mind. Little Davey Chance sat two pews over from our family. When Father Shudders—director, treasurer, accountant, and self-proclaimed Grand Marshall if you will—assigned baking blueberry pies to Mrs. Graff and lemon tortes to Ms. Smirk, Davey's legs twitched. Weeks later, when Father assigned the Country Store to Mr. Stevens and the Cherry Tree to Mr. Barker, Davey's shakes were full-blows: jerky and rapid. How that boy shook, enough quivering to be my moving calendar.

With each passing week, Davey's jiggling excitement grew, and that became contagious. Even the adults got into the act, their speech revving up with all the fun, and their hand movements faster and punchier. By the time July drifted in, our ship slipped into the harbor, and we were snapping messes of bewilderment.

Well, my first social stop was the country store. Although I had played it a few times the prior year, Mother offered to show me the ropes.

A dozen numbers formed each of three sides of a rectangle, and a prized-filled table formed the fourth side. Prizes included boxed games with their cellophane still intact: Monopoly, Sorry, and Yahtzee. One choice included a poker game complete with two decks of cards. A holster toting two cap guns loaded with a roll of caps each (and one extra in cellophane) rested near the front, while a game of Chinese Checkers beckoned to passersby. And then there were the baked goods: deep-dish apple, cherry and peach pies. A chocolate cake sweated near the rear, its richness sucking in moisture from the sultry air.

"Now choose a number and place your bet—uh, nickel—on one of them," Mother coached me. I picked number 24, my birth date, and I plopped my considerable sum of money onto it. When all of the numbers were covered, the spinner and barker heaved ho to twirl the wheel: a circle of lacquered wood with red numbers stenciled around its circumference. Two nails partially pounded into the wood on either side of each number fenced them in. As the wheel spun, a stationary leather strap struck the nails to sound "clackety-clack" over the head of each smiling gambler.

As the wheel spun round and round, each player held his breath. Clackety-clack, clackety-clack, clackety-clack the strap spitted. Then, it slowed with our growing suspense. The wheel passed 24 once, twice, and a third time, but it kept right on going. It slowed dramatically. "Come on 24. Come on 24," I chanted.

"Clack, clack, clack 20, 21, 22." The strap snapped into 23, and it almost stopped. "One more," I pleaded.

C-l-a-a-a-ck, the wheel stopped at 24. I won! "Mother, did you see that?"

Mother grinned nearly as wide as I did.

Since Mother was my good luck charm, I figured she was entitled to help me select my prize. We'd split my winnings. A few of the prior winners, usually the men, took their time to claim a prize. Eyeing the table the way a coonhound eyes a downed bird (as if waiting for a master's signal to retrieve his prize) each man acted weird. After "my" win I understood why. You see, rummaging through prizes happens to be the best part of winning. Well, Mother and I chose a homemade, deep-dish apple pie, the most delicious one I'd ever tasted. "Look at what I won for a nickel!" I bragged to my friends.

"Lucky strike," one friend said.

"Beginner's luck," said another. "I'd just as soon have picked the brownies, though."

Father Shudders and I happened to stroll up to the Ladies' Alter Society's Bake Sale as Mrs. Chance finished her table browsing. With a nonchalance few actresses might muster, Mrs. Chance eyed the largest, most luscious chocolate cake on the table. She said, "Ah . . . I'll have the . . . chocolate one, please."

I was relieved that a physical law hadn't been broken. Mrs. Chance always asked for the biggest and best chocolate cake, her choice as dependable as is the apparent setting of the sun.

"Excellent choice, Mrs. Chance," Father said.

"Isn't it? It's my son's favorite," Mrs. Chance licked her lips.

Who was she trying to kid? I mean, really . . . her son?

Father Shudders had already unzipped the church's Bank of Louisburg deposit bag, and he had commenced to count bake sale proceeds.

"How are we doing, Father?" the Altar Society President asked.

With only a sly look, Father said nothing. But his look meant, "Darn fine."

"Better than last year?"

"Neck and neck, I'd say. But I haven't been to Concessions yet. I'll let you know how things look once I've finished this afternoon's rounds." We all trusted Father Shudders with the money, right along with most everything else.

Turning away from the bake sale table, I nearly collided with Mrs. Chance's little boy Davey. His quick dodge set off-kilter the two-scoops of ice cream crowning the cone he was carrying. Before he could adjust it, that fool ice cream demonstrated Newton's First Law. It kept going after Davey stood still: "splat". Davey sheepishly glanced around before scooping up his mixed-up blob. Then, he plopped it back on his cone. No one was the wiser, or so he thought. Licking his palm, Davey wove through the crowd, and he made it halfway across the lawn before his ice cream made a repeat performance. That made Davey two for two.

Aiming to win a slingshot or a squirt gun, I sidled up to the Cherry Tree, a dead tree plopped into a metal bucket and filled with gravel. One year the kids propped it up on criss-crossed lattice boards and loaded it with red tissue balls pressed into nearly round objects they called "cherries". For a dime any player chose a cherry to unwrap. If they were lucky, they'd find a slip of paper with the name of a prize scrawled on it (sling shot, squirt gun, one dozen cookies, one dollar). Not every cherry had a piece of paper hidden inside. And not every cherry with a piece of paper had a prize written on it.

Although Knights of Columbus members oversaw the Cherry Tree, teenagers were in charge of making the balls and running the game. I thought it was mean the way some of them grinned while teasing eager players. Sometimes they dangled "extra" big cherries on the tree. Of course to most players a larger cherry meant a fatter prize. When these players opened their cherries, more than a few of their faces dropped, and so did their hopes. I didn't win anything, but toting around my pie more than made up for it, shielding me from embarrassment.

Anyone who wanted hot food headed for the gymnasium. Gliding in there, I reckoned I'd walked into a green house bursting with the sweetest blossoms on earth: home cooked food. Aromas blended to form a dancing bouquet of crimson and brown, and that mostly meant steaming country fried chicken with all the special herbs and secret seasonings that might have pestered even "The Colonel", his shame seeping from his skin to match the steam that wafted over the chicken. The meat was tender enough to melt right on the bone—like an ice cream cone on a too-warm day.

Full and groggy, I moseyed outside and leaned against the school just to the left of the gymnasium door. Chubby Graves, his face an alarming red, semi-stumbled through the door. He was chuckling about God knows what. Chubby owed his nickname to parish elders who made a game out of mocking him. I asked Dad why Chubby drank so much.

"To numb the pain of his tortured spirit. He tries to laugh it off, and that's too bad. There's nothing sadder than a jolly man sloshed with pain."

I was thinking of him when a woman said, "Look Billy, it's Sean Redmond. He spent four years in a wheelchair. Remember? He's healed now. Isn't that a miracle?" Mrs. Crinshaw gripped the handles of her son's wheelchair. He'd spent most of his fifteen years in it.

"Hello, Billy," I said. "How's the day treating you?"

Billy's head bobbed and his eyes darted, but eventually they rested on me. His intelligent eyes probed me with silent questions: How did you heal? How does it feel? Did you ever think you'd walk again? Is there hope for me? If so, will you pray for me?

Billy Crinshaw was the fourth son born into his third generation, hard-working Kansas farm family. At age 47 his mother learned she was pregnant with him—a risky situation, even by today's standards. People believed Billy's many disabilities might have been due to her advanced age. No one knew for sure. Anyway, we didn't ask about "such things", and we surely didn't ask what was "wrong" with him. That would have been downright vulgar.

"Sister Marie William toted Sean a bottle of holy water from Lourdes, France," Mrs. Crinshaw told Billy. "She says that's what healed Sean. That's right, holy water—and faith. What do you think about that, Billy?"

Billy knew about faith, at least that's what Mother said. "That boy has faith without end—or beginning. It simply is."

"What kind of faith?" I needed to know.

"Simple. He has a 'I-know-I'll-be-healed' kind of a faith. He simply knows it."

I have faith too, I wanted to say. But dare I tell him I'd pictured a way to heal before Sister Henrietta ever strode up our walkway with her small bottle of water in tow? Did I dare tell him I'd fantasized for years about how my bones might heal? Might I tell him how I'd labored with my secret friends: Lambda Helios, Omega Bluebonnet, and the Little Country Deuce?

Billy and I shared a bond because we'd spent years in a wheelchair. (Actually, my wheelchair got more use as a cart for Mother's heavy laundry basket than for me.) No, I guessed my case wasn't at all like Billy's. But, how could I tell him what I was thinking? Did he understand we were alike in some ways but different in others?

Oh, he understood. His eyes told me so. He knew that I imagined my bones would heal. Most folks guessed that he was "retarded", unable to understand simple conversation. But they were dead wrong. Billy knew and understood more than he let on. In fact, I'm sure he knew and understood my thoughts.

Mrs. Crinshaw chimed, "Billy's oldest brother named his new baby Billy in this young man's honor." Mrs. Crinshaw ruffled Billy's hair.

Pride gulped up and all around Billy's face. He smiled, his lower lip all scrunched up.

"Can I leave you with Sean for a few minutes?" Mrs. Crinshaw asked.

Billy jiggled his nod.

"We'll be fine," I said.

A grumbling man charged through the gymnasium door. He joined the food line for the third time.

"L-e-e-ggg," Billy eked out.

Billy was right; it was Mr. Legg, known to me as the scoundrel who panted to swipe our land for twenty-five cents on the dollar. Before Dad declared wage earner's bankruptcy, "that man" sniffed our need and commenced circling like a vulture. Had the Bank of Stanley and Grandfather not taken charge, "he" might have taken our farm. I guessed he was satisfied only for the time it took him to devour his prey. His brand of hunger couldn't be sated by wealth—or food. Mr. Legg left the gymnasium, his overloaded paper plate dripping stickiness. I doubted he'd eat all he snatched. His dark world of greed highlighted Billy's misty, light world of happiness.

"Billy, are you happy?" I blurted out. Although I reckoned he was happy, I needed to ask him, and I did so before I could stop myself. Anyone might want to know the same. How can anyone carrying such burdens, overflowing with pain, be happy? I shifted my weight and fumbled to shroud my tactlessness.

Rotating on a unsteady axis, his head bobbed and trembled toward me. A smile leaked across his face. "Ye-e-e-s-s-h" he said in a tone defying his physical wobbliness. "Y-e-e-e-s-s-h, Sh-sh-sh-on. A-a-u-u-n-d-h y-o-ou-h?" his voice slid down and then up again, as if it had decided to go gliding.

I bristled like the tail feathers of an old Tom turkey. Was I happy—I who had been healed? If an adult asked me such a thing, I would have thrown up my smokescreens. I'd have answered coyly. Around adults I'd need to cloak who I was and what I felt. While there was no telling what they might do, I trusted Billy.

"Well, yes I am—for the most part. Still, I don't like what happens. I mean, I'm mighty sad to think about child abuse, murder, and poverty. I'm angered to know children starve while others waste food. That's a sin, if you ask me. And I worry about–"

The right corner of Billy's mouth moved askew while I droned on, and his nose crinkled. I'd never before seen a person act that way when I spoke. Heck fire, he really listened to me!

When I finished citing my list of reasons for sadness, Billy smiled. His left hand wavered and then plopped on my right knee. Struggling to utter the words, he said, "Be happy, Sean. Be happy."

Billy's eyes glowed, as if particles or stardust filled them with light. Were his eyes spearing starlight right into me? I knew a work of art had fluttered down from the sky and into my sight, and that living artwork spoke solely to me. My throat felt large and dry, as if I'd packed it in cotton. My heart fluttered with a jumble of feelings. Sadness, anger, frustration, and then peace drifted nigh, and I struggled not to cry. I did not want him to see me cry. Heck, he might reckon I was a baby.

Then it happened. A glowing peacefulness quivered out of him, and into me. It overfilled us. I saw it in shards of radiance that warmed the lawn and table and trees. I felt it as loveliness that no flower, food, or perfume could match. And I knew I shared something "important". Is that how eternity felt—warm and unbounded, without motion or time, and with no weight? Did eternity rest in Billy's reply: "Be happy," now and always, simply and fully?

A scent tweaked my nose: jasmine perfume. It was Mrs. Thomas wafting by, one arm gesturing wildly while she jabbered, the other hugging a stack of notebooks and her purse to her side. Watch out, I thought to say, but before I spoke, Mrs. Thomas slammed into Father Shudders. Her purse shot out of her hands and spewed its contents onto the lawn.

"Oh," Mrs. Thomas squeaked. Her face went red as she crouched and grabbed for several pink makeup compacts, her black and her red address books, her prayer book, and a cigar. She groaned, mortified, when she snagged her frilly pair of nothingness and shoved them into her purse.

Father moved to help her, but he stopped short. "I beg your pardon,

Mrs. Thomas. I wasn't watching where I was going."

"Um . . . thank you . . . I mean . . . yes, okay," she said.

I turned my head away, and so did Billy.

We watched a toddler teeter by, his mother's hands out in case he should fall.

"Billy, how do you cope?"

He smiled and leaned his torso forward. "Be happy," he stammered. "Just be happy."

"It's that simple?"

He bobbled-nodded.

The parishioners' gaiety overtook us for a while. I guessed they'd forgotten their troubles, their brows unfurrowing in our day of pleasure. Was our summer social their way of finding a kind of center or balance —a place of peace?

"You know," I started, "I think we're all tight rope walkers trying to balance. We're tested, and then we find our balance by using gifts. Some of them might be powered by opposing forces, but they find a center or equilibrium."

"Really Sean? What's that?" Billys expression said.

"It's what happens when opposing chemical reactions find a resting place. One reaction goes one way, while the other one works in the opposite direction. But there is a balance or equilibrium where they find peace."

Billy agreed with me. I reckoned he strove to find his way, too.

At that moment I saw Billy differently. Sure, he was challenged, but I didn't see him as a disabled person who was imprisoned in his body. I saw him as a pool of cool water on a hot day, calm except for eddies swirling to form patterns. He made me feel more at ease than I'd ever felt before.

Mrs. Crinshaw made her way back, and I guess Billy must have seen her approach. He turned toward me with import on his face. "R-e-e-e-m-e-m-m-b-a-a-a m-e-e," he said. "Remember me."

Of course I'll remember you, I thought, as I will all of my friends. Then, in a twinkling I knew what he wanted. He'd asked me to remember what we talked about and to share it with others.

"Oh yes, I will remember you. I'll tell your story, too. Really I will. I'll tell it the best way that I know how."

"Billy," Mrs. Crinshaw sing-songed, "it's time to play bingo." I could tell by the way she gripped his chair that her wish was really a command.

My, how I wanted her to leave. As Mrs. Crinshaw turned to wheel Billy away, I touched his right hand. "I'll remember everything. Don't fret. I'll tell your story, the best way I know how."

I confounded Mrs. Crinshaw. For starters, maybe she didn't know how Billy and I connected. Did she suspect what we knew? That was the last time we'd see each other. He died in his sleep later that month, and we felt it coming. I knew it—that he would not last another six weeks. We both knew it, and that made saying farewell tougher.

Billy Crinshaw's death proved a small comfort, for I knew his pain had ended. But his story lived on. I've been carrying it some thirty years now, and I've hoped countless times that I might be able to tell it clean and crisp: as clean as a pin.

"Perfection isn't needed or even wanted," Billy would reassure me. "Compassion and persistence mean the most." Sometimes, all that folks need is for us to be there for them—simply to comfort them. When we show up, we receive much more than we give. We'll be all right, in spite of our faults. With that comfort, we've nothing left to fear—nothing at all."

Dad's 1960 Dodge

One Friday morning after he tinkered with Dad's 1960 Dodge to "tune it up", my seventeen-year-old brother Paul declared, "I'd better take this for a spin—test the brakes."

"Huh? What's wrong with them?" I asked. I'd been watching Paul work, and he hadn't so much as peeked at the car's brakes.

"Not reliable. Need testing."

I was convinced.

The call went out, "Who wants a ride?" Leo, Greg, and yours truly answered by piling onto the car's wide front seat. Paul drove sensibly enough out of our yard, but in no time he proceeded to pace the car—like a caged Siberian tiger—on the west road that framed our section: a half mile out, a half mile back, a half mile out, a half mile back . . .

Then, as if the tiger's cage door suddenly flew open, Paul "floored it", bounding downhill to freedom. Faster and faster we sped until gravity nudged us past seventy miles per hour. Wind screamed through the open windows, and Paul grinned. Greg, Leo, and I huddled against the dashboard, and we held on tightly enough to whiten our knuckles.

Paul pushed the car faster, and then "whomp" he tromped the brake pedal. We boys splatted against the dashboard, and we welted underneath its girth. An otherworldly grinding—exponentially more grating than fingernails being dragged down a chalkboard—echoed through the valley, tingling the small hairs on the back of my neck. Then, a miasmic dust cloud mushroomed skyward before it pettered out, fluttering back to engulf us.

I wondered if the car had "passed" in Paul's rush to the edge. After I peeled myself off of Greg and Leo, I spied Paul's face. It held a going-in-for-the-kill look. Paul panted with a huntsman's shallow breathing, showing me that more lay in store. As much as I would have liked it, I didn't dare ask, "What the hell are you doing?" I sat red-faced next to the boys, all of us hoping to return home without wet accidents.

On our final eastward approach to the driveway, Paul exclaimed, "The brakes are gone!" as he commenced to pump the pedal.

"Not funny," I squeaked out, hoping he was funning us.

Paul's rapid-fire expletives showed me otherwise. He pounded his foot like some dazed fool playing a Souza march on a pipe organ (the kind that's fed wind by foot power). The brakes kicked in a tad, but they were too late. We clipped forty as we neared the left-hand turn into our driveway. Someone (was it me?) yelled, "We're goners!"

The way I saw it, Paul had two choices. He could forget the driveway and nose the Dodge east and downhill toward the spring. We'd fly down that road, primed by our still healthy speed, and we'd likely bottom out at eighty. That meant passing the spring at lightning speed before the uphill piece near the rock quarry stopped us. Then, Paul could shift into park and breathe. Would our savior be that section of the gravel road above the spring, the one that shot up at a ridiculous grade (far steeper than that of runaway truck ramps)?

The other choice meant easing the tires—an unlikely possibility since we were doing forty—into a right turn southward onto the dirt road leading to the main road three miles south. The car would tucker out along the way, the same as would a too-tired hound after romps through weary hills. Gripping the dashboard again, I felt my eyes bug out, and I chanted, "East, east, east!"

Presently Paul divined a third option as he shouted, "Hit the floor!" He aimed to maneuver a left turn into our driveway, but momentum said otherwise. Careening toward our mailbox, we shot for its resting place midway up a terrace above the dirt road. It lay nestled in a ten-gallon milk can filled with gravel. Did it sweat as the car lunged toward it? The Dodge scooped up the mailbox—milk can and all— dragging it beneath us. That wedged mailbox dampened our speed until the Dodge ground to a halt.

We made it, I thought—too soon. Paul bellowed, "Get out. It'll blow!" The four of us scrambled for our lives.

Well, the Dodge didn't blow. It did rest at a weird angle, propped up by our crumpled rock-filled barrel, though. Had the car gorged on the barrel, grown sleepy, and demanded a nap to digest its prey? The fender and grille were bashed in, but the rest of the car looked unscathed. (We later learned Paul had bent the Dodge's frame, rendering it unsafe to drive farther than thirty miles at a shot, its vibration wearing the tires thin before their time.)

Jacking up the car, we pried and dragged the mailbox's remains from underneath it, and I asked Paul, "What . . . what will you tell Dad?"

He brushed the question aside with his right hand. "It doesn't matter.

The Dodge needed its cobwebs cleared. We all know how touchy the brakes are, don't we?"

I can't say whether it was Paul's answer or something brewing in my "gizzard", but I felt dazed. "Dad's not gonna buy that," I said.

"Listen, we did the old man a favor," Paul snapped.

"I don't think so," I fussed, butterflies banging around in my stomach.

"To hell with it, then!" Paul growled, stomping away, swirls of dust echoing his retreat.

Did Paul have something to prove? Did I?

Later that day, Leo and I crept up to Paul on the back porch. "May I borrow your BB gun?" I asked.

"Why? What for?"

"Target practice."

Was I thinking clearly, seeing as how that Daisy hand-pump BB gun could spit a BB no more than a hundred yards? Besides, the BBs fancied silly arching paths, not the clean ones of grown-up guns. What target was I expecting to sight, much less hit?

Paul cocked his head from side to side, as if studied a too-ripe banana. "All right." He shrugged. "Stay here." He fetched his "rifle", along with a soft-sided red container that swelled with hundreds of BBs, from our long shed (home for our fryers, ducklings, goats, and a granary tucked behind closed doors on its west side).

"Break it, and you'll both pay. Got that?" (Didn't that go without saying?)

Perspiration trickled down our brows as Leo and I took turns toting Paul's rifle up to our sharpshooters' roost in the mulberry overlooking our barnyard. We aimed to ping a metal drum that loitered next to the chicken shed. Instead, we wafted BBs all over the barnyard, including the corrugated tin roof of the chicken shed, the wall of cinder blocks on the south side of our long shed, and a rusted Burma Shave sign that rested against the shed for only God knows why.

We didn't make one strike in ten. After firing off a dozen more rounds—shots—Leo said, "To hell with it, anyway."

"Let's aim for something that's important," I muttered, pointing the rifle barrel toward the green roof of Dad's Dodge. He had parked it south of our chicken shed.

"Why bother shooting at it? You won't hit it anyway." Leo said.

I took that as a dare, and I aimed to hit the Dodge, or least ways cuss myself for not trying. Pumping the rifle, I brought the butt to my shoulder, squeezed the trigger, and sent forth a BB. It traced an unpredictable arch before it struck near the roof. The only trouble is, it twitched down at the last instant to connect with the front passenger window. It shattered the glass into a web any spider would envy.

"Jesus H. Roosevelt Christ, Sean!" Leo yelped.

"I can't believe it!" I gasped. "I thought safety glass was 'shatter resistant'." It didn't put up much of a struggle, especially given our fool gun's weak muzzle velocity. "How can one miserable BB do damage like that?"

A chill shot down my spine, and the blood in my legs froze, numbing them. "What'll we say?" I needed to think.

Leo nodded, burying his hands in his pockets.

"Let's roll up the window, punch out the glass, and then roll it back down. No one will know the difference for a while." I needed to buy time, and I figured stealth was my dry tender.

Leo kept watch while I handed Paul his so-called rifle. Then, we snatched a burlap sack from the granary. Into it we plopped the broken glass, lumped in three chunks still clinging together—spidery veins and all. We disposed of "the evidence" in our dump, a spot in our northwest pasture, and we vowed to keep mum.

Just home from his week at Argentine, of course Dad took a notion to drive to town. As luck would have it, a storm brewed. Dad tried to roll up the front windows . . . er, window.

"Say Sean, do you know anything about my missing window?" Dad asked slinking into the living room where I watched "Gomer Pyle, USMC". Out of the corner of my eye, I spied Leo walking our way. He turned "about-face" and hightailed it into the kitchen when he heard Dad.

I gulped, "Yes sir."

"What happened?"

"Well, I accidentally shot a BB through it, and it shattered."

That was part was true. I hadn't bothered to tell the part about swirling mists of my misguided energy that focused on his car. I also did not utter a word about how Paul's car abuse and answer to my questions had infected me, or the part about feeling duty-bound to attack his 1960 Dodge. (Was that my job?)

Dad grimaced and shook his head. "I won't even ask about the mailbox." He scuffled into the kitchen.

Stunned, I thought, Is that it? Won't he yell at me or punish me? Will he do anything? Isn't that what Dads are meant to do? I felt a gnawing in my stomach. Did Dad's soft manner mean "weakness"?

Dad drapped a dark plastic over the hole to shroud what once had been his Dodge window.

No sooner had news of the second "mishap" trickled through our family when Mark, all of sixteen years, reckoned it was his turn with Dad's car. It was Saturday, and Dad napped in the downstairs bedroom. Mark drove the Dodge past the clothesline to the gate of our newly mowed fescue field. Parking it near the spot where our king cottonwood had reigned, he aimed to keep company with a girl who was even smarter than she was pretty. Our neighbor Bonnie had skipped a grade on account of being bright. She lived a mile south of us. Almost daily in the summertime, she galloped her father's horse to our farm.

That day both the horse and Dad's car raced. (I spied the action from the top of our pear tree in the northwest pasture.) That poor horse had more than a workout, what with galloping to save himself from a hideous mechanical monster commandeered by a hormone-dazed teenager. I declare, Mark traced enough rings to earn a contract with Daylight Doughnuts. As impressive as that looked, his finale lay in store.

Although the fescue had been cut, Mark sweated to hold his bearings in the field. From where I sat, I could tell he lost track of where he headed or what might come next. Whirling the car about, he gunned it and headed for our pond, barely twenty feet ahead of him. When he saw his imminent dunking, it was too late to swerve. Mark "floored it".

Well, the Dodge hit the pond's slight embankment and went airborne. And it might have had a sporting chance of clearing the pond on a good day, but this wasn't one. The wind blew other plans, pinning down its speed. The car lit on the water's surface, skipped a few feet like a flat rock, and sank to a stop near the pond's far shore. Although the car's front tires met the bank, its rear ones hadn't. They were mired in a foot of mud, clay, and cow poop.

Well, it's sure that Bonnie's little horse never guessed it'd be conscripted to rescue the very monster that had tormented it. Using a rope from our milk barn, Mark attached it to its bridle. The poor thing heaved dutifully, coaxing the Dodge to slurp out of the mire. He needed three tries and more than four minutes.

Once he'd freed it, Mark gingerly eased Dad's mud-bombed car back onto the north driveway, and then he parked it south of the chicken house. The horse and rider followed a healthy distance behind.

Climbing down from my viewing station in the pear tree, I trotted to Mark. Whew! I had to stop before I reached him. Had a stink bomb exploded inside the Dodge?

Mark was climbing from the driver's seat when I approached. "Did you see that?" he started to chatter, waiting for my congratulations.

Lifting my eyebrows, I nodded.

Mark commenced his jabbering at Bonnie like a sassy jay, ignoring me. "I'm sure I'd have cleared the pond if the winds hadn't been against me!"

"The car's a mess, Mark." I said. "It smells like-"

"It's nothing! I'll swab that up inside of a few minutes!" Mark didn't let on when the "few minutes" might commence. Well, Mark flirted with his guest, and soon he decided to escort her home. He strutted alongside the horse as happy as you please, his hand glued to its bridle. The pond ooze ripened in the late morning sun, and I took Mark's "few minutes" to mean sometime after Dad stirred.

The trio had cleared our yard when our sleep-dulled dad strolled up to check on something in the chicken house. Why hadn't I thought to disappear before then?

Dad swiped his palm over his mouth and nose. Then, he muffled, "What in the name of Jesus, Mary, and Joseph happened?"

Stuck with the truth, I started, "Mark dunked it into the pond in the northwest pasture. But he'll clean it up in no time. Besides, the car runs all right, even with that heavy layer of gunk." (Once in a while, my mouth kept moving long after my brain had signaled it to hush up.)

Dad's heavy sigh sucked out whatever air—or will—remained in him. He turned away from the car, from his hellions, and from anger. Shaking his head, he made for the house.

"Dad, Mark's still within earshot," I silently pleaded. "Call him home. Shout 'Get back here, Mark, and I mean now!'"

Dad didn't hear me. His shoulders hunched, as if they wanted to hold and comfort the rest of him. What kind of father would let Mark get away with such carrying on? Shouldn't Dad at least ground him to let him know who's in charge, especially since Mark had fallen short of dry ground on our pond's far shore? Maybe Dad was too tuckered out by wage earners' bankruptcy. Did he feel tired because he missed his brother Jim? Maybe . . .

Grandmother scolded, "You and your brothers are like a pack of bluetick hounds, Sean. You're all begging to know who's in charge."

Grandmother had heard about our mishaps. She knew that Paul,

Mark, and I had them now and again. But I reckon she was generous in use of the term "mishaps". Did our shenanigans qualify? Mishaps are innocent, unlike intentional acts, which are another animal altogether.

"Well, I reckon you might be right," I mumbled to Grandmother.

"*Might* be right? I am right, darn tooting. You boys are provoking your dad into showing his teeth, just the way young pups nip at the lead male until he snaps." Grandmother stared at me. I didn't answer. Had I ever seen Dad snap?

Well, right about that time, Leo must have been shedding his milk teeth because one night the following week he took to nipping at Dad.

First he stripped off both of the Dodge's windshield wiper blades—like a famished man who might gnaw the flesh from a tasty drumstick. Next, he freed the driver's side wiper arm, and then he mangled the passenger's side wiper arm. (Did that shape look like the weird path of the BBs?) Maybe Leo guessed Dad wouldn't notice.

Of course, Dad noticed. Not only did Leo's deed blur Dad's vision, but in a downpour it also clawed at his hearing. When he switched on the remaining wiper, it screeched at him.

Dad knew Leo authored the work. Was he suspected, seeing as how he was the next boy in line? Maybe Dad knew any more damage wasn't worth the bother for us older boys.

When confronted, Leo managed only, "Greg did it."

"Greg's too small to crawl up onto the hood," Dad countered, "least ways, strong enough to strip the wipers clean that way."

Leo stared back, daring Dad to continue, and Dad stopped short. In fact, he simply sighed and walked away—again—his breath in long draws.

"Please, Dad, punish us!" ached to blast out of me. "Get angry! Lunge! At least give us a deep throaty growl . . . anything!"

But Dad never budged from his defeated (or even dead) stand, and that felt like no leadership at all.

Maybe some of the tension between fathers and sons draws from a need to know who's in charge. Can knowing that cushion angst in an uncertain world? Didn't we want Dad's attention? Oh sure, Dad came home, but at the same he hadn't come home—not really.

Amazingly, after all of that, Dad's 1960 Dodge still ran all right. Its looks fueled humiliation tall enough to shame anyone, but Dad drove it nevertheless. He clattered it to Argentine on Sunday evenings, and then he shimmied it back home on Friday nights.

But soon the shame loomed too hefty even for Dad, and he took to parking it south of our chicken house. He left it there to rest. Since we toted Janice to Spear's Chiropractic College on Troost Avenue in Kansas City, Missouri most Sunday evenings, Dad rode along to Argentine.

Who's to say how long Dad's 1960 Dodge would have lasted had we boys not fiddled with it to raise Dad's eyebrows? As it was, the car did not amount to much anymore, scuttled that way. Its frame lay bent, its front fender mangled. Only jagged edges of greenish glass remained on the passenger-side front window, a sheet of dark plastic doing its best to convince raindrops to stay outside. It wanted a windshield wiper arm on one side, and its sole wiper went without a blade. Winged grasshoppers whirled onto its hood to rest a spell. Shade weeds thrived in its shadow. Although the car boasted of an automatic transmission, that didn't cushion its disgrace. Dad's 1960 Dodge had surely seen kinder days. And thanks to his boys, so had Dad.

Our Personal Lab

Although we'd never let on, we kids grew more partial to our farm than Thomas Alva Edison "claimed" he was to his Menlo Park lab. Like Junior Edisons, we concocted towering inventions. Unlike him, we tooled with lowly supplies. That meant improvising as we often cut corners that were best left unrounded.

Mostly, our creations defied mighty forces for a shining moment. Oh, gravity invariably spewed turmoil our way, and it broke loose along with our gadgets. Then, pain sat in as we lay scuffed and bruised on the ground. When our gadgets and we kids crashed to earth, we asked, "Why us? What went wrong?" Through it all, we treasured glorious moments when we fancied something to behold.

A more sober view tells me our inventions couldn't have impressed a too-drunk hog. Our launch pads held bound-for-heaven rockets that ignited there before daring to twitch even an inch skyward. But we never said die. No self-respecting kid could ever quit. My two younger brothers, Greg and Leo, panted to help, throwing their weight behind our escapades. Four years my junior, Leo was in second grade. Greg was only four.

Invariably, our homemade "ships of state" rocked on the deep spot in our creek before they gushed with leaks. Tilting dramatically, they floundered, swamped, and hit rock bottom.

Each time our inventions collapsed, we dropped to our knees to catch our breath and to lick our wounds.

Undeterred, we tunneled into the musty earth to dig secret tunnels until limestone in bedrock drowsed our dreams. Our holes from those encounters exposed rocks that only a snake might fancy for sunning, but that pleased no one—maybe not even the snakes.

When we crafted palaces from hybrid bamboo canes, our cattle found their own use for them. They commenced rubbing the base of their horns against the canes until their itchy motion swept our empire into a heap of rubble.

Once we unearthed a drainage pipe in our barnyard which trickled to moisten a spot that called for inspection. There we crafted a dam of gravel and mud to form a muck-filled pond, which we stocked with minnows. That was part of our dreams for "trophy" fishing without leaving home. Instead, the pond sweltered into a breeding ground for mosquitoes before Dad leveled it one day as he slurped his 1960 Dodge through that mud hole. Our pond wilted.

Perhaps more startled than wounded, more puzzled than hurt, we wondered again, "Why us? What went wrong? Why can't one of our designs work?" A better question might have been, "Why do we need to invent? Why hatch such dribble?" Did we aim to leave a mark in stone, even if it was edged in crimson? Did we need to tame nature in some small way?

While some little boys wore capes and jumped from barrels to fly, we invented. We simply had to try, although that meant bruised limbs and dashed hopes. Dad once told us that old Alva had tried thousands of compounds before deciding that tungsten would work in light filaments. He'd taken many hits, too, and we boys knew we could not quit. After all, great inventions come with immense sacrifice.

One unsavory incident involved a rocket engine that exploded on the launch pad. That blast charred my undershirt. A welt blossomed on my right hand—the offending agent that lit our engine.

Spotting me as I trudged up our sidewalk, Mother tried not to laugh, what with my blackened undershirt and puffed hand. The burn was only first degree, and that meant she'd lay it on me again—the first degree, that is.

"Soak your fingers in here." Mother poured a glass of milk for me. "It'll help soothe your skin." Then, after convincing me that no surgery was needed, she lightly bandaged it.

I lost track of the number of times that I wandered to the house for help. "How did it happen this time, Sean? Were you playing with matches?"

Had that been the case, I might have felt better. Instead, I had to tell Mother that I had spent two whole dollars on an Estes rocket engine. (We kids didn't have the money for the fancy ignition switch to work the engine properly.) I had to confess that I'd tried to fire the engine the "old-fashioned" way. Leo and I had snuffed our way through half a box of Diamond brand matches.

"Well, I hope you learned to follow directions. Those engines are unstable. Do you know how lucky you are? Why, you might have been seriously hurt—maybe even put out an eye." (Once Ann had caught her eyelid on the side of a tuna can that heaved skyward with the help of a firecracker. Mother never let us live that down.) "Think through a prob-

lem a couple of times before you take action." Mother knew what to
say to make me feel better and worse.

Besides treating burns from rocket experiments gone mad, Mother
also iced fingers mashed by heavy objects—like tree houses. Dad had
replaced the living room door, and he told us boys that we could use it
for whatever we pleased. That way, he wouldn't need to burn it.
Naturally, we wedged that door against two mulberry branches to craft
our treehouse. We didn't want to kill the tree—no sir—so we didn't
hammer any nails into it. Our hearts were in the right place, but I can't
say as much for our wits.

One morning Greg, Leo, and I were lounging on our fine tree house
door. I was lying on my back, and the boys were stretched on their
stomachs when a bee landed on my thigh. Startled, I jerked my leg, and
that threw us off balance. With that, the door commenced to slip. It
tobogganed earthward to pick up speed, just as did our heartbeats. One
moment our home was safe, and the next moment it was a rattling
death trap. A pile of hay cushioned our impact. If it hadn't done its
work, our injuries might have blossomed way beyond Leo's pinched fingers and the egg on my noggin.

Mother usually mumbled, "Chores are waiting," as she aimed to coax
us back into the real world. We knew she tried to put up with our pal-
pable need to invent, but enough was enough (and sometimes too
much). Mother comforted us when our dreams ended up splintered on
the ground along side of our latest contraptions.

It wasn't always poor planning that doomed our designs. For example, one summer day I wandered along the ditch of the dirt and gravel road that skirted the south side of our yard. Marooned in thought about how to solve a technical problem in our latest nautical disaster, I didn't see it—a stout Canada thistle—stretched out in front of me. As I passed, it clawed at my arm. I spun about to escape, but it was too fast for me, and it latched onto my britches. Squirming to work loose, I lost my balance and slammed face first onto the ground. That thistle had tripped me! Before I could right myself, a car raced by to spew grit over my face and shirt. That fool thistle had thrown me to the ground, and it held me there until I was covered with dryness.

"Well I be go to hell! Thistles are horrid pains in the ass!" I declared.

Dusting myself off and peering around to ensure no one had seen what happened, I ambled to the barnyard where our free-roam Rhode Island chickens scurried about. Leo was watching the fowl from his nest, a platform in our mulberry.

That ancient tree towered at least fifty feet above the barnyard. It must have been a whopping hundred years old, and its trunk showed it. Girded with thick hunks of bark that crinkled out at least an inch, that powerful tree begged us boys to adorn its branches with treehouses of the mobile persuasion. (They fancied wandering about like a bug on a hot night).

Hoisting myself up to join Leo, I announced, "It's about time we hatch another adventure, don't you think? This mulberry deserves it."

"Yeah, we need something cool, like what the Swiss Family Robinson did," Leo answered.

A collection of platforms rested in the mulberry, but we needed a better way to rise from the ground to any one of them. We'd been toying with an elevator design.

"We'll need a shell to build an elevator," I began. Our eyes swept the barnyard before they settled next to the chicken shed where an abandoned metal drum glinted in the afternoon sunlight.

"There's our shell!" Leo and I yelped. We scurried down the tree and over to the drum. It looked perfect. Its rim showcased four holes around its mouth at ninety-degree angles.

"We'll thread the ropes through those holes," I instructed.

"What ropes?" Leo sighed. "Do you see how small those holes are?"

Greg left the porch to join us after he saw us run for the drum.

"Bailing twine," I said.

"You mean 'hay rope'," Greg corrected.

"All right, have it your way. Yes, hay rope will do."

We boys fashioned a girdle of baling twine that radiated from the mouth of the barrel. To this we attached two strands of twine as our main cable. Then, we heaved that cable over an unsuspecting branch.

"Gravity, move over," I said.

Tugging at the main cable, we managed to hoist the drum a pinch. As the drum lifted, the rope chafed against the branch and stalled. Greg and I beamed. Our design had worked a little.

"Oh, that's fine," Leo huffed.

"It isn't too bad," I said. "So what if the rope rubs."

"What do you mean it isn't too bad? This piece of crap doesn't work enough to spit."

"Well, if we raise the elevator slowly, it'll work," I assured him.

We really needed a pulley, but as it turned out, friction was the least of our problems that day.

With our experiment working, we commenced phase two. We needed a willing victim—er, candidate—to pilot our invention. That lucky fellow would whisk to his stately tree chalet, offering a splendid view of our barnyard, grazing fowl and all.

Naturally, we chose our youngest brother Greg, four years old and barely forty pounds. In such work the youngest and lightest brother is always chosen. Greg graciously accepted, and he climbed into the drum. I scampered up to a platform to keep vigil while Leo stayed on the ground to work the cable. Then, down went the rope. Up sailed the metal drum—heaved by inches with each pull, but who was keeping track? Up and away it sailed with Greg.

"My gosh, it works," I exulted as I peered over the side of the platform. I knew the day would be ours, and we'd have our way. Gravity was going down for the count. Swiss Family Robinson, move over.

Perched on our platform, I gazed down to see Greg, who clapped and bounced, the dust clouds flying up from his feet. (Given our inventive haste, we'd forgotten to clean out the drum.) No points were earned for neatness, and that was more than offset by how our cussed elevator worked. Greg stopped bouncing long enough to clasp his hands and to hold his breath. He was suspended in heaven, and he needed to taste his glory.

Then I heard it—chafing of the baling twine as sharp metal edges ate into it. Our design flaw began to rouse from its slumber. With more chafing and cutting, one cable snapped. Its side of the elevator sagged, and Greg shifted to the opposite side. Snap! The other cable gave way, and disaster loomed. It marched punctually, homeward bound.

I must save him, I thought, as I leaned over the platform to catch the hellish sight: our vehicle and it's hapless pilot hurtling to earth, as if in slow motion.

"I'll save you!" I hollered as I stretched out my arms to grasp Greg. At the same time, I lost balance. In short order, I mimicked the elevator's descent, and that slow motion scene changed into a speeding one that might have dazed "The Flash" himself. My arms froze outstretched as I reached for Greg. (I'd forgotten to ask, "If I'm saving Greg, who in the Sam Hill's saving me?") I excuse myself, as such details are easy to overlook at age eleven.

A great cloud of debris rifled skyward as Greg's steed crashed to earth with an attitude. A jarring thud echoed from the metal drum, and an ominous dust cloud mushroomed from it. Greg wailed, more rattled than hurt. Then, faster than I could say Jack Robinson, I clumsily bounced off of both the drum and Greg. When I struck, my pupils were dilated for action. Luckily, I cushioned myself with my arms, and I protected my ribs.

"What'd ya do, Greg?" Leo hollered. "Why'd ya break it?"

"You yellow-bellied sapsuckers!" Greg pelted back. "You two planned this! I'll get you for this. I be go to hell, I'll get you for this!" Slowly, his anger waned with his wind. With fewer colorful words, he bellowed, "You two planned this thing, including Sean's falling out of the tree onto this piece of crap." Greg reinforced his accusation with a string of profanity aimed at both of us in general and at me in particular

Friend, I'm telling you I didn't fall from the tree and hit Greg and his drum to frame his woes. Since gravity works faster than I can think, I hadn't planned it. Still, we were fairly shaken, and distress beaconed from our faces in silent droves. Although our consciences were clear, our designs were clouded.

How could I explain to my brothers that our troubles were a tribute to our old nemesis—gravity—that had beaten us again? Gravity had pulled the elevator down, and it had spanked us in the process.

I couldn't talk for a while, but I felt a tinge of laughter in my chest along with a dull pain in my ribs, which was fitting. Hadn't our scene rivaled any from "The Keystone Cops"?

Greg shook with conspiracy theories, Leo shook with anger, and I shook with pain. But because I had meant to save Greg, I didn't shake with guilt. While my face and shoulders were pretty scratched up, I couldn't have shouldered my guilt had I not tried to save Greg. At least on that count, the day had proved successful. I suspect that Mr. Edison and his loyal assistants might have agreed.

Lo, A Twinkling Diamond's Evening Glow

Summer mornings in the sauna that's eastern Kansas swell with stickiness until a body feels cocooned by tatters of glistening fly paper. By afternoon the sultry air mugs unsuspecting guests, sweltering anyone fussing over whether or not they have enough juice left to spit. That goes double for souls who toil over soils. A searing sun sets parched lips into fits of quickening quivers.

Adrift in a growing family, I winced at how my list of chores didn't shrink. It grew. Stooping to pick strawberries or bush beans, a creeping numbness slithered down me, commencing around my waist. My shirt become part of my skin, and it clinged to me like tree frogs. As I swatted at buzzing flies with an attitude, my bangs speared upward with my heated puffs. Drenched in sweat, would my clothes need to be cut off of me? On milder days hope might huff its warm breath. On those days, I reckoned that I'd be found. My would-be rescuers could spray me down with "Off". Then, they'd power-hose me, stripping off tattered remains of one-time clothes.

As I picked green beans, the sun played tricks on me. The soil reflected heat, which I felt and saw in hazy patches of breathless air. A slight breeze stirred up dust over the rows, and the sun rays bounced off of packed soils. The hundred-degree heat freed aromas, some metallic and bland, but most dusty and dry. Heat has the final say with scents in crofts, and I smelled every rude degree.

Aromas hatched in warmth told me where I stood, and I could smell my way from row to row without looking. Moistness trickled past my neck until it settled in the small of my back. Aching for relief when a whiff of wind stole by, I tasted the heat of airborne dust.

Does sweat change flavor with rising temperatures? The saltiness of ninety-five degrees toyed with me, followed by the acrid smell of a hundred degrees. Dust seeping into my mouth tasted different than on cooler days. Does salt in dust gauge itself with every degree? Heat waves made their sounds known—withered leaves that rustled in heat streams rising from clayey soils. Torrid summer days stretched on with our work. Grandmother often declared, "It feels like were a mile from hell, and the gates are all down."

Lulling fans were upstaged by a newcomer, our window-mounted air conditioning unit. We found a home for it in the east window of our living room. When no one watched, I pealed up my tee shirt, and I lapped up cooled air. The thrill of chilled air on wet skin showed me heaven lives. While it stunned me at first, that didn't stop me from flapping the bottom of my tee shirt to lick up all that delicious air.

"Stop it, now! You're soaking up the coolness!" Mary snorted. She fussed that I blunted the cooling magic in our living room. On top of that, a whiff of my saltiness blended with the air. Sucking up heat and moisture, the unit sweated great globs that leaked from its back side, which peeked outside. The ground moistened with those warm droplets.

We counted on four o'clock and its promise of a visit with the family at Collinswood Manor for the latest episode of "**Dark** Shadows". Simply to watch those waves pounding against cool, stone beaches roused our heat-seared brains. Our television sat in the living room, and that meant degrees of relief, courtesy of that blessed window unit.

I craved the show for two reasons. First came a rest from the heat. More importantly came a flight of fancy. I could feel myself in that coastal Maine town, the ocean sploshing along the rocks and misting onto our sun-drenched faces. The salty foam felt better than it tasted. In those evening mists, I made out a faint tapping sound of footsteps drawing nigh. Had Barnabas come calling?

After "**Dark** Shadows", we tore ourselves from our cool hovel to commence evening chores. At least once a month, I mowed our considerable yard and terraces whether they needed it or not. While no one told me what time of day to mow, I knew not to commence after nine in the morning or before late afternoon. The time in-between, that no-man's land of torridness, was when some folks bellyached about their air con-

ditioned offices where they worked. Didn't they know the heaven that
was theirs?

One July's late afternoon I had finished mowing the lawn, and I commenced working on the east and south terraces. I drifted. My mind went
anywhere other than there. I estimated surface areas for cross sections
that I mentally sliced from curved objects. I was "occupied". Our butcher's meat slicer and scale appeared. I could slice any curved object into
slivers. Once I knew the cross-sectional area of each piece, I estimated
their tiny volumes. By adding the volumes for thousands of such slivers,
I estimated the total volume of a curved solid.

Once I knew the volume, I computed its weight. But first, I needed to
estimate its density. Sometimes, I practiced this game as I watched our
butcher slicing briskets. "Take your time, Mr. Hamlet," I offered, imply-
ing I wanted no accidents. What I really wanted was time to cipher. To
know the weight of the meat stack, I worked out the volume for each
brisket slice. Then, I added them for its total volume. I multiplied that
total by the meat's weight per cubic inch. (I kept a list of densities for
various meats—ham, brisket, pork chops, etc.) Finally, I tested my
answer by glancing at his scale. After all, a butcher's scale is only a kind
of adding machine to total the weight of meat slices. It measures the
force of gravity on the volume of meat heaped on the scale. I'd been
computing the weights of such objects with estimated volumes and densities for more years than I could spit in feet.

As I mowed, I worked out weights of weirdly-shaped chicken shed
roofs, their heaving tin in waves like the ocean. Other times I crafted
riddles or stories. Without such pastimes, I'd have been bored blind.

Shoving our mower up and down the terrace on the south side of our
yard, I came near the mailbox that Paul had "crinkled" with Dad's 1960
Dodge. Glorious, swirling thoughts had marooned me on a distant
shore. Without warning, I flinched at the thud of the mower, which had
died. The mower fell victim to an old poke wanna-be, laying hold of the
blade to stop it cold.

"Well, I'll be go to hell!" I muttered. Judging by the evidence, I
guessed that the cotter pin had been bent by the lusty weed. Did that old
poke get its grins by whacking the mower blade silent? The weed in
question was a particularly juicy Canada Thistle that I'd disliked forever.
It was the same kind of troublemaker that I'd only recently begun to
wonder about, imagining that I might find a pinch of goodness in its
heart.

"No account, piece-of-shit weed! Boorish, invasive weed!" I sputtered
as I marched to the house to find some pliers, a screw driver, and a
spare cotter pin.

The other kids had not stored the tools in their proper place in the tool box resting in the entry room to our kitchen. That vestibule doubled as a place to hang sweaters and coats, as well as a storage room for tools, boots, and our wooden step ladder. (It was folded, resting against the west wall.)

As I stumbled out of the storage room to walk back to the mower, I huffed with an attitude. "That's all I needed," I fumed. Delays riled me because I knew that after I finished mowing, there were cows to be milked, chickens to be fed, and hogs to be slopped. Supper would follow.

Then, after all that fuss, I'd slink away into the darkness, blending in there. Mother'd expect me to help her water our garden, which swelled to nearly one acre, a size that meant her watering projects stretched late into the evening. Why should I risk being nabbed for one of Mother's water crews?

As I trudged out of the house, the sound of two shot gun blasts caught my ears. "What? What's happening?" I sputtered.

Then, a strange sound of pain personified stunned me. It was the sound of an animal howling in agony. A strange man toting a double-barreled shot gun stood on the gravel road fronting the south side of our yard. That sight startled me, my breath coming in rapid puffs as I dashed toward him.

"Was that Mr. Crocker? Had he come back to finish old business?" I gasped, the image of his sad and terrified eyes seared into my memory. I recalled the day our drunken and estranged neighbor pounded on our farmhouse door with the butt of his shot gun. That day Mother shouted him down. Did he grip that fool Peace Dollar in his sweaty palm, and had it lived up to its promise?

Well, I could see that it wasn't Mr. Crocker. This man was much heavier, a sizable pouch girding his midsection. Taking aim toward something writhing on the gravel road, the stranger raised his weapon. Before he shot, I caught sight of a bloodhound sprawled in the dust and gravel. The hound yelped, his cries chilling my blood.

As I reached the stranger, he fired. A sickening sound blasted from his shot gun, echoing into our valley. The hound's tormented body went to twitching, then to stillness.

"Mister, whatcha doing? What happened to your bloodhound? Why did you blast him?" I asked in rapid fire.

"Diamond back rattler got him, right on his snout. Had to put him down," the man murmured. His fingers were crumpled to form a half fist, only his index finger mostly straightened as he stood pointing at the remains of his "best" friend. (His quaking voice and misty eyes told me so.) I stopped looking at the man's face to cloak his embarrassment.

"We were hunting on your land. Mr. Redmond said it was okay. My hound snooped where he shouldn't have. Look," he motioned as I traced the direction of his outstretched hand. On the terrace not five yards west of our mailbox rested the remains of a diamond back. The hunter had blasted it to pieces, and its tattered remains rested in bloody strips. Pieces of its mangled body wrapped around sturdy weeds and fescue stems on the terrace.

The sight of bloody snake guts, twisted and draped over and around weeds, sent a shudder down my spine. The snake innards were spackled onto them, making a hybrid of plant and animal, which was an odd chimera. The stranger's shots had done their work, and I imagined that some of those weeds looked like they were part snake and part old pokes.

"Were you mowing this terrace, son?" the stranger asked, motioning toward my broken-down machine.

"Yes, sir. I was," I muttered as I swiped sweat from my brow. I had come within a dozen feet of that diamond back.

"Looks like Champ did you a favor." The man's voice quaked, and his eyes misted. "God, I loved that dog. He was my best friend . . . had to put him down."

"You mean he did me a favor by nosing into that diamond back? I might have stumbled onto it if Champ hadn't beaten me to it."

"Yes, I reckon that old Champ did you one powerful, big favor," he mumbled as he lowered his head, swiped the back of his neck with a red handkerchief, and headed toward the remains of Champ. He moved the hound's body to the side of the road. "Tote me a gunnysack, boy. I need to wrap up Champ."

Dashing toward the granary next to the chicken shed (where we kept our gunnysacks), I raced over the events of the last few minutes. Indeed, I was grateful that Champ had rousted the snake. But I felt sad for him and for the stranger who'd lost his best pal.

When I made it back to the south terrace and the gravel road fronting it, I saw Dad talking to the stranger. Dad had been napping, and I guessed the three shots had awakened him. As the two caught sight of me, Dad motioned for me to hand the gunnysack to the stranger crouching over Champ.

"Much obliged," the man mumbled, squatting down to pull Champ's carcass into that musty gunnysack. "Much obliged," he repeated, finishing his gruesome chore, knotting the sack with the red handkerchief with which he'd swiped sweat from the back of his neck.

On the gravel there murmured traces of fur and two wicked blotches of crimson. The stranger straightened himself as he pulled together his mouth in a twisted and sad shape. Then, he began "pawing" at the gravel with his boot—at the spot where all that sickening redness lived. He scuffed his boot over that spot dozens of times, even after the redness vanished in a shroud of dust and pebbles. The stranger continued to rub his boot over that spot in a rhythm that reminded me of a dirge. You know, it's the sad cadence of church hymns that drag too slowly, as if the parishioners are not fully awake and are droning on to hear themselves sing, perhaps to startle themselves awake.

As the stranger took his leave, I gazed up at Dad, a large set of questions poking from my face. While I knew I'd need to talk with him about it, I also knew that some things are better left in peace for a spell. Knowing that this was one of those times for peace, Dad pursed his lips together, waved, and said, "Sean, there're cows to be milked, chickens to be fed and, hogs to be slopped. There are eggs to be gathered, and trash to be burnt. Get to it." I knew Dad wanted me not to dwell on what I'd seen.

Are some matters better left untouched for a spell, their memory tarrying in shadows that are more easily stalked with later talks?

As the afternoon bloomed into evening, we finished all of that work. We took our supper in the kitchen as the sun began to set. Next, there were bushes and shrubs to be watered, and an enormous garden to be tended. I retreated into the shadows to rest for a spell.

Mother told us, "The best time to water the garden is in the evening because the water soaks in better when the temperature drops along with the sun." Also, evening watering didn't risk the chance of scalding the plants, which was likely if we watered them while the sun blazed. Generally, we did not commence watering until after seven o'clock.

By eight o'clock watering wasn't finished. It might not be missed, unlike most chores. For example, if we didn't milk Mum and the other Jersey cows, they would bellow in pain. Also, Mother would ask what we'd done with the milk. If we didn't gather the eggs, the empty cartons would herald our failure. But, if we didn't water a row of green beans, who'd know? Well, Mother would know.

Mother always knew where our efforts had fizzled. Relying on smell, she knew that a freshly watered row of beans smelled different from one left dry. The sun-baked soil softened and wafted tender aromas, like those of alfalfa or strawberries, depending on what a person wants to smell. Water from our cistern swirled with the plants, the fertilizer, and the clayey subsoil. Does a body need to rely more on smell than on sight when it comes to toiling over summer soils in Kansas?

Mother took command of the garden hose, which she brandished like a baton. That hose had many extensions, stretching nearly as far as the landing strip of our county airport. Despite its ungainly length, Mother handled the monstrosity with the aplomb of a pro, for indeed she was a master.

She timed her waterings like a maestro. Rushed to relieve each row, she tarried only an extra minute with her favorites: her melons and cucumbers in the northeast corner of our garden. She offered them generous drinks. She preferred the watermelon patch most of all. Spanking the sides of the largest melons with water, she thumped them to judge sweetness. "That one ought to take a blue ribbon in the fair," she declared, striking it once again with cooling streams.

We had our staples: green beans, onions, beets, carrots, potatoes, turnips, sweet corn, lettuce, Swiss chard, mustard, raspberries, and strawberries. Mother also experimented. There were patches of rhubarb, thick and reddish green as it grew ever nearer to our kitchen table. There were Virginia peanuts, which were not nuts at all but legumes, thank you very much. Mother somehow knew how to prepare the soil for that special crop. Next, we endured a patch of kale. Wow, did I flinch at that stuff. Kale is one plant that totes a natural insecticide. It grew bitter enough that not even the *pests* wanted anything to do with it.

During our evening watering sessions, the sun was long gone, and the thankful earth wafted waves of heat from its scorched hide. Soon came time to start our oversized hall fan, a lumbering beast two feet high and three feet wide. Its metal blades were powerful enough to pull a partial vacuum that sucked cool air from outside, pumping it into our stifling upstairs hallway where it swished in tiny drafts into our bedrooms. Our clumsy monstrosity made bearable many a summer's evening. By leveraging cool evening air, we soothed our memories of noonday heat.

As Mother labored in the garden, I knew we could scamper away to "drink in" those lovely evening breezes. I needed to "thaw out" from the heat, to melt the redness on my face which held fast the recent memory of a torrid day. Maybe a glass of iced cistern water or a few more moments in front of that window-mounted unit would do the trick. The night was mine to catch my breath after the punishing heat and toil of day in those soils of clay. On nights that pouted with lingering warmth, I sat on the fron porch cooling myself with an oversized glass, overbrimmed with ice.

Our front porch became our favorite spot on breezy summer evenings. Gazing across the fields and down the hill toward the spring, we spotted an occasional car on our lonely dirt road. What welcomed company! At first we waived at our guests, but as the car sped away we grew surly.

"Get off our road, you coon dog!" spouted from our mouths once we knew for sure the driver couldn't hear us. To call someone a coon dog meant they stopped at nothing to fetch what they wanted, even if it meant stomping all over the rights of others. No doubt about it, to call someone a coon dog wasn't a compliment. "How dare they dust our road without stopping to thank us. The gall of it all! How rude."

Finally, at about nine o'clock we stared off toward town to spy a summer's evening glow. It flickered from the lights at the ball field six miles distant. If games were played that night, we'd know by the glow. If there wasn't a game, darkness lived. Ann crept to the porch and paced as she strained to view that glow even on nights when darkness ruled. Our sister Ann cared most about that glow. She'd played the game and excelled at it.

Ann couldn't bear its absence on dark nights. There was no mistaking it; either the lights were there, or they were not. Even so, Ann took no chances, and she peered dutifully into the distance before she huffed, "Well, there must not be a game tonight."

We all gazed toward town and that missing glow.

Then we'd sigh, "Yes, you're right," in a tone sharing her sadness, half hiding our chagrin. Well, there was no need to add to her disappointment, for Ann was our spokesperson when it came to longing for the light missing from darkened baseball diamonds.

Invariably, Ann toted a frosted mug filled with crushed ice and cola, which she had doctored with cherry syrup. Donner's Drive-in served it, and Ann grew to be its greatest fan. The owners knew what she craved even before she spoke.

Each of us had grown to love it secretly, too. Its sweetness excited the lining of my mouth after torrid summer days. For Ann, the drink was best stirred—not shaken—which flew in the face of the way some folks doctored martinis. She ensured that all of the luscious cherry flavoring mixed with the tartness of cola. Swirling her ambrosia as she paced, she gazed toward town to search for that special evening glow. Sounds of her spoon clanked against the glass like clockwork, perfectly timed to her front porch cadence. I suppose that watching Ann with her cherry-flavored cola over crushed ice meant a lot to me because of the heat of the day contrasted with her elixir.

Ann knew the finest things in life. She happened to be the smartest student in high school, and she was an athlete to boot—just as Mother had been in her heyday with the class of '42. She'd also served as class President, and she'd been voted most likely to succeed. That tasted luscious to me in a way that came to light as I watched Ann handle her cherry-flavored refreshment.

I often spied on Ann as she swirled it, and I spotted some of her secrets. Maybe some of what I saw ran tandem to her in my newly created vapors as I peered into her hidden world. But it sure felt like her intentions leaped up in the glory that was her frosted cheer-cola loveliness.

Ritually at nightfall, she meandered into the kitchen for a tray of ice, a cutting board, a rolling pin, and cheesecloth. A washcloth wouldn't do since she needed something that provoked air flow, letting her ice *breathe*. Of course, she cracked and crushed only ice fresh from the freezer section of our GE refrigerator.

In a select, darkened corner of our kitchen, she primed her labor of love by covering the cutting board and rolling pin with the cheesecloth. Was she like a wine connoisseur puttering in a wine cellar where temperatures and light are controlled?

Then, she misted over to the fridge to pull out a tray of ice that she had filled the prior night; nothing older or fresher would do. Through all her efforts, she'd learned that the ice must be precisely twenty-four hours "new", born of cistern water.

Ann repeated the ritual many times, and I guessed she ran on autopilot. After moving the tray of ice to the cutting board, she plopped out exactly six ice cubes. No more and no fewer would do. The rest she left for us kids and for our ice water. Arranging the cubes in the center of the cheesecloth in three rows of two cubes each, Ann wrapped the cubes stealthily, as if she bundled a secret formula. Glancing over each shoulder in turn, she detected any prying eyes. Of course, she knew I was watching her because her lips curled a faint smile.

After wrapping the cubes on the cutting board, she began to rap them with the rolling pin, cracking them into pieces. The end of the pin worked best. That was step one in her evening ritual.

Stage two meant breaking the ice into many pieces. She laid the cheesecloth flat and began whacking the ice with the pin. Then came stage three wherein she crushed the ice. She welded the rolling pin, crinkling it over the ice. Did she fancy rolling out brittle, iced cookie dough? No, she aimed to crush it, not to craft a sheet of pastry.

In each step, Ann reminded herself that the ice must breathe. She also paused between the three steps to let the ice rest. "We are both tired and need to rest for a spell," she declared when I asked about the pauses. Is that the way a master pastry chef lets dough rest before baking?

Once she finished crushing ice, Ann paused to wipe her brow with the left sleeve of her white blouse. After all, creation calls for concentration, and that's thirsty work. She paused to take a gulp of iced cistern water to counter the heat conjured by her labors.

The next steps are best described at a distance, for I believe she had no set recipe. She relied on smelling, seeing, hearing, feeling, and tasting. Into a ponderous sixteen ounce tumbler, she added an unknown quantity of cola, its brand name hidden from view. (Ann steamed off the labels from the bottles to guard her secret ingredients and to nurture mystery.) She favored the same gold-tinted tumbler, which shrouded her efforts and proportions from anyone viewing at a distance. She hinted a glimmer of her secrets only to the intrepid few who watched right over her shoulder. Her pour rate and time told me that she filled the tumbler about half full.

Next, she welded a tablespoon to tote a dollop of crushed, aerated ice into her creation. This called for at least four tablespoons in a first pass, sometimes five. Did the exact number depend on the temperature and relative humidity that evening? Then, she glanced over her shoulder as she slinked to fetch her secret ingredients in the cabinet. It was a flask of cherry syrup (and other elixirs) to which she had periodically added her own "boosters" to fortify it. No one dared see how many squirts of this ambrosia she added. Let's just say she coated the cola bubbles and ice liberally, wafting the cherry syrup aroma near her nose, just as a wine connoisseur might test a rare vintage. She grew partial to a plastic spoon to swish her ingredients. Metal wouldn't do, as that might bruise the flavor.

After testing the mixture for bouquet and color, she held it near her right ear to hear hissing cola in ice and syrup. Did she fancy a certain pitch, one that showed her when to stop squirting syrup over ice? Was she a maestro tuning an instrument mellowed with age to create a richer tone that only a trained ear might hear?

Next, she repeated this leg of her creation so that the tumbler filled to the brim. At that point, she pulled up a pinch of ice to top her creation, as if she added a cherry to a glorious ice cream sundae. Peering at the cola bubbles, she needed to inspect their patina of cherry flavor that colored the gritty skin of each bubble. She wanted the right number of bubbles with their skin colored to her perfection. In a few sections, the cherry syrup might overpower the cola's dark tint, but she let that happen in only a few token cases.

The skin of the bubbles in a few spots screamed of cherry refreshment. Those bubbles held a sheen like gasoline on water, leaving streaks of rainbow colors. The bubbles felt like ecstasy.

After all of her labors, she fetched her glass mug, which she had chilled in the GE refrigerator section for precisely one hour. Any less time meant it was too warm, dulling the flavor. A longer time meant the cold glass might swipe part of the sudsy goodness and rob her palate of its aromatic splendor. With one twitch of her wrist, she found a new home for the concoction as she poured it form the gold-tinted tumbler into her frosty glass mug. Another creation lived, oozing life.

After fussing over her drink, Ann pulled out one white and red straw from the carton in the kitchen cabinet. She insisted on the straws with white and red swirls, which reminded me of the display in front of a barber's shop. Those fool straws also looked like peppermint candy canes at Christmas, a favorite for all of us treat-starved kids.

With a swirl of the straw and one final glance, Ann swished the straw to the side of her glass mug. Wishing that the flavors had mixed well, she drank from the straw poised on the edge, never in the center. To do otherwise was unrefined, akin to gorging oneself on the heart of a sun-ripened watermelon or on the center of a freshly baked cherry pie that lay cooling in the window. Now that would've been a shameful waste—and a kind of sin.

With her collage of perfection, swirling with the right temperature, aroma, color, sound, and flavor, Ann meandered onto the front porch to find us kids gazing toward town. That sight and glow from the town's lights entranced us. We relished the cooling summer evening breezes, and we searched for the glow of the town's baseball field diamond, trumpeting a game or two of ball would be played that very night. How we hoped to spy the twinkling diamond's evening glow, wafting over the evening air to soothe our senses. That inspired us, what with all those sporty efforts in town six miles away.

Our eyes hungrily followed her every move as we consoled her on dark evenings. After all, we had our own interests at heart. We knew that she'd share some of that cherry cola if we watched her and made our apologies at the proper time. How delicious it tasted.

I swear, Ann might have worked for a soft drink company, seeing as how her tastes were way far ahead of her time. That's what we kids thought as we struggled to cool ourselves and to free our minds. Ann invariably gave the drink a final, furious swirl, grasped the straw in a corner of her mouth, and seemingly inhaled it as she cocked her head to one side. She beamed, meaning it passed.

As I recall those summer evenings long ago, I taste the frosty heaven of Ann's cherry-flavored colas. I see the glow from that ball field, and I feel the excitement on nights when we beheld it. We were all young, full of hope and life, and brimming with tall dreams, taller than Ann's iced mug of cherry refreshment. That cherry cola embodied all of this, making us feel special. Did we control a piece of our world, and might anything come true? Had we made the cut, fitting in despite a lack of money? Since Ann was one of us and popular, hope lived. She excelled at studies and at sports.

Could all of us do as well as Ann? Might we take up the baton in academics and in athletics? If so, would we be popular and successful?

When we sipped that frosty cherry cola, we fancied that we'd have a chance to tap into such success. To drink that treat felt like the privilege of a well-rounded, successful person. In that sense, the drink held an ambiance all its own, one perhaps undefined. The joy bubbling in that drink fizzed up far past its refreshment.

To this day, when I want to celebrate, I need a cherry cola. No champagne, merlot, chablis, or cabernet sauvignon comes close. For in that cherry cola rested genius. In it rested our hopes and our dreams. In it rested the reluctant control we'd wrestled from the relentless sun and from a farm that twitched with labors of love and of dying hounds. It held a sense of winning over toil and sweat, of defeating summer days on the farm we loved to hate.

To this day, I reckon cherries are special ways to say, "Thank you for a job well done. Now, it's time to relax. Now, it's time for a bit of heaven."

Paradise overbrims with sun-rippened, sweet cherries. How could it be any other way?

Let Us Dance!

When I was still quite young, I noticed all the fuss swirling around Mother. At first I'd felt awkward or embarrassed when I noticed it. As I grew older, I resigned myself to accept it. The men in our church simply had to stop and fiddle with their coats or pretend to read an announcement posted on the bulletin board whenever Mother "happened" to be around. I knew better, because I watched them as they watched Mother walking toward them. They stood uneasily fidgeting in the vestibule or near a collection plate. Sometimes, they stared blankly into space as they waited for her.

Oh, one man needed to ask about our farm. Would we sell any acres? Another wanted to know if she could come to a barbecue. ("If Mr. Redmond is on the road, you ought to have a night off," they would say.) Still another wanted to know if he could stop by to buy free-range eggs. That excuse sounded unlikely coming from a man with a flock of Rhode Island Reds ten times the size of our flock. You can't believe the variety of excuses and ruses the men found to say hello to Mother. Well, at least they grew resourceful. I knew right then how lucky I was to call Lola Juanita Kearney Redmond "mother", and I reckoned most kids in the parish agreed.

Mother took it all in stride—their awkwardness and nervous laughter. They needed to see Mother, and it shone with the light in their eyes and the ease in their steps. When they shuffled over to greet or to chat with her, they changed into young men for a brief moment, free and full of light. They stood erect, and they spoke in excited sprints of words that left them breathless. Sometimes their words made no sense at all, as if their racing minds blunted their logic. Mother understood, though, and she treated them all kindly. How lucky each of them felt simply to speak to her.

Then, as their talk ended, each one slinked away, their shoulders began to slouch, and their feet began to drag, as if lead weights were strapped to them. Broad smiles faded. Their spirits fell as they trudged toward their cars. Weren't their own families waiting for what seemed to be ages?

No, there was no mistaking it. I guessed Mother was the most popular and attractive woman who ever graced our parish, and that was the opinion held not just by the men. Most of the women also clamored for a word with Mother, too. I guessed folks saw her as a glamorous movie star who happened to grace their lives.

So, from my earliest youth, I knew what charm and grace meant. People melted and went limp. Others bumped into the edge of kneelers, and one man fell right into one. Heck fire, I saw its effect on countless folks—both men and women! Even the women whose husbands fawned over Mother looked like they didn't mind much. Who could? After all, it was Lola Redmond. I once heard one older gentleman mumble something about how she must have came straight from Hollywood! Few ever disagreed, for that's exactly how they treated Mother. She was their Grace Kelly and Debbie Reynolds, with a pinch of June Allyson and Doris Day for good measure. Her smile made them wobbly, weakening them right in the knees.

In those days in northeastern Kansas, ballroom dancing and champagne music had a heyday. Every Saturday evening, we tuned in to see "The Lawrence Welk Show" from Los Angeles. If we had been watering our garden or tending to chores, all that came to a halt when Lawrence took to the air.

I'd race across the living room floor, which we had just lined with a large patch of vinyl flooring that rolled up like a rug. Then, that piece of floor covering felt the rapid swishes of my body as I slid from the dining room into the living room, not wishing to miss even a second of the best program on television. We watched with wild abandon, our mouths drooping, and sweat beading up on our foreheads.

Oh, how we dreamed of all the lights and sounds that were Hollywood! We tapped our shoes to keep time with all of those magnificent tunes, like "To Dream the Impossible Dream", "Climb Every Mountain", "Walk On", "I Believe", "Yankee Doodle Dandy", "Give my Regards to Broadway", or "Born Free".

Arthur Duncan tap danced, nudging me to buzz with tales of adventure. The Lennon Sisters appeared too pretty to be real in their white linen dresses with blue satin sashes. Norma Zimmer, the Champagne Lady, appeared to enchant us with her songs from heaven. Parishioners often told Mother that Norma and she must be twins separated at birth. JoAnn Castle pounded away another Ragtime tune on her piano while she positively beamed at all of us. I declare, one time when she rendered "It'll Be a Hot Time in the Old Town Tonight", her piano burst into flames!

Oh, how we clapped—and I mean hard—whenever Lawrence took a few turns around the dance floor with each of his female cast members. As the show closed, we knew to keep a song in our hearts, just as Mr. Welk had advised.

Then, every Saturday evening, I imagined that I heard a Southern

Pacific Railroad locomotive clattering westward. I hoped to board any train that could take me to Hollywood so I could hold a piece of that glamorous fun. There I would audition for a part—any part—in the show.

After Lawrence and the cast bid us goodnight and reminded us to "Keep a smile on your face and song in your heart," Ann often took matters into her own hands. She plotted to "get us kids ready for bed to surprise Mother." She guessed Mother would be thrilled not to manage that chore for one evening. "Quick, wash up and bathe," she directed as soap bubbles flitted in the bathroom, not unlike the champagne bubbles in Hollywood.

"Comb your hair. You youngest kids, use a yellowed toothbrush to press down your hair. It's too fine to brush." With that, what had been innocent, downy locks became Jackie Gleason's bartender hair, slicked back with extra grease.

After being scrubbed pink, we dressed in our pajamas and lined up in descending age and size on our stairway. The creaky stairs groaned with all the weight, as if to protest. Then, Ann ceremoniously led Mother into the dining room to inspect the troops: to deliver her "surprise."

"Mother, come into the dining room to check out the table we polished," Ann began with an air of innocence. Mother looked straight ahead, focusing on that table. (The slight curl of her lips told me she knew what was up.)

"Oh, that's fine. It looks great," she declared. Then, "Oh, what a surprise!" when she happened upon the beaming faces of nine children—not including Ann—smiling at her from our banister. Well, Mother probably knew what was up, but it was all such clean fun to pretend she had no idea what had happened until Ann unfurled the fruits of her efforts. Mother was like that, don't you know.

As summer passed into fall, Mother commenced to plan our Thanksgiving Day celebration: a feast followed by dancing. She invited a few families from the parish—families whose children were about as old as the kids in our family. She also invited our cousins, our grandparents, and any guests who our oldest sister Janice (age eighteen) requested. One year, Janice asked her landlady Mrs. Riseman from Donnelley College in Kansas City, Kansas to visit for the day. Mrs. Riseman was a stately, older lady who had grown lonely and who had often told Janice as much. Her stories added to our fun.

Mother knew all of the best recipes for simple but delicious food. Besides the traditional Thanksgiving dishes, we relished wonderful casseroles and soups, marinated vegetables from our garden, and dishes fresh from the oven that radiated their spicy aromas. There were steaming kettles of minestrone soup and chicken noodle soup, drawing on both the garden and our barn yard. There were tuna fish casseroles and salmon patties (a holdover from our Friday menu when meat was not allowed), and yeast rolls steaming from the oven, sweating for us to gobble them.

That's not to mention the amazing cakes and pies Grandmother Kearney churned out. When she was a young lady, the Great Depression meant that anyone who could afford sugary desserts was wealthy. Hope sprung eternal, and laying out a peach or rhubarb pie—or even a chocolate cake that glistened with richness—meant that we had made it: poor no more!

Grandmother Kearney oftentimes gave directions. A petite and highly intelligent women, our irascible grandmother knew just what to say and how to say it both to shock and to correct us kids. Groans took to the air of "Lordie, were you kids born in a barn?", or "Would it kill you to turn off a light switch?" or "You kids act like you don't know how many beans make five. Now hush."

In spite of her sometimes gruff manner, she grew partial to all of us. For example, when our youngest brother Greg was born, she stayed at the farm for an entire week. After each meal, she declared, "Any Redmond child doesn't know where his mouth is. I mean really!"she fumed as she stooped to sweep up messes under the kitchen table.

A few days later, as we drove to the farm with Mother and Greg (child number ten) from the Paola hospital, Grandmother heard Greg wheezing. "Now, Lola," she insisted, "He sounds like a little jackass. And don't you dare think about having any more children. After all, this little guy almost killed you." Mother had endured blood poisoning (sepsis) after Greg's difficult delivery. We ten kids proved to be more than enough.

Another time, when my sister Jean poured cream over her piece of gingerbread cake to moisten it, Grandmother stated, "Why, I would slap any child who did that. What an insult—to pour cream over perfectly fine cake!" That comment broke my sister of her habit, this despite the fact that Mother told Grandmother Kearney that we kids poured cream over cake at her proding.

On Thanksgiving Day of my eleventh year, I had been decorating the dining room. One of my projects involved tracing leaves onto white paper for name settings. Grandmother cornered me and looked me straight in the eyes. She thundered, "Sean, do you know what you want to do when you grow up? You're not from a wealthy family, you know."

How did she know what I'd been thinking? Heck, I shouldn't have been surprised, seeing as how she always knew. (I'd been wondering what I wanted to do for a living.) Hesitating to find the right words, I said, "Well, I don't know, although I fancy dreaming and telling stories. I write stories now, you know."

Without missing a beat, Grandmother barked, "I know you do, and let me tell you, if you ever take that up, you better know what you're doing."

Needless to say, my leaf tracing halted.

"Don't you ever confuse your reader, 'cause if you do I'll be there to swat you. So, you better make sure you know what you are talking about."

"Grandmother . . . ," came through a nervous giggle.

"If you don't know what you're talking about, then don't write a single word. Imagination may be fine for you, but a wild imagination does not help anyone else."

"Yes, ma'am."

"All right then, if you can't tame your imagination, then sit down and hush up!"

There was no arguing with Grandmother.

Before noon on that Thanksgiving, I chanced to see Mother all alone in the utility room. Now, it wasn't unusual to see her in there washing clothes. But on this occasion, she was "occupied". She held a wash towel to her chest, and she commenced to move around to a beat, as if she aimed to dance with someone who was as partial to it as she was. As she stepped in time with the music swirling, her fingers fluttered as if her hands and she were thistledown wafting o'er windswept prairies, grand and mysterious.

As she danced all alone, I remembered Dad telling her, "Lola, I don't really like to dance."

No two people could have been more opposite when it came to dancing. In fact, Mother once told Dad, "Tom, when you are in a mood, you can hang black crepe paper at any fiesta without even breaking a sweat."

As I watched Mother silently dancing by herself, I somehow knew that she and Dad wouldn't be combing gray hair together. She glided silently around the room, only a slight rustle and sweep of her dress to break the stillness. Her eyes were closed, and her lips were drawn. Knowing that she would divorce Dad, I wondered how she'd reconcile that with the Catholic Church. Besides, I couldn't fathom what it would mean to all of us kids.

Well, by and by the guests commenced to arrive: After Grandmother and Grandfather Kearney came Mary Riseman (Janice's landlady), the Kramerichs, the Qualizzas, and Aunt Laura Lee and her family. Mr. Kramerich worked for the FAA, and Aunt Laura and he had worked together in the same office in Olathe during the late 1950's. Now, years

The adults as youths again had the world at their beck and call . . .

later, they became reacquainted at Mother's party. Aunt Laura was Mother's only sibling, and the Kramerichs had become our best friends.

Mrs. Qualizza and Mother attended nursing school together during WWII, and they had known each other for upwards of twenty years. Mr. Qualizza had a crush on Mother, but that wasn't much of a secret.

As it turned out, Mother was the pivotal character in all of these friendships. I don't think most of these families cared much for Dad, as he seemed preoccupied. Was he consumed by his internal ghosts, by all of those long-ago battles?

Once all of our guests were accounted for, we commenced feasting . . . and, we kept right on feasting for what seemed like hours. While the adults rubbed their midsections or bellyached about "overdoing" it or poured another hot drink, we kids danced in front of the still-steamy and goey-from-the-overn Toll House cookies. Their chocolaty flavor and meaty walnuts were framed by oatmeal and raisins in globs. We were riled up enough to devour them, and we often hit our mouths with striking blows. Some of the cookie ended up on our cheeks and lips. (If a body does not know where his mouth is, he might shove the cookie in the general direction of his face while missing the mouth; he could slide his face around until he found it.) That might explain the semisweet chocolate smeared all over our faces, making us all look like runners up in a local mud slinging contest. Perhaps Grandmother had been right after all when she declared, "You all look like a bunch of bull frogs wallowing in Missouri mud!" I declare that no mud seemed so rich or luxurious as that chocolate seeping throughout all of those tollhouse cookies.

After our rich interlude came mandatory group photos. Ann always got into the act to organize "the group". She was an amateur photographer and organizer. "Come on, everybody, out to the front porch for a group photo," she chirped.

We never knew if the front porch could hold such a crowd, even if we used four or five rows with the smaller children front and center. Somehow, we always managed to squeeze in everyone.

Well, after all of the feasting, desserts, and hot drinks, we normally hit a lull in all the doings. Folks regained their strength to clear away the furniture in the living room and to prepare to dance. After suffering through all of this bother, then and only then came the music and the dancing. Away flew the furniture, back against the walls, as we cleared the dance floor for action. Our RCA record player ground out the recordings of polka music, like "Roll Out the Barrel" or "The Pennsylvania Polka" on 45 rpm vinyl, one right after the other. The adults chose a partner, usually commencing with their spouse. Then, they began to shuffle and spin across the dance floor. Their faces grew filled with happiness, and their eyes became drunk with laughter. Mr. Kramerich began moving to the beat of the music, and a broad smile lit up his face. Mr. Qualizza began cavorting around the room with his spouse in tow. It was all such sweet fun.

As I watched from my viewing chair, I imagined the adults as children again playing in the dawn of their youth, the whole world beckoning to be explored, enticing them to behold its wonders. From my viewpoint, I saw the joy in their faces and the life in their jaunty steps. The adults seemed free for at least that moment, and my spirit drifted with theirs. (I felt connected with freedom.)

After the first dance, each person could choose a new partner. The men all clamored to dance with Mother, which seemed a bit much. While I reckoned Dad might be jealous, he didn't let on. It was more likely that Dad hadn't noticed, what with his shadow occupying his chair. There was an undertone of good-natured pouting and of hurt feelings on behalf of each man's wife, yet the women were friends with and loved Mother. That helped soothe hurt feelings, and no one harbored grudges.

As the dancing and music droned on, the older children began to fuss that it had lasted too long. They fancied playing board games or talking. So, invariably our party splintered off into subgroups. The adults remained to steal a few more turns around our linoleum dance floor as they relished those vinyl-coated tunes, including, "Don't Sit Under the Apple Tree", "I'll Be Seeing You," and "Smoke Gets in Your Eyes".

When we kids had to break away from the fun to care for the animals, we rushed through our chores to stretch our time back at the celebration before it all ended. As we ran up the sidewalk, we smelled pies and allspice, gingerbread and freshly-brewed coffee wafting redolently over the lawn. Memories of onions and garlic, of sage and rosemary teased our taste buds. We could hear the din of laughter and of music. We sensed the glow of that merry celebration, and we could feel its warmth. I imagined this must be an oasis in the half-light, framed by the lengthening shadows of that late autumn's twilight.

The day flew by, as if it had been a hawk that spied its dinner in a distant pasture. Darkness had fallen all too soon on this day of light, of laughter, and of celebration—of life and of one another. In those moments, no one seemed to care about work and overdue electric bills, about varicose veins or overly-spirited kids. Folks forgot about all of those worries for a few hours. Our spirits lifted. While it's true we'd faced ill health, bankruptcy, disappointments, and possible divorce . . . , we hadn't failed. No one is a failure . . . no one who has laughed and danced, shared and cared, comforted and hugged, smiled and loved. No one fails who in time ekes out some wisdom through "The awful Grace of God".

So, on those days, no matter the circumstances, we all became light-hearted and free. We enjoyed ourselves and one another. The adults, as youths again, had the world at their beck and call. In spite of their troubles, the light in their eyes and the glow in their faces heralded that they surely had not failed.

You see, at Mother's celebrations, everyone and everything were sheer successes. And besides, as the party ended, we knew to keep a song in our hearts, just as Mr. Welk had advised.

Simplify

One summer morning less than two years after my legs had healed, I'd been swept away in daydreaming for quite a spell on the couch upholstered in raised green fabric in my grandparent's living room. Heck fire, before lunch I'd already dueled a gunfighter in Dodge City, Kansas at the OK Corral. We battled in that one-street town, creaking with moaning sounds that were muffled only by the whistling wind's cries. I was the only man in town with enough gumption to face down the marauder, although I hadn't even fired a six-shooter before that showdown! Luck was with me, which is more than I could say for the outlaw.

Then, leaping ahead more than a century, I blasted off for a mission to Mars. Standing in a space suit on the surface of the Red Planet left a lump in my throat. Next, before I could say Jack Robinson, I was wearing a crisp white laboratory jacket. I held a curved flask, and inside it bubbled a potion to cure the common cold. I watched myself grinning, my face framed by tousled curls in need of trimming.

After several flights like that, I smiled wearily. Shooting down an outlaw and finding the secret ingredients for such a potion is tall work, and that takes something out of body! Colorful liquids in bubbling glass flasks spouted grumbling torment. All of the details in those stories became part of me, just as I became part of them.

Suddenly, I noticed a slight shuffling poked into my stories. Was it a bloodhound dragging a bank robber by the shirt collar? Nah, it was Grandmother's wheelchair rolling into the living room. Following surgery to remove cancer from her small intestines, she formed a blood clot that lodged in her left leg, which became gangrenous. So, her surgeon removed the leg and the clot. True to form, Grandmother was back in her housekeeping routine within two weeks of her surgery. Her home remained as spotless as ever. Grandmother had been confined to a wheelchair ever since. Two months had passed since she lost her leg.

Leading up to the time that Grandmother lost her leg, I know she suffered. One day I watched her as she rubbed her left leg, as if she tried to bring it back to life. Startled pain rested on her face as she slowly worked her fingers over her left calf. Grandmother was careful so that she did not do more harm than good; she took her time as she worked warily with ease. She wore a pair of light green tennis shoes and tan slacks. As I watched her, I knew that soon she wouldn't be needing those slacks or those shoes. I guessed she would take to wearing gingham dresses and a single house slipper. Mother had told me about her circulation problems, and no amount of soaking or rubbing helped. Not even her special liniment poultice did the trick, and it held a bevy of secret ingredients from a recipe that Grandmother's great aunt had invented. That recipe had been handed down through three generations, but not even it could help mend her left leg.

The next week her surgeon operated. Two months had passed since tha spring day.

"Do you have enough light back there, honey? Don't strain your eyes. Each of us receives only one set."

"Yes, Grandmother, I'm fine."

Seeing Grandmother sitting in her wheel chair with a stump left for her left leg looked and felt odd. A stump loosely wrapped in bandages remained where once had been a mighty leg that had powered the petite lady to do just about anything. Where once had stood a lady swift of foot, now sat one wheelchair-bound.

My grandmother still seemed formidable. She held herself with a certain dignity, as nothing stopped her from being herself. And, my oh my . . . she was wise—patiently tired—which I knew whenever I gazed into her face. She'd stare gimlet-eyed at me as if to ask, "Now what in the hell do you think you are doing this time, Sean?"

The loss of her leg did not stop her from doing all of her household chores. Her home sparkled. When she needed to go into tight corners where a wheelchair would not take her, she scooted on the floor. That is something I had done a lot before my hips had healed, and I marveled that this petite lady of nearly eighty years scooted so well, rivaling my skill. In spite of her loss, Grandmother's home was as spotless as ever! On days that were harder than most, she grudgingly hired a cleaning lady. Otherwise, she made do, and she kept on going. Did keeping busy help take her mind off of her operation? Maybe not thinking about it buffered her from haunting pain. Despite her determination to shirk its company, phantom pain remained her steadfast companion: pain where her left leg had been. She spoke softly about the pain shooting down her leg, the pain she still felt in a limb that was then long gone.

"When are you planning to go outside to join the rest of the kids?" Grandmother asked me.

"Oh, I don't know. Maybe when I finish this chapter." I held up my book for her to see: *Treasure Island*. Only seconds earlier, I'd been daydreaming—a fact not lost on Grandmother.

"Sean, why in the world do you waste your time reading and daydreaming?" Grandmother's question was more like an accusation. "You need to be outside to experience life. Don't just think and read about it." Before I could sputter an answer, she shot at me, "I swear, each day you become more of a damn bookworm." Grandmother pivoted her wheelchair toward the kitchen. Then, she ordered me, "Come on out to the kitchen. It's time we talked."

With a pregnant sigh, I put down my book and began to wend my way there. While I took enough time to show my reluctance, I came quickly enough so that I wouldn't rile her further.

Grandmother had brewed a pot of coffee, and she'd laid a fresh sleeve of Saltine crackers on the kitchen table covered with a red and white checkered tablecloth. Since her operation she had a poor appetite. Often her meals consisted of nibbles on a stack of Saltine crackers washed down by sips of black coffee. She laid several crackers on a saucer next to her coffee. Then, using the fastener at the top of the sleeve, she rolled the sleeve back up against itself to seal in the remaining crackers. I had never seen anyone do that before or since! Why, in our house all of those crackers would have been goners in one sitting, anyway. I had imagined that most folks simply waded up the sleeve or (at the most) gave it a single twist.

"Now, Sean," Grandmother began as I sat on a chair opposite her. "What do you plan to do for a living? I mean, what will you do with your life?"

I stared at her, my ten-year-old mouth drooping. The room grew pregnant with my hesitation. "Well," I began, "I'd like to be an English teacher or a writer, but I reckon I'm not cut out for that. So, I guess I'll enroll at a university where I'll major in engineering, business, and finance. That way, I'll make a living without making a fool of myself."

Now it was Grandmother's turn to pause. After nibbling on the edge of a Saltine, she gestured with what remained of it.

"That's all right if you want to do that." She swallowed hurriedly and continued, "Your future is nobody's business but your own. Well, maybe it's yours and God's business. I won't tell you what to do, and I won't dissuade you."

But . . . ? I thought. Go on Grandmother. But, what?

"Just tell me one thing. Why do you think you aren't cut out to be an English teacher or a writer?"

I bristled at her question because the past Thanksgiving Grandmother had laid into me but good! She informed me that my wild imagination wouldn't make sense to anyone, nor would it help anyone. She assured me that if I dared write a word about what I imagined, I'd make a fool of myself. She even went so far as to say she'd be there to swat me if I did. How could she have forgotten?

"What is it, Sean? Was it something I said?" Grandmother batted her eyelashes. I knew then that she had not forgotten—that this might be her way of apologizing for being kind of rough with me the past fall.

I sighed my answer, "Well, yes and no. Maybe. You told me if I chose to become a writer, I'd better know what I'm talking about. You said, 'Imagination is fine, Sean, but wild imagination doesn't help anyone. Keep it to yourself.' My eyes darted from Grandmother's piercing watch, and I gazed at the carpet as I uneasily pawed my right foot in patterns over its surface.

I had been a little reluctant to recite those lines to Grandmother, but I suppose they had bothered me enough that I needed to clear the air. She wasn't angry with me, seeing as how she offered me a Saltine and smiled faintly, her head nodding.

"Would you like some peanut butter on that cracker, dear?"

Taking courage with that gesture, I continued, "You said that imagination is fine, but unless I am very clear, I'll confuse the reader. That's a problem, I suspect. I usually don't know exactly what things mean. I'm in a cloud and daydreaming a lot, too. I know I would ramble. So, I'd better not be a writer."

Grandmother smiled, "Well, you'll find in life you have a few choices, Sean. You may take advice from other people or not. It's all up to you. A smart boy listens to the advice, and then he compromises. Do you know what that means?"

Well, I thought I did. After all, I was a whole decade old, and that must count for something. Acting cute, I offered, "How about if we play a few hands of gin rummy instead, Grandmother?

"Acting cute doesn't become you, Sean. Now, reel back in your silly chin and answer."

I'd stuck out my chin in her general direction, (in my best Franklin D.

Roosevelt pose) trying to disarm her. She cleared her throat as she directed her gimlet-eyed stare at me. Knowing when to quit, I sighed and began, "Well, it means when folks with dueling ideas try to reckon how they can both be happy," I stammered. "They change what they want. Although nobody gets what they first asked, what they get is tolerably close to it." My face grew red because I guessed that I'd made no sense. I spied Grandmother's uplifted eyebrows, which beaconed her weary patience wearing thin.

"Oh, that's close enough," Grandmother offered with a wave of her left hand, her bruised skin grown thin with age. "Folks may not get exactly what they wanted, but it works. They're happy enough, after a fashion."

Her generosity relieved me.

"Now, when people give you advice, you might make a compromise by thinking hard about what they say. You are allowed to change what they tell you a little and take their advice for the most part. They may even help you make a better decision. Then, you will still work for what you value most. Then, I'll bet you'll be happy for the most part."

Seeing me grimace, she continued, "Now, Sean, don't fret. You might not be as happy as an old bullfrog a'wallowing in Missouri mud. You might not be as pleased as a coon dog hunting in the Ozark hills, either. But . . . , you'll be happy."

I scrunched up my face. "Well . . . you . . . will . . . But-"

"Whatever happens, remember never to give up on your dreams, at least not entirely. Always keep some part of them alive. If you don't, you'll grow old before your time." I'd heard something like that before, but where? Then, I remembered where: at the Union Station in Kansas City, Missouri that night we rode west with the night on the Santa Fe Chief. John Jansen advised me never to be too disappointed, for that would lead to bitterness, which is a kind of poison. He reckoned bitterness makes a body old before his time.

I'd been staring at Grandmother because I wanted to remember all that she said and how she said it. Her voice was steady, and she emphasized words like dreams, life, alive, and old. As she finished speaking, she reached for another Saltine, which she nibbled before taking a swig of black coffee.

Although at first I didn't like what Grandmother said, I had to admit that her words made sense. In fact, I can't remember a time when Grandmother didn't make sense.

"So, you're saying I need to be my own person, that I can change some details of advice when I need to, but I must never forfeit my dreams?"

"Yes, that's about it. You decide what you want to do. Keep an open mind, and never give up on your dreams, the ones you hold most dearly," she huffed.

"Well, all right, Grandmother. Suppose I do write something one day. What if it even makes sense? Then what?"

Grandmother answered in rapid-fire, "Then, you might have something."

"Really?"

"But then again, you'll need to ask yourself one question: will my story make sense a century from now?"

"One hundred years from now?" I halfway whined.

"The mark of a fine writer is how a story holds up. Does it say something today as much as it did a hundred years ago . . . or a hundred years hence?" she challenged.

Her standards seemed too tough to reach.

"Grandmother, I don't even know what life was like a hundred years ago, and no one can rightly say what it will be like a hundred years from now. That's impossible. How can anyone know what you are asking?" I gasped with bother.

"Do you know what makes a story timeless?" she quizzed.

I knew this was a tough question, so I searched my vast storehouse of knowledge from that huge span of ten years that I'd lived. In a moment I began, "Well, I think I do. Take my illness. All kinds of people get sick, whether they lived a hundred years ago, now, or will live way in the future. Folks can see a body struggling and sense something like that in their own lives."

"Go on."

"If I can see things in relation to a bunch of times and places, then maybe I can take a specific story and make it general. If I can see my stories against a background that is common to all people, then I'm liable to make it universal."

Grandmother smiled. We understood one another. "That's right, Sean. Find what has meaning now and tomorrow and a thousand years ago. Meaning is a whole other dimension that you may tap. Your story will be only the plot or backdrop to provoke a wider meaning."

"Yes, ma'am."

"If you do this, then maybe you'll have something. Then, I won't need to come back to thump you for making a darn fool of yourself."

As she spoke, her abbreviated body twitched with a rhythm in her chair. She accented certain words to match her gestures: words like meaning, everybody, story, thump, and darn fool.

"Then, you'll have a compromise that is really a better story for us all, one that doesn't serve only your purpose," she smiled as she slowed down and relaxed her fingers, which had become clinched. I imagined that some of the phantom pain in her missing leg had gone searching for a home in her hand. Does pain troll for places to live? Does pain add another dimension to life, one that readers will sense?

"Sean, become a writer if that's right for you. But remember what this old woman told you. If you don't grasp this grand design, then anything you write will be only a bunch of words, not amounting to a dung heap in a drought."

"But Grandmother, what if my imagination clatters away like a run away train on the tracks of the Atchison, Topeka and the Santa Fe? Hmmm, 'The Atchison . . . Topeka . . . and the Santa Fe,'" I hummed the melody for the words. Without thinking, I lit on the set of an MGM Grand musical. Catching a glimpse of Grandmother's displeasure, I hushed.

"I see we have some work to do, Sean. Thoughts and feelings may be powerful allies or mighty enemies. It all depends on how you manage them. Take your wild imagination, for instance. It healed your legs, and that's fine. Don't let it run too wild. Don't let it become a rogue. If you do, then it won't do you or anyone else any good, like common thistles. They spread in a bramble and take over, hatching a thicket to crowd out everything else. Do you see why that's wrong?"

"Yes, I see. Grandmother, I know that's selfish and thoughtless of ornery thistles."

"It's plain wrong. Although their purple flowers are pretty, thistles left untended brim with thorns and prickly points. That does no one any good. Besides, other plants deserve a chance. It's not that thistles and wild imagination are bad. They simply must be controlled."

"Yes, ma'am."

"Thin out thistles so they don't crowd out the rest of the flowers and crops. And, thin out your ideas. Cultivate only the richest ones, and then you'll reap a bumper crop, a 'timeless' bumper crop." Grandmother's face relaxed.

"Yes, Ma'am."

"There is beauty and goodness in everything, just as there is ugliness, too. You'll find both if you look hard enough."

"How will I find the beauty instead of the ugliness?"

"Know where to look. The trick is to find the beauty, and that's one large balancing act," she advised as she rubbed the stump of her left leg with her knotted fingers, stiff and aching. (I knew she hurt far worse than my head would even if I did disappoint her, and even if she did come back to thump me for being foolish.)

With her words my face lit up, and I beamed, "Yes, Grandmother. I know. I remember watching a tight rope walker in a dusty big-top circus tent when I was a little boy. He might have fallen, but he didn't."

"All right."

"And Dad leans gently into the wind when he tries to balance his life, to do more good than harm on balance."

"Stop. You think that by leaning into the wind to do his best, he makes a difference?"

"I sure do, Grandmother." She looked pleased that I understood how important it would be to find balance. . . . and to control my wild imagination, even though she didn't care much for Dad.

I even wondered if her advice might be timeless. On that day I made a compromise. I told myself, If her advice isn't timeless, it is about as close to it as I'll ever hear. I decided that if I felt others could understand my stories now and in the future, then I might try to become a writer. If I didn't think my stories would make sense, I wouldn't write a single word. That was my compromise.

Grandmother finished another cracker, sipped her coffee, and sighed. "Since my operation, no one listens much to me. The only one waiting for me now is the undertaker, and even he doesn't appear to be in much of a hurry."

A certain air of sadness swished through the air as she steered her wheelchair to the room north of the kitchen. There she raised ferns and African violets. Grandmother misted them daily, gently wiping their fronds to clear them of dust.

She wheeled herself there swiftly, seeing as how our talk had put her behind time.

Stairs Came Crashing Down

The Crawford girls held up under physical problems that persuaded most folks to call them "retarded". Both Linda and Nancy stumbled into the world with damaged heart valves, high-pitched squeaky voices, and straw-like hair. Their poor eyesight meant wearing glasses with "coke-bottle" lenses, all on account of their father's sin, townsfolk asserted. Mr. Crawford did double duty as grandfather and father to Linda and Nancy, while Rita Crawford (whom Mother welcomed as a new neighbor several years before) was their sister and mother: "Sister Mom".

Mr. Crawford never denied "seeding" a second family with his daughter. Rather, he boasted of it. "I beat the Missus at least once a day, whether she needed it or not. When she got all uppity and stopped sleeping with me, she did me wrong. A man has his needs, and it's a crime if'n his wife goes cold on him. Well, I denied myself until Rita turned ten—a proper age for learning her to be a woman. It wouldn't have been Christian to learn her sooner." Mr. Crawford nodded like crazy over that, priming his audience to applaud. "The Missus got all jealous on account of our carryings-on, and she up and left town. 'Good riddance,' I say. Well, me and Rita kept house regular ever since. I gotta admit she ain't much to look at, but she sure can keep me company— if'n you know what I mean." With that, he puffed out his chest.

While most townsfolk were horrified, they also *strained* giddily to catch whiffs of Mr. Crawford's whiskey-steeped truth telling. Mind you, folks trashed Mr. Crawford behind his back, that is. But no one ever got up a head of steam to tell him to his face—that he'd sinned. In the Kansas of my youth, folks reckoned that Mr. Crawford's deeds were a "family matter". To stick one's nose where it didn't belong warranted meaner frowns than did any of Mr. Crawford's nasty habits.

"There're too many strikes against those girls," townsfolk whispered. "They won't amount to squat."

Linda and Nancy thought differently. "Nancy and I will be the first

Crawfords in the county to graduate high school," Linda announced. Her words turned my throat cottony.

Watching the girls huff to make the grade, I knew they worked something powerful in school—unlike many of their "lightly-starched" classmates. And the last class bell of the day didn't mean rest for them; no sir. They held part-time jobs. Nancy helped our town's librarian, and Linda sorted medications at a nursing home.

Could they live on hard work and hope? It seemed they had little else.

One day Linda climbed our dusty school bus steps while a dazed Nancy followed close behind. "Well, you'll never guess what happened," Linda said to our bus driver, Mrs. "Bubbles" O'Grady.

"What?" Bubbles asked.

"Our stairs came crashing down."

"How'd that happen?" Bubbles puzzled, whacking out two Bazooka bubbles in rapid-fire order. "Is everyone all right?"

"Oh, Dad planned on tending to dry rot in the stairs years ago, but he didn't get around to it. The other day, the stairs commenced to pull away from the wall. Then, last night right before bed, they collapsed as Dad started down them. A ball of dust spewed over our living room. Dad, he fell no more than ten feet. He was booming mad all right, but unhurt." Linda's story felt cartoon-like.

"What will you do?" Our driver cracked another bubble.

"Dad, he tossed a rope over the rafters up in the attic. Said we'd need to scale the rope to get upstairs. Since I don't climb, I'm wearing my clothes from yesterday."

The Crawford home had once been stately, owned by a wealthy family. It was sold in an estate auction, and its owner lived out-of-state. He rented it to tenants, his first ones none other than the Crockers who skeddadled. After a spell, in moved the Crawfords. Upkeep did not appeal to Mr. Crawford. He perked up only for boasting, hunting, swilling whisky, and incest.

Within a few years the house was a tumbledown mess. How could anyone trash a house in a few years to the point of its collapse? I wondered. Had that kind of crumbling seeded in Mr. Crawford's mind?

Linda's story reminded me of Edgar Allan Poe's, "The Fall of the House of Usher", of the mansion of gloom owned by a thoroughly agitated Roderick Usher, and how the house tumbled down after rotting. I reckoned that the Crawford home also reeked of decay, a home enveloped by "a pestilent and mystic vapor, dull, sluggish, faintly discernible, and leaden-hued". Faced with abuse, a body either crumbles alongside it or flees (as had Mrs. Crawford).

The Crawford home fit snugly into the mold of dreariness Poe described. It conjured despair in droves, rendering the Ushers and their mansion giddy by comparison.

Nancy and Linda didn't look vexed about the crash—only inconvenienced. They spouted news of their second-floor access rope with lightness, quipping, "We'll tie a half dozen knots in it to help us climb." Did their levity help them cope?

"That sounds oddly exotic," I mumbled, "but oddness wears thin." I reckoned a bunch of weird details fray thin and snap after reality sets in.

The Kent boys, though, were more trouble to the girls than were any fool stairs. Unlike the stairs, those boys didn't go away. Instead, they taunted the girls as if they were paid to do so. (They were high school friends of my brother Paul.)

"Aw, don't worry about wearing your filthy clothes two days in a row," the oldest Kent chortled after hearing Linda's story. "You smell like monkeys anyway, with or without fresh clothes." Several kids chirped with delight.

Another Kent followed up with, "Why, you monkeys must be thrilled to pieces to have a rope to swing on now."

With that, the youngest Kent (in my grade at school) began scratching his ribs and shrilling monkey sounds. Before long most of the high school boys and some of the younger ones rattled our bus windows with their zoo chorus.

Bubbles sputtered, "Watch your language. Hush, now!" Her voice was a wisp amidst the clattering bus, jarring all of us senseless by the ruckus.

Next came a hale of spit wads. As they spewed their ammunition at Linda and Nancy, I saw the youngest and quietest Kent boy sweep his left hand over his leg where he rested it on a hole in his jeans, frayed bare. While I couldn't have cared less about holy jeans, I did care about what kind of people reckoned they were duty-bound to taunt a girl when she's hurting. Didn't my friends warrant kindness instead of cruelty? What were the Kents shrouding under their attacks?

Did Linda and Nancy need a "symbolic" rope to pull themselves up in life?

I remember a cartoon in *The Kansas City Star*. President Nixon implored a poverty stricken child, "Pull yourself up by your bootstraps!" Sadly, the child stood barefooted.

After the "stairs" incident, I couldn't help but stare at Nancy as she stepped from the school bus and trudged up the inclined sidewalk to the high school front door. (Linda was two years older than Nancy, and I paid her no heed.) Bubbles delivered the senior high school students first, and then she drove to the grade school. Teenagers had tromped up that sidewalk every year since the "new" high school opened its doors in 1926. While most glided up that slight slope, Nancy managed to do otherwise. Moving in a peculiar fashion, almost twitch-like, she commenced to lean forward as she launched her books from her side. Did they prod her? She tapped the books' forward motion to power her steps toward the front door, and I heard her self-satisfied squeak, "I'll make it. Really, I will." No one dared tell her otherwise.

For weeks I studied Nancy. Every other afternoon she boarded the bus and flopped down on the seat in front of me. (The other days she worked at our town's library.) Without fail, she snatched her hairbrush from her battered handbag. More bristles were missing than not. Brushing her sandy-colored straw-dry hair, she crinkled the air and managed to kink her hair further. Mother once said, "Nancy's hair is damaged by weak genes, owing to inbreeding. Nothing will fix that."

Mother's words made me boil. Had she forgotten that she once tried to hand laundry detergent to Rita Crawford who refused it on the account of making her own soap? It was an odds-on favorite that Nancy washed her hair with that homemade soap. It stripped moisture and luster from her hair, much the way Mr. Crawford stripped life from his oldest daughter. I'd wager that soap also played a role in Nancy's greasy complexion, begging taunts from the Kents.

Nancy grunted as she ran the brush through her hair. She tried to smooth her kinks before she tucked the ends under at her shoulder, but her hair would have none of that, and it sprang back up. It stood straight out as if she hadn't bothered. But Nancy seemed satisfied, and after a spell she exhaled with a broad grin.

Mother took offense at more than Nancy's hair. One day while I studied at the library, Mother tracked down a book. Steeped in one thought or another, I was startled by Mother's voice. "I said I don't want this copy. Look at it. Pages are grimy, and its corners are dog-eared. Aren't you listening?" Mother scolded Nancy Crawford. (Didn't Mother know Nancy kept a folded picture in her purse: the one in the article about Mother winning an award at the Paola Nursing Center? I'd tried a few times to tell Mother how Nancy admired her. She craved her approval, but Mother would have none of that.)

Rushing over, I intervened. "Maybe that's the only copy in the library, Mother."

Mother glowered at me.

"I think Nancy is doing a fine job." I winked at Nancy.

Traces of a smile crept over Nancy's face. "I'm sorry, Mrs. Redmond. I'll look for the other copy," she promised in her thin, high-pitched voice.

"Damaged from birth," Mother sighed as Nancy scrambled away.

"Give her a chance," I begged. "She's really trying."

Mother fumed.

I scribbled on a piece of paper, "You're the best librarian I know. Thanks for your help."

When Nancy jogged back with the book, she handed it to Mother who tersely thanked her. Then, she huffed, "Sean, come on. It's time to go home."

As we left, I handed Nancy the note. Almost to the door, I glanced over my shoulder to see her reading it. Nancy smiled.

When we reached the car, I sputtered, "I know you don't care much for Nancy, but I don't reckon that's fair. If you'd give her a chance, you'd like her."

"Oh, yes? Why?"

"She's sweet, and she tries hard. Whenever I see her, I want to stand, wave, and cheer. Anyone who tries, no matter what, must be a fine person—even Nancy. You really would like her if you took the time to know her."

Mother snapped back, "Try not be too sensitive, Sean. I don't dislike her. I'm simply not partial to white trash in the library, that's all. She's unseemly there."

That was the lone time Mother disappointed me. I guess we're all entitled to our mistakes, but Mother made a doosey. She seemed prejudiced only against what she called "white trash". Nancy deserved better.

On the school bus the next afternoon, Nancy told me, "Sean, you're the only one who has thanked me for my work. You're the only one who appreciates me at the library, and that's too much to take." The day before, she'd fled to the bathroom to shroud her startled, misty-eyed misadventure.

Nancy finished high school, and she went on to study nursing. I reckon Mother's example edged her in that direction. If she had a daughter, she may have named her Juanita in honor of Lola Juanita Redmond, my mother. Linda finished school two years before Nancy. She moved away, too.

As William Wordsworth said, "The meanest flower that blows can give thoughts, which often lie too deep for tears." Nancy and Linda fit his ideal on all counts. They tunneled into rocky soil, and they thrived when no one gave them a chance. A silent dignity sprouted from their efforts, noble and undefiled. Their persistence dwarfed any I've seen before or since. Their example of working hard to overcome prejudice and misfortune felt fine way back then, and it feels even finer now.

One afternoon as I cast worn stones into the pool next to our leaning cottonwood, I basked in echoes of their golden reflections.

$\mathcal{M}$r. Bentley and the $\mathcal{M}$elon Snatchers

The creek that sauntered through our valley headed south, more or less, for nearly a mile beyond the concrete bridge that spanned it on the dirt road east of our farmhouse. That bridge sprouted in 1959, fresh with smooth concrete walls and a cement slab for a floor. Water trickled over its floor even during dry spells because our spring kept churning, come rain or shine.

During wet months rains swelled our creek. Then, water gushed over the bridge's cement floor to fill a pool on its south side. Standing on the dirt and gravel crust that topped the concrete bridge, I spied what I could in that pool shimmering beneath me. Nearly eight feet deep at its center, that watering hole became home for healthy-sized channel cat, bass, and bluegill. Those fish, fat and sassy, glided through cool waters. The swirl of a few eddies showed me that mighty fish, powered by crescent tails and fins, plowed their way through murky waters. Water spiders danced on its surface, and flies droned nearby. On the east side below where the bank rose sharply to cloak itself in a thicket of gooseberries, the remains of evergreen trees rested under water. Their rotting branches crafted a welcoming home for contented channel cat, drowsed and lazy, nesting there.

That spot became our private fishing and swimming hole. On Saturday mornings after our chores, we kids swiped hunks of raw bacon for bait, and we headed down to the water hole to fish. Algae and mosses thrived in the skim of water that seeped over the cement floor of the bridge. After picking our way over pockets of slime, we planted ourselves on select spots around the pool, usually one shaded by a weeping willow or cottonwoods. There we armed our cane poles with wads of bacon and our patience.

If fish didn't bite, or if the day felt too warm, we threw our poles and restraint to the banks. We swam, fancying ourselves mighty channel cat and masters of our fishing hole. A few times Paul tried his bare-knuckled snatch of a channel cat resting in a hollow of evergreen branches that soaked on the east side of the pool. He called that "noodling". Although he often nudged up against a sassy catfish, its whiskers brushing against his leg, he never did catch one that way. Fishing and swimming remained our prime pastimes, and noodling became a "lost art" for us long before we found it.

We didn't insult our watering hole by resorting solely to fishing and swimming. My brothers often launched homemade boats, crafted of weathered boards and tin sheeting that we hammered over the boards to crinkle a metal skin. Each one routinely sank. Some things never change, as predictable as is the apparent rising of the sun. Our boats floundered even if we slathered tar to shore-up holes in their sides.

Our creek headed south, for the most part, until it grazed Mr. Bentley's farm. There it snaked southwest to hatch a clutch of serpentine banks. (Did our creek hesitate to head southwest, preferring to meander in protest?) The land next to the banks sloped gently down toward the creek. During springtime our swollen creek overfilled its banks, leaving sand marooned in puddles.

Mr. Bentley grew the largest and sweetest vine-ripened melons with ruby red flesh and jet-black seeds tailor-made for spitting long distances. I guessed that swirling waters, well-drained soil, and a little care made for the finest melons in the county, and I guessed right.

Mr. Bentley was a widower who shared his farm with Duke, his twelve year-old coon hound. He had once howled as the county's champion coon hound, and the pelts Mr. Bentley tacked up along his smokehouse echoed Duke's glory days. While Mr. Bentley didn't need to embellish tales of Duke's fabled skills, he did improve on them with time. After all, that is what he did best—next to raising melons, that is. Mr. Bentley added a certain flair or swagger to every story he told.

Mr. Bentley raised chickens, ducks, and hogs, and he did himself proud with an otherwise no-account field of alfalfa and milo, a mere afterthought in size. His real interest rested in watermelons, his specialty. I reckon all the care he doted on them left scant time for keeping up his home. It suffered patiently amidst swirls of fretting over his precious melon patch.

He lived in the frame of a railroad caboose that he'd plopped down fifty yards west of the creek and thirty yards east of the main dirt road. He'd framed his caboose home with cinder blocks topped with a row of bricks. I figured those blocks welcomed snakes to slither into them to make a home of their own.

Mr. Bentley added a room to the car, which he waterproofed with a covering of tarpaper. One spring day he got a wild hair and added a wooden lip to his home, which he called a porch. He rocked himself on that porch as he oversaw his kingdom of hogs, fowl, and melons. If anyone or anything came calling, he shoved at the arms of his rocking chair to pry himself up and out, mimicking an engine with a pair of faulty pistons. Then, he spied what crawled up his one-lane dirt road, rock-strewn and cruelly rutted.

Mr. Bentley's farm housed many relics, and his 1940 black Ford pickup truck topped the list. In it he hauled supplies from a wholesaler all the way up north in Kansas City, a whopping thirty-five miles distant. He sputtered there twice a year to restock the wares he stored in a shed tucked between his smokehouse and the hovel where his chickens roosted.

So as not to embarrass himself much when neighbors called to buy supplies, Mr. Bentley revived his pickup every six months for a supply trip. His truck coughed to life after many protests, the way grouchy kids mutter the third time they're called to morning chores. Spewing a cloud of grumbling sounds, the pickup revved up.

Well, Mr. Bentley overflowed his truck with everything from hardware and wire to liniment and duct tape. How did his truck hold up? Maybe the secret rested in his caution. I'm sure that he never drove it faster than forty miles an hour. Well, let me see . . . Mr. Bentley's pickup might speed that fast if he gunned the engine, threw his weight forward, and sped downhill with a favorable wind at his back.

When folks stopped to buy a special fence tool or a certain kind of wire, Mr. Bentley scratched his head, rubbed his chin, and slapped his left leg with his right hand. His loosened coverall strap on his right side made more room to wave his arm about. "Well, I'm slap out of that!" he often declared, puffing himself up like a rollicking toad as he began to rattle with laughter, as if steered his 1940 pickup over a washboard surface of rutted and hard-packed dirt.

Folks began calling his place the "Slap-Out Farm" because that is what he often told them when they came calling for supplies. So. they hadn't saved a trip into town after all. And to add insult to injury, they had to endure his long-winded tales.

He usually commenced with the high cost of the supplies, and then he ambled into something or other like, "My second cousin over in Franklin County can't afford a thing, not even half price. All he does is sit on his duff by the fire, cradle his hurt toe, and whistle hard times. Why? 'Cause he's as lazy as a drunk hog. That's the cousin who up and married his very own half-sister, God forbid! But their children didn't come out all deformed, and they earn a living, unlike their no-account pappy. If he ever shows his face on my land, I'll give him what for—the old skinflint! What did he mean swiping a roll of barbed wire without so much as a thank you? Sounds like a Yankee, if you ask me." Mr. Bentley rambled about any subject, and his supply favors amounted to squat. He ended each story with an attack on the general character of Yankees and of city folks—not to mention the specific character of Republicans.

Mr. Bentley was a dyed-in-the-wool Democrat, fussing about how President Taft didn't know how many beans made five (and how he had likely gobbled them before he could even count bean one). Drawing enough wind to let loose his blustery blasts, he carried on about the generally low moral state of Republicans. "I wouldn't trust one of 'em Republicans as far as I could throw him, and that ain't far, seeing as how they suck up anything not moving."

When Dad declared, "Teddy Roosevelt was a Republican, and we thought he was all right," Mr. Bentley grew more riled.

"Leave it to Teddy to swipe what weren't his, I rest my case," he said. Then, not resting, came, "Teaching any Republican not to lie and steal is akin to working on an egg-suck hound—learning him to steer clear of the chicken shed. Just you try it. He throws a hissie fit, as if I hurt him." Nothing could convince him otherwise.

Dad offered, "How about Mrs. Coif, the kindest lady in the county. She's a Republican, and she wouldn't steal." Mr. Bentley would have none of it. "Why, turn your back one moment, and she'd make a snatch at your wallet, like a duck on a June bug. That's all them no-account Republicans are good for: swiping what doesn't belong to them, elections a specialty. When they're caught, they scrunch up all mopey-faced. A pack of no-account thieves and liars, you're darn tooting!"

Mr. Bentley's firm opinions meant he was self-assured about nearly everything but slap-out of most things—except for vine-ripened melons. He bragged about growing the best melons in the county, and his rows of ribbons from the county fair proved some merit for his claim. One year he scooted to the Kansas State Fair in Topeka with his best specimens. He took Grand Prize there, which meant that folks figured he grew the finest melon—not only in the county but in the whole blame state.

The first time I saw him carrying on, I watched his face redden with laughter. Had he sucked up enough hot air to gain lift, threatening to go airborne? I should have known better, that he would remain earthbound, for his heavy laughter weighed him down as if he had gobbled lead shot, something akin to Mr. Twain's Fabled Jumping Frog of Calaveras County.

Appearing to be a hobo living in a grounded railroad car, he strutted like an overfed hog grunting for air on a hot summer's day. His mouth drooped open like a widder women's pig. He coolly folded a wad of tobacco into his cheek, the dark globs in his mouth calling to mind over-sized watermelon seeds prime for spitting. Mr. Bentley spat more often than not, and he made a show of doing so. Now, spitting properly is an honorable sport, and anyone who does not spit by the rules dishonors himself and the sport. He marshaled a particular rhythm for his spitting, especially when he rested in his rocking chair. First, he relaxed by loosening the right strap of his coveralls. He always did himself proud, spitting only as he rocked himself forward, seeing as how that primed the thrust for his wads. How far could he sling a dollop of spent chewing tobacco? No one rightly knows. As he spat, he reared up in his chair and grabbed both arms to brace himself for greater distance. As he slung that spent glob of chewing tobacco into the air, Mr. Bentley crashed back into his chair.

Quality knew its price, and Mr. Bentley knew how much he could charge for melons without killing his repeat business. That didn't mean they didn't grumble about "highway" robbery. Anyhow, medium-sized melons were $4, large ones were $5, and the extra-large were a whopping $7 each. The medium-sized ones were what most folks would call large; Mr. Bentley never grew any small ones; the patch and Mr. Bentley would hear none of that. The land, water, and sun conspired to make sure all of his melons were respectable in size.

Even so, what Mr. Bentley's melons boasted in size, they outdid in flavor. Why, those melons tasted so sweet that it positively hurt my mouth to nibble them. Not knowing if I could take it slow since it tasted so fine, I managed to restrain myself so that I would not injure the lining of my mouth. Whenever I ate a slice of his melons, I took care, the care of a tired body carefully edging into a too-hot bath. First I licked and then gnawed on a crimson wedge.

Our master melon-grower never gave away a melon to save himself. Did the word "gift" register in his mind? It's not that he needed all of that money or would have missed $7 here or there. I suppose he wanted his customers to appreciate the melons. If they paid for each one, they would savor their flavor even more.

One July day when I was ten years old, Dad and I stopped to buy a few ducks from Mr. Bentley. As Dad drove up the rutted dirt road, I felt creepy. The undergrowth and bushes whispered, "Danger." And on a crudely scrawled wooden plank, words in red paint warned, "Bewar of Dog".

I whispered to Dad, "Is Mr. Bentley what people call a hermit?"

"No, not really. However, if he had his druthers, I reckon he would be."

"Where do hermits live?"

"Far from here, back in the low spots, tucked between wooded hills."

"How far back is that?"

"Far enough back so that a body needs to wipe owl poop off of the clocks to tell time."

"Dad . . ."

Mr. Bentley sat rocking on his chair and chewing tobacco as he watched the creek, its swirling waters teeming with sand and dirt. His chicken and duck shed looked no worse than his caboose-frame home covered with tarpaper and a few loose boards.

"Help yourself to the ducks, Mr. Redmond," he shouted when Dad handed him $5 for a pair.

Before walking to the shed for two ducks, Dad said, "Sean, rest here." Mr. Bentley's hound Duke, sprawled on boards nearby, didn't budge.

Mr. Bentley wasted no time. "Son, did ya know ya have new neighbors? Some city folk moved down. They built a summer home and then decided to live in it year-round." Snorting, he sputtered, "We'll just see how long that lasts."

"Don't you think they'll stay?"

Mr. Bentley rocked a few rounds in his chair before he answered, waiting for the proper timing with his rocker to begin a sentence, like a trapeze artist waiting for the right moment before lurching forward to grab the rope.

"Well, maybe. For a year or two, anyhow. Then, just you wait and see. They'll tire of country living and head back to the city. Once city's in their blood, they can't purge it." He ceased rocking for a spell and leaned forward, as if he was fixing to tell me a dark secret. "Why, I even heard the mister took a trip to 'New York City' to hear an opera. What a waste of money. The idea . . . a bunch of sloppy folks in baggy britches, prancing around a stage and shouting at each other like a pack of bloodhounds baying at the moon. Old Duke would take 'em if ever he heard that ruckus, I guarrraantee!"

Agreeing since I did not know what else I could do, I offered, "A shameful waste . . . he sure could've bought a fine truckload of melons with all the money he blew on the opera!" Was Mr. Bentley more peeved that the new neighbor hadn't come calling to buy melons?

"Son, if that stranger wanders around here asking to buy a melon, I'll declare that I'm slap-out of 'em. Money ain't everything, you know. I declare, city folks reckon they're too good for all of us."

Mr. Bentley spit out part of his tobacco wad, staining the gray dirt.

"Yep, gone before you know it, as unfaithful as a Yankee I'd say, which is what most of them are."

"Yes, sir."

"We farm folks are the real people, the permanent ones. We do all of the work, all of the living and dying in these parts. The city folk are stuck-up jokes," he snorted in disgust as he slapped his right hand upside his left thigh. Being slap out of patience for city folks, he figured he would be slap out of whatever they wanted.

"Are city folks as mean and cussed as Yankees?" I asked.

Mr. Bentley wobbled back and forth in his rocking chair before biting down hard on another wad and tearing loose a mighty glob that he spat to his left side. He slurped his mouth with his shirt-sleeve, streaked and spackled with brownish traces of juice. His lips sputtered to action, as if they had been primed by his saliva.

"Well, no. I reckon no one is as low as them lying, burning, raping Yankees!" He let out with a self-satisfied howl and thumped his left leg against the creaky boards of his porch that moaned in reply. Then, even though he hadn't drooled or spat, he smeared his face with that shirt-sleeve again.

"You know how low those Yankees are? They're so low that I would not sell them a watermelon, not even if I was out of money for tobacco. Why should I? Well, I'll be go to hell—there ain't no law saying I gotta sell my melons to anyone toting a wad of loose bills in their britches. Who knows where all that loot come from, anyhow, hmmm?"

As Mr. Bentley droned on, my eyes flitted toward the creek bank where I saw a bunch of thistles in full bloom. The soil was filled with rocks, and I wondered how all of those thistles had managed to find a home there. The ground could not have been much good. If it had been, Mr. Bentley would have commandeered it for part of his melon patch. Those thistles made a bumper crop in that rocky spot, and they managed to do that without any of the care that Mr. Bentley lavished on his melon patch. They must have tunneled their roots into the rocky soil to find a few pockets of soil between the limestone and shale. Those thistles reminded me of the farm folk who had settled in those parts, managing to tend marginal farms with a quiet dignity.

"Maybe their Daddy stole it, don't you know! No Yankee's gonna taste my watermelons 'cuz I won't sell 'em one, and they ain't smart 'nuff to swipe one," Mr. Bentley shouted as he slapped his left leg once again with his right hand, the loose material on his sleeve flapping.

"Has anyone been smart enough to steal them?" I shot back. I figured it would be not much of a stretch at night. Of course, Mr. Bentley kept watch on his patch by day, but nighttime was a different matter. He had to sleep sometime, I reckoned.

"I've worked this here farm forty years, and I knows every square inch of it. I knows its looks, and I knows its smells. If a damn Yankee ever set foot on this farm, Duke and I would know it. The thing about a Yankee is they're so stuck up, they think they don't stink. Well they do, I tell you."

Dad crept by with the mallard and hen in tow as Mr. Bentley finished his lecture. Mr. Bentley sat chomping on a slug of chewing tobacco, rocking himself in his chair. He spat juice out of the corner of his mouth, first to one side and then to the other. The wind tried to persuade him which direction to spit, as nearly as I could tell. Since he was indeed a mighty spitter, he spewed as often into the wind as he did with the wind. Likewise, some of his stories rambled one way, while other times they meandered another way (the ones not covering Yankees, city folks, or Republicans, that is). Take his second cousin over to Franklin County. He let on, "I can't figure it. My kin's employed! There may be hope for that old codger after all." No matter the details, Mr. Bentley's mission was to set the world straight about his newly reformed relative. While speaking, he fussed and pawed at ideas, the way a bloodhound fusses and paws at the base of a mighty chestnut where a coon's treed. No matter what the subject might be, Mr. Bentley let us all know he was an expert. He wound up with a frontal assault on Yankees, his defining theme, as if that was his paid job. We all could rely on his Yankee hatred.

"Thank you kindly, Mr. Bentley. We'll be leaving now, and I'll see you again next month for supplies," Dad offered as we headed for our white Plymouth station wagon that rested in the shade of a cottonwood.

"Mr. Bentley was hard at it again. Do you believe all he spouts about Yankees, son?"

"I don't know. He sure sounds like he knows what he's talking about, but I don't know. Every time someone disagrees, he either gives an example to make his case, or he rattles off on some other meandering."

"He sure does."

"Mr. Bentley reckons only a lying, thieving Yankee would dare steal one of his melons. Anyone else would leave them be. Only a Yankee would stoop so low."

"Believe what you wish. I don't think Yankees are as sorry as Mr. Bentley says. You'll need to decide that for yourself. I doubt they are much different from most folks living in these parts. I reckon Mr. Bentley has an old bee up his bonnet that's pestered him these many years."

"Well," I thought, "Yankees may or may not be different from us country folks, but Mr. Bentley did claim that only a Yankee would stoop so low to swipe one of his melons." Sure, a Yankee might snatch a melon, or maybe a boy would. Could any boy resist taking a dare, risking being caught, to prove he could do what an adult says couldn't be done? The little wheels in my mind spun rapidly as all of Mr. Bentley's protests about Yankees birthed an idea. I could smell the flavor of bubbling waters on a range; my hen was on.

Andy Franz, my best friend from school, planned to visit that weekend on our farm. We'd camp near the creek about a half-mile north of the Bentley farm. The last month when Andy had visited, he asked me what was wrong with that "old man", Mr. Bentley.

"Oh, he's all right. Set in his ways, I guess, but he's okay." Since Mr. Bentley lived near our farm, I stood up for him.

Crinkling up his nose, Andy scoffed, "Never mind defending him, Sean. My uncle stopped by Bentley's farm last summer, and that old coot wouldn't sell him a melon. What kind of a crazy fool is he, anyway?"

I didn't have the heart to tell him that Mr. Bentley probably thought Andy's uncle was a Yankee.

"I'll bet we could snatch a melon right from under his nose," Andy boasted.

His words sent a tinge of fear down my spine to tingle my skin.

Although Mr. Bentley had been civil with me, he scared me. There was no telling what he would do if he spied a couple of boys snatching his melons.

"Andy, that's a powerful weak idea. Forget it!" I shouted, aiming to kill the idea in its tracks. (Even though I'd already toyed with it.)

Andy would hear nothing of it. "Are you afraid, Sean? Does that old goat have you scared of him?

"He'll catch us for sure, I figure."

"Not if we take some precautions," Andy mused, the edges of his mouth curling up with a spicy plan. "If we play our cards right, we'll be feasting on melon and telling stories by our campfire tomorrow night," Andy assured me.

Andy's plan was this: We'd rest at our campsite until midnight, and then we'd hike over to the stream which branched away from the creek to snake within twenty yards of Mr. Bentley's watermelon patch. Then, all we'd have was a barbed wire fence between us and our pick of melons.

Once we had our melon, we'd hightail it back down the creek until we found the southwest spot where the stream merged with the creek. Then, we could head northeast up that stream until we made it back to the dirt road. One half mile of running later we would be safe back at our camp. "The old man and his hound will be hopelessly confused when they lose our scent in the water."

Andy's plan seemed all right. Against my better judgment and because I didn't want Andy to know that Mr. Bentley did scare the poot out of me, I agreed to the plan.

For dinner we roasted hot dogs over a crackling fire. We gobbled tomatoes from our garden, and we also roasted corn on the cob that we wrapped in aluminum foil, well greased with hunks of butter.

For dessert we fried doughnuts. First, we melted Crisco, and then we waited for the hot oil to spatter and to sing. That told us the oil had reached just the right temperature. A few degrees cooler would have made the doughnuts soggy with oil, and a few degrees hotter might mean they would burn. Next, we popped Pillsbury biscuits from a tube onto our palms, and then we stretched the dough to make holes. We plopped those odd-shaped biscuits into the oil to fry them golden brown. Finally, we doused our doughnuts in a mixture of powdered sugar and water. Our doughnuts rivaled any we could buy in a pastry shop.

We turned in at dusk after setting the alarm clock for midnight. As my head hit the pillow, I began dreaming about our getting shot as trespassers on Mr. Bentley's farm. Then, the clanging sound of the alarm clock warned me that midnight had come—and with it our hour of destiny with that melon patch. The crescent moon shone with enough light for us to see where we were going, but not enough light to make us easy prey for Duke and Mr. Bentley.

Although I wanted to call off the raid and tumble back into my sleeping bag, Andy shouted, "Come on. Time's a wasting!" I knew I'd reached the point of no return. But stealing was wrong, even if old Bentley had dared me. That moonlit night, we'd either have our prize watermelon or have hell to pay.

Wordlessly, we galloped up the dirt road that took us clear through to the Bentley farm. About one hundred yards shy of his farm and the patch, we took the stream southwest until it joined back with the creek nearly two hundred yards away from our target. Then, we moved carefully through the creek waters until we spied the patch. Three strands of barbed wire and weathered wooden posts protected it from anyone with enough guts to raid it. My heart pounded as we squirmed beneath the fence's barbed wire strands.

As we stood to spy which melon to plunder, the hooting of a screech owl sent a shiver down my spine, and a gasp shot out of my mouth. I had imagined that was Mr. Bentley shrieking—booming mad. I'd be a matter of seconds before he was on us.

"Shoosh, now. Just hush," Andy whispered.

My fingers felt stiff from the cool water, and my throat felt funny. I knew stealing was wrong, but we had our pride at stake. We had to outmaneuver Mr. Bentley and Duke.

Our eyes flitted over the patch to spy the largest one. Then we saw it. Half hidden in the undergrowth of vines, it rested in a swirl of straw: the roundest and largest melon I'd ever seen. It taunted, "Snatch me if you can! I dare you. I double dead-dog dare you!" Light from the crescent moon glinted on the waxy surface of the great melon, as if it was an egg of a monstrous bird that waited for it to hatch in a sandy nest. But where was the giant bird? Would it wing back to the nest after finding food for its soon-to-be hatchling? What would it do when it saw us pawing at the egg, fixing to nab it?

I watched myself as if I was someone on the outside looking in. My breaths came in short pulls followed by moan-like rasps. My teeth began to serenade us.

We gasped with no control. Andy zipped out his pocketknife to sever the cord.

The vine didn't give up without a fuss, even under the supposedly sharpened blade of Andy's prized Swiss Army knife. With each tug, I hoped the vine would snap. But, with each gnawing try, thick dullness remained. Then, after three tortured swipes, it snapped. The melon was ours!

My heart was in my throat as I lugged our beauty toward the fence. I rolled it underneath, and we sidled behind. Only the creek and the curving stream stood between us and the dirt road—that is, provided Duke didn't sniff us out first. As we stumbled along the creek and then the stream, our thoughts grew long as we drew breaths in short pants. Where's the catch? I fretted. This has been too easy. Is Mr. Bentley lying in wait just around the next bend?

We stumbled along with as much caution as we could muster, taking turns toting that large melon. The rocks in the creek slowed us down, especially the ones covered with algae, as slippery as all get out. Staggering a few times, we lost our balance, and then we plunged into the creek, soaking ourselves up to our waists in cold water. Gasps shot from my lungs. Falling into the creek after being steamed shocks a body! On top of that, my legs were covered in slime. The chill persuaded my teeth to rattle harder than ever before, so much so that speaking was out of the question. In fact, my teeth rattled like a hog chewing charcoal.

As I fell, my right leg shot out from beneath me, pausing before it rested in a V-foot-hold of two sharp rocks, which skinned my right shin. For a second or two I felt my right foot oozing into mud and gunk at the base of those two rocky spears, and I wondered if water worms lodged there, too.

"My God, my foot's stuck!" I wanted to holler. Will I die in this muck-hole of darkness? Will I meet my end like a dinosaur trapped in a tar pit? Will Andy scamper off without me?

The gooey mess of mud felt like plaster as I heaved hard and slurped my foot out of the crevice. A sucking sound grudgingly sighed my release. Gasping, I wiggled my way clear, my treasure still in tow on our chilly night of dares.

By the time we reached the dirt road, we were soaked and panting like two coon hounds returning from a night of romping through weary Ozark hills. Our legs told us the half mile run back to the camp seemed to stretch for hours, but it also felt like mere minutes. Each second we felt more sure that we would not be caught, and yet we dreaded what

might happen in the very next instant. Maybe the old man waited with his shotgun just over the crest of the next hill! We couldn't be sure of our fortunes until we reached camp safely.

Finally, we slogged into camp, but not before we stopped a short distance away to inspect a suspicious shadow. Did the old man aim to ambush us in our own camp? Our lurker turned out to be a coyote—maybe kin to the one I met ages ago?

We changed into dry britches, and only then could we cheer at our "Bentley" success. Then came our reward. Andy sliced into its flesh with his Swiss Army knife, and we commenced to devour about half of that melon under the light of the crescent moon. Although the day had been warm, the melon tasted as cool as all get out. Even after our adventure in the cooling night air and creek water, we were hot, the sweat trickling from our reddened faces after all that excitement in our midnight foray.

Speaking of taste, that melon was so sweet that it positively hurt my mouth. Andy tore into his slice, but I had to take mine slowly. To eat it any faster would have done real damage to my mouth, like hemorrhage it with pleasure or something. As I slurped that melon, I decided that if anything came close to heaven, it must be gnawing at a melon at midnight under a crescent moon. The taste of that melon might come close to what preachers in purple robes squawked about, ad nauseam. Did some of its sweetness also come from outsmarting Mr. Bentley?

I reckon we needed to prove to ourselves that we could do that—snatch a watermelon by the light of the summer's crescent moon. Our plan had worked. Excitement gave way to drowsiness as we finished feasting on the melon. We wrapped its remains in a copy of *The Kansas City Star*. We'd "do in" the rest of our prize for breakfast.

The next morning, Dad drove Andy and me into town to run some errands. As we passed the Bentley farm, Dad said, "Sure enough, Mr. Bentley revved his truck to the city yesterday for supplies. I hear he decided to stay the night at his buddy's place."

Well, Andy and I were fit to be tied. Still, I wondered if our plan would've worked had the old man and the hound been on the farm that night. Sometimes I think we would've made it, and sometimes I think we would've been caught. Maybe Mr. Bentley had been right when he declared that "no one" was smart enough to steal one of his melons, not right from under his nose—and Duke's. We'd stumbled into some old-fashioned dumb luck, just as surely as we'd stumbled and fallen into the creek swimming with algae and undercoated with slime-covered rocks.

When I think about that melon we snatched, I imagine that most things are uncertain. I couldn't for the life of me be sure about them, not the way Mr. Bentley was with his firm opinion on everything (including Yankees, city folks, and Republicans). I reckon that life's a mixture of white and black to form mottled shades of gray, just as were those unworldly shades of gray from the shadows cast by moonlight, just as I'd felt both poorly about what we had done and glad that we'd done it. I imagined that it all depended on the way I looked at things. At any rate, I knew I'd be saving my money for months to slip under Mr. Bentley's doormat. I knew that I must pay for that fool melon. After all, right is right! (That's all I knew for sure.)

Maybe Gary and I needed to prove to ourselves that we could do what we'd been told we could not do. My memories of that raid—when we snatched a large melon at midnight, when chilling creek water dripped from our britches, when we imagined an old man and a coonhound lay in wait—are too luscious not to remember fondly.

Gary and I needed to pull a few stunts like that to show we were becoming big boys, capable of doing whatever we had the courage and resolve to muster. I wondered if hounds feel that way the first time they hold up all night, treeing as many coons as they can corner: as many coons as they're smart enough to trap.

I declare, I suppose that I don't feel too poorly about snatching that fool watermelon after all!

Jim's Song

Although Dad mentioned Uncle Jim more sparingly with each passing year, I'll wager he thought of him daily. Eventually, Dad ceased talking about Jim altogether. Well, that is except for our trips to visit his grave on Memorial Day in St. Joseph's Mt. Olivet Cemetery. I pretty much expected Dad to tell his *usual* Uncle Jim stories then. Each time I learned some new tidbit that made me more curious about what really happened to Uncle Jim in St. Joe. Then, on the Memorial Day after I turned ten, his story blossomed.

After Mother and the kids had leaned flowers against the graves of Uncle Jim and Dad's parents, they turned back toward the car. Dad commenced talking. The look on his face told me I was in for a news flash. "Sean, you already know how lonely Jim was toward the end. Aside from Uncle Bill his doctor, I was the only who bothered to visit him. No one else seemed to care much. Oh, I know we're all busy, but you'd have thought that someone else might have popped in to offer him a 'Happy Birthday' once a year."

"But his parents were gone, and low feelings stewed in our family, right?"

"That's it."

"And Aunt Muriel visited, too? How about her?"

"I suppose. No matter. Just know that Jim felt lonely. I mean really lonely."

Dad had spent much of his free time with Jim. Visiting whenever he could, Dad often drove to St. Joe more than a time or two weekly. "I'd fill him in the best I could: bits of family and world news—anything I could think of to cheer him up—while I clipped his nails."

"You clipped Uncle Jim's fingernails—and even his toenails?"

"Yes, he didn't feel up to doing it himself, and the hospital staff didn't care to notice, let alone care for him."

"And Uncle Jim didn't trim his nails on account of how sad he felt?"

"What . . . ? Oh, yes . . . sad. Yes."

Tales of Dad's loyal visits etched him as a giant in my mind. That made me feel tall, even though I was only a whisker under five feet.

"I showed him our farm in words," Dad began, his face taking on a faraway look. "I'd tell Jim, 'We live on a prairie farm where we raise cattle and sheep. While some think that strange, much of our land is rocky and hilly, while another part of it is flat and thick with topsoil. We also raise goats, and chickens. Let's see, we fish and swim in the creek of our Old Redmond Valley. (You know, the way we did when we were boys.) My oldest boy Paul hunts for fossils along its banks, and Sean helps. Hmmm, let's see, what else . . . oh yes, we grow corn, wheat, milo, trees, and bushes.'"

"Did Jim ever ask questions?"

"Not often. He sat there listening, though. 'We swirl cow poot with straw to help persuade trees and bushes to grow. We tend pear, nectarine, and apple trees, too.' Jim didn't blink. He only stared off into the distance, as if his eyes wanted to drift into another world."

"Was that a trance?"

"Maybe. Now and again, he managed to nod. He let me know he listened. Once when I told him about our apple trees, he grimaced. I felt bad about that. I'd aimed to remind him of graceful times in our father's orchard. Instead, I reminded him of that horrid day in May, the day I committed him."

"No you didn't," I argued. "Even I know you can only 'commit' something wrong, like a crime or a flashy robbery. But no one can commit a person."

"This is different, Sean. Jim was struggling. And, he wasn't right . . . that's a fact."

"How so?"

"He'd stare for hours on end out across the prairie, his right hand draped over his left one, his eyes glazed over, and his breathing shallow. He wouldn't get up on any account. Maybe he was in a trance, and that's no show."

"I suppose not."

Dad paused for several seconds while he pulled weeds from around Jim's headstone. "It was late May, and the apple trees were in bloom. Our Sunday dinner was flawless. After dinner we moseyed out to the apple orchard."

"You mean you drove, right?"

"Yes, of course, we drove. Once at the orchard, my brother John and I relaxed with Jim on a walk. As the three of us returned to the car, I said, 'Jim, it's time.'" Dad's voice cracked. "A storm swept over Jim, and he commenced to pant. Sweat beaded on his forehead and around the sides of his nose. His right foot pawed at the dirt, and his eyes darted like a cornered coyote that searches for a way to escape."

Mr. Carl Zettle had breathed like that when I caught him slinking away from our kitchen early one morning. He was headed to the Osawatomie State Hospital. Hadn't he also said, "It's time."?

"Poor Jim, there wasn't anywhere to run. But just as swiftly as it hit, his storm of panic dribbled away. Jim stammered 'yes', and we drove away. I wonder if Jim knew that was the last time he'd see Dad's apple blossoms peaking," Dad sighed.

I waited for Dad to continue. The faraway look in his eyes drifted yet farther afield. "Oftentimes Jim's trance broke when searing pain swept in, startling him back into this world. (The 'red death' wouldn't let him be for long, and sometimes suffocation was even worse than the pain.) His trance wasn't one of oblivion."

"Dad?"

"He didn't stare into space without thinking about other folks. Most said he might be a vegetable. Not Jim. He cared too much."

"About what?" I asked.

"A world gone mad, one groveling. It smears the stench of uncaring over itself."

"His trance world was more sane than this one, right?"

"Yes, his world was more sane than this one. How can we say that this world is anything other than mad, where money means more than life, where things mean more than do souls—even tormented ones that ache for relief?"

"Such a world must be insane," I agreed. Does anyone care to recognize it?"

"Oh, how he cared about people. And his caring engulfed his heart. That ate up his mind."

"More than the way the red death ate up his lungs?"

"Yep, more than consumption. Dad turned toward the car, and then he turned back. "I mean, how could folks say his mind was ill? Why, he cared more for people in one day than most anyone else could in an entire year."

I shrugged. My thoughts were still huddled on the idea of cares eating up a heart and mind, far more hideously than the way consumption ate up the lungs.

"Gliding into the State Hospital, he talked to patients the way an ambassador might. He'd bow and wave, smile and shake hands. He looked the way a straight politician ought to look?"

"Dad?"

"You know, a straight one. Not a crooked one. Not like most of them, who remind me of the time that the polecats littered under our barn. That sure had been one stinky time."

"That sure was," I sniffed, the skunks' odor outdone by some folks who knew better but did as they pleased.

"Jim smiled, introduced himself, and observed, 'I'm here only for a brief rest.' And even though he really needed the help himself, he looked after other patients—special soul that he was."

"Good for him."

The doctors didn't give up hope for your uncle. They unleashed a bunch of procedures to snap him out of what ailed him. Why, they even tried electric shock treatments," Dad shivered. "Powerful jolts meant to jump-start brain waves and help the victim—er, patient—think again. Jim stopped thinking altogether for a long spell. He was worse than before we committed him. Yet my brother surprised me."

"Like how?"

"Like on the Fourth of July, 1958. Although catatonic, he followed me to the end of his hallway. From the window, we watched fireworks. I said, 'I'm partial to red pyrotechnic displays. How about you, Jim?' He didn't answer. Then, just as well as you please, Jim whispered, 'Lovely fireworks, aren't they, Tommy?' My God, I thought. 'Jim, how are you feeling? May I bring you something? Do you know where you are?' Well, that was it for a month. Imagine that. 'Lovely fireworks, aren't they, Tommy?'" from out of nowhere.

I started to laugh but slapped my hand over my mouth.

"That's okay, Sean. I thought it was funny too." My head drooped.

"Honk! D-a-d!"

Dad waved toward our car, mumbled something other than, "I'm coming, I'm coming." Then to me, he sputtered, "There's more . . . The first time the doctors actually 'left Jim alone' it was already too late. They stopped bothering him the morning he died. That morning I peeked into Jim's room to find him still in bed. This is strange, I thought. (He'd grown partial to sitting in his chair to wait for me.) I asked an orderly if Jim was ill. 'Oh, no, he's fine. Just resting, that's all. Go on in.' Well, Jim wasn't fine, not by a country mile. He was dead—rigor mortis set in. Were my innards being yanked out then?"

"I suppose you were mighty sad."

"Yes, but you know, I'd never seen a more peaceful look on anyone's face than Jim's. He looked as gentle as a suckling lamb. He glowed, the light radiating from inside of him and spearing into every corner of that room. It's as if he'd returned from a dreary place to offer light to a world gone dark. Naturally, I spent my special time with Jim before I let on to the hospital staff that he was gone."

"Honk! Honk! Honk!"

Dad looked between the car and me. "Before we go, I need to tell you a few secrets."

With that, I almost jumped for joy. I said I *almost* did. "You mean I'm old enough now?"

"What? Maybe. Listen, don't tell anyone what I'm about to say until I've been dead and buried for at least ten years."

"Sure, Dad. I'll wait *twenty* years after you've gone, if you'll feel better."

"Promise?"

I nodded, but what I really wanted to do was to hug him. Would I finally know Uncle Jim's secrets?

Inhaling deeply, Dad began, "I forced myself to do something for my peace of mind. Edging over to Jim's side, I pulled off his socks. His toenails had grown too long. You see, I hadn't visited him in a week because I'd been working overtime. Well, I needed to do something for him. At the very least, I could trim his toenails before those bastards put him in the ground."

A certain chill surged down my spine. "You clipped a dead man's toenails? How did you find the nerve?"

"I didn't find it. But someone needed to care. I *forced* myself to clip his toenails, that's all."

My skin twitched with fright. Well, I didn't rightly know if it was fright or something else. All I knew was that a powerful feeling had snatched me. Maybe it echoed how much Dad loved his brother. It's a kind of love that twitches in soils and flutters over deep pools. It's the kind of love that sweeps up from the very soil into the soul to nest and litter there. I still can't fathom its depth. Love that strong makes a body weak, and it seeped from Dad's pores. While he talked, I felt a love powerful enough to tumble down walls and to blast its way into eternity.

"After slipping Jim's socks back on, I sat looking out his window for a spell. After a time I rose and said, 'Jim, it's time.' I rose to fetch a nurse. But before I left the room, I spied a mockingbird perched in a lilac bush. He'd been twittering a 'special' melody. I tried to make out what bird's song he was mimicking. But try as I might, I simply could not place that tune: sweet and sorrowful, sad and hauntingly lovely." Dad's breath started to catch.

"Driving to the funeral home, I stayed glued together by that melody. I thought about it: 'Jim's Song' all that day. What bird claimed that melody? None. At the funeral home again I saw Jim's face peacefully at rest, and the sight of him lit in my mind, melding with that mysterious melody . . . Then it hit me."

"What?" If I had a seat, I'd have been on the edge of it.

"The mockingbird's melody wasn't a bird's song at all." Dad lowered his voice. "He was singing 'Jim's Song'. Can you imagine?"

"But . . . Jim . . . was dead"

"He may have hummed his song earlier. Maybe Jim's soul sang that song in death to say good-bye to me," Dad sighed. He gripped my shoulder. "Perhaps I was too sad to hear him singing, so the mockingbird sang for him."

"The mockingbird sang Jim's song because you were too sad to hear it?"

"Yes," Dad swallowed. "Sometimes, beauty rests smack dab in front of us. We don't see it, seeing as how we're all drawn up in our world. Mockingbirds might help us hear all songs, even those of dying men."

"And the world is better off hearing those songs of dying men, who die of broken hearts, right Dad?"

"Yes, absolutely. The world is alive with music, with songs from everyone. It beats with your song and mine. We all have a song, and they all ease in from a font, one echoing and twitching with life."

"Yes, sir."

"Never stop listening. Never give up. You'll hear it. You will." His hands trembled, his eyes red and misted.

"Honk! Honk! Honk! Honk! Come on! We've been sitting her all day!"

"We'd better go," Dad said.

"But Dad, how do you suppose the mockingbird learned Jim's song?"

"The mockingbird nested in the lilac bush growing next to Jim's window where he sat on occasion. A black, wooden chair rested there. That's where Jim gazed onto the open pastures, where he saw songbirds frolicking near his window, where he spied that mockingbird fluttering near the window. That's where Jim and that bird eyed each other."

"But Dad, anyone knows that when a bird flutters at a window, someone's going to die. Do you reckon he was telling Uncle Jim that he was a goner."

"Maybe . . . But it was more than that. Your uncle could listen to music and to poetry nonstop and still thirst for more. Seeing as how the hospital staff didn't permit books, radios, or phonographs in his room— as if that might make him feel better, who knows? I think Jim took to crafting his own music. He might have whistled."

"Do you remember him whistling out of his window?

"For a few years it was enough just to coax Jim out of bed. Then, in his last year Jim perked up. I often found him swaying in his chair next to the window that overlooked a small knoll. He could see the lawn and all of the grounds rolling out onto the prairie. I suspect that stilled him.

I imagine Jim whistled his melody while he sat there. That mockingbird may have heard it even when Jim was silent, though.

"Do you think mockingbirds can listen so well that they can hear a tune when it is not sung aloud?"

"Maybe. Perhaps they're more gifted than we assume. And somewhere on a windswept prairie, a poppa mockingbird is teaching his newborn that hauntingly lovely tune: 'Jim's Song'."

"HONK! Honk, Honk!"

"Hellions," I muttered.

"Tom?" Mother called.

"Why don't we hear such songs?" I asked.

"Most of the time we're too wrapped up in our day. Maybe we're not willing to listen. Some folks don't want to be touched by songs both lovely and haunting. I'm willing to listen, but usually I don't hear it. Since Jim died I've been straining to hear his song—soothing and mysterious—once again."

Walking back to the car, Dad paused. "I think the finest work we may do is to listen and to tell the stories we hear, even if they aren't sung as well as the mockingbirds can warble the songs of the brokenhearted."

"But those are songs, Dad, not stories."

"The *notes* are their *words* and the *melodies* are their *stories*. But we can try. I reckon the finest work any of us can do is to listen so we can tell the stories the best way we know how. Who knows how that may help someone flailing for something to hold onto . . . something to remember those who have been lost," Dad sighed.

A few steps from the car Dad said, "There's more to 'Jim's Song', but you're still too young to hear it. But soon-"

"Tell me now, Dad. Please, I'm old enough. Really I am . . ."

As I spoke, I saw how Dad's eyes rested on the head of a dandelion that was in full bloom. Its wispy tinsels of fluff ached to heave up to parts unknown, grand and mysterious. One or two of the hairs twitched heavily with ease as if it waved farewell.

An eerie feeling crept over me like the time I watched dust swirling in our hay barn. Didn't that dandelion's head appear to be the Earth? Wasn't the down aching to fly up like spaceships that yearn to blast off, voyaging to stars? And maybe the dandelion was a whole planet ready to venture to other worlds, and . . .

Honk! "Let's go!"

"About those songs . . . does it matter if I sing a pinch off key?"

"Nope."

"What if I don't know all of the notes?"

"No matter. Do your best, and let gravity be your guide."

"Is it all right to hum the parts that I don't understand?"

"Sure, why not?"

"May others sing along?"

"That's what we hope they'll do. That makes a richer tone. That makes a choir: One voice, one song, one heart."

"And what if someone doesn't like the song?

"Then walk away, but hum the tune while you leave."

Back in the car Dad spoke for all of us to hear. "I declare, Jim looked mighty peaceful at the home. How sad that he had been so troubled in life, relaxing only in death. His service began just as serenely as his expression."

There was a collective groan from everyone. Even little Leo and baby Greg moaned.

"Monsignor Daley from the downtown cathedral agreed to conduct Jim's service. We were seated in an alcove. A red velvet curtain separated us from the rest of the funeral home. In the main room next to us lay in state a wealthy farmer who made a career of buying up land for cents on the dollar during The Depression. Half-way through Jim's service, townsfolk shuffled in to pay their respects to the rich man. Without lowering their voices, they jibed one another over baseball games or made small talk about the weather. One man, mind you, even had the gall to drone on about his dog's case of diarrhea."

"That was powerful rude of them," I stammered.

"It was. But the mockingbird's song—'Jim's Song'—pulled me through. That bird had cared enough to share 'Jim's Song' with me."

No one seemed to notice Dad's comment about the mockingbird.

"Didn't the funeral directors care?" I asked.

"I guess not. But Paul did." Dad smiled faintly.

Mark jeered, "Aw, Paul, such a good wittle boy."

Dad said, "As Jim's service drew to a close, Paul—all of seven years old—strutted up to the red velvet curtain that divided us from the wealthy farmer's wake, and before you could say Jack Robinson, he yanked it back to show a room crammed with crying people. 'Knock off that noise, you yellow-bellied sap suckers!' Paul said. You should have seen their faces." Dad laughed.

That was the first and last time Dad spoke of the mockingbird's melody, of "Jim's Song". It wasn't the last time he recited Jim's funeral story, though. Every time he told it, I hoped it would be laid to rest. Like Mother often said, "Tom, that's enough. It's not healthy for you. You must move on."

I can't think of Dad without seeing his haunted spirit—haunted by his life in St. Joseph. During the spring of my eleventh year, when Sister Colette announced that I was to be confirmed, for my confirmation name I blurted out, "Joseph". Without thinking, I chose Joseph.

"Fine choice. That name of Jesus' Foster Father, St. Joseph," Sister Colette offered.

"Yes, Sister. It sure is," I stammered, my head nodding.

Really, I chose the name that had been whispered in darkened corners for years, a name shrouded in mystery and intrigue. The name I chose was the town of Dad's obsession. What had happened there? Could Dad ever let it all go? That town happened to be named after Jesus' Foster Father, seeing how early French Catholic fur traders had settled there on the banks of the Missouri.

And what was the meaning—or feeling—of "Jim's Song"? What about that tuft of dandelion down revving to take off for parts unknown, grand and mysterious? What about thistledown that twitches to journey into the unknown pitch stillness of night to glimpse a reflection of itself?

Most of my life I wondered if Dad could relax and let go. Might he be free? Now, I run from sentences that commence with "If". Why? After all my long thoughts about Dad, after all of my struggles to understand him, I've yet to decipher his stories and misty riddles. The mystery of what might have been linger.

Now, after a lifetime of pondering his life, I've come to one stunningly simple conclusion. Dad did his best, and knowing that makes all the difference.

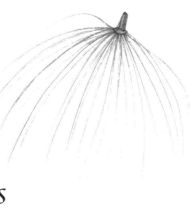

Spiders Spying
Gunnysack Genius

Spectral images flickered across our television screen one summer's eve. The date was July 20, 1969. Two astronauts swayed and lurched in puffy suits—human-filled marshmallows that sprang to life from a too-strange story book. Who had blown air into their suits to fill them? Darting over the lunar surface, they might not last long before a certain spell broke, sending them to flutter back onto the pages of a tall tale.

Their movements looked curious, as if they had been drugged for power and speed, the side effects leaving them too sore to move quickly. Were lead weights in their shoes holding them down so they didn't drift away, or did the moon sweep them into a state of chicken fits—bursts of action followed by twitching of worn-out nerves. Would they dance one last time before silence hovered over them?

The astronauts teetered on their toes, as if a brisk gale worked to blow them off of their feet (quite a feat with no atmosphere there). Finding their balance, the astronauts reminded me of how my brothers stood on tip toes atop the Wallace Park swimming pool high dive before they plunged in. The pair hopped and moved about, laboring to stop.

The astronauts moved like kids cavorting through fields of tall sweet corn during cool summer play. Their images panted and swayed, and their forms quivered across the landscape in an otherworldly manner—owing to the fact they were on another world!

Reporters began covering the Apollo XI voyage about a week before blast-off. I remember seeing the gigantic metal platform with the tank-like conveyor that groaned as it inched the rocket (one sprocket at a time) toward the launch pad. I watched endless interviews with official-looking scientists in Houston and in Cape Kennedy. The control panels flickered and flashed, dancing to persuade Apollo 11 to shove off on a voyage of discovery. I recalled Irwin Allen's "Lost in Space" with Will Robinson, the Robot, Doctor Smith, Major West, and the other Robinsons. But alas, the capsule could hold only three men: Neil Armstrong, Buzz Aldrin, and Michael Collins.

Knowing the astronauts planned to walk on the moon during the evening of July 20, I staked out my spot in the living room by five o'clock. I planned to be sitting at my post next to the south window of our living room as the Eagle descended to the lunar surface. I could glimpse the July moon out of the corner of one eye; I saw the astronauts close-up with my other eye. This way, I'd miss nothing. I nearly writhed with excitement. I yearned to fly away, too!

"Well, man's gonna walk on the moon on my birthday," Mark announced as we waited for the spidery Lunar Excursion Module ("The Eagle") to land. Mark declared, "They'll do it on my birthday. They'll walk on the moon on my birthday! Is anyone listening?"

His birthday would be made famous by Apollo 11. Would that help him meet Tina Louise in Hollywood, and would his knowing her help him get started? Pillows swished by my face from his direction.

"Could all of this be real?" I wondered aloud as I blended the familiar with what seemed to be science fiction, like Jules Verne's *From the Earth to the Moon*? "Could this be a dream?" I asked.

For the second time in a few minutes, Mark tossed a pillow at my head, the dull ache in my neck and shoulders assuring me that this was no dream. Nope, this was real! Two men had landed on the moon, sure enough!

Mr. Walter Cronkite choked out the action, his words echoing, "Wow! It's like Buck Rogers!" haltingly.

I kept thinking, Please don't cry Mr. Cronkite. I liked him, and I didn't want him to lose his job.

Mother was swept away by it all too, exclaiming, "Kids, just think they are up there! Can you believe it?"

Her words sent my brothers and sisters scurrying out onto our front porch to stare at the moon. Darting fireflies flashed their intermittent lights to greet us all. It was real! Our jaws hung low, and I wondered if Jules Verne himself might pinch himself to know it was real.

Then wonder transformed into worry. Could the crew return safely to the Earth. What if something went wrong with the engine on the Lunar Excursion Module, the LEM called "The Eagle"? What if a meteorite sliced a hole through "The Eagle" as it rested on the lunar surface to catch its breath? But there is no air on the moon, so how could it breathe? With no atmosphere, meteorites might do real damage. Oh well, "The Eagle" was only a machine, but that meant its engines might not work, right? How could they work with no oxygen in space or on the moon? Oh, the scientists sent Apollo with its own canisters of oxygen so that the engines might light. What if an asteroid punched a hole through the Command Module Columbia? And so went my flights of questions . . .

That LEM, a spidery contraption looking odd enough to work a mite, reminded me of a metallic virus wending its way to the moon's surface! Now I ask you, could anything that goofy-looking work reliably? Its spindly legs made me think of an enormous spider lowering itself gently onto the surface from a string many miles long. The astronauts were lucky the cussed thing hadn't crashed.

Who could tell me if the LEM might make it back into orbit to dock with the Command Module Columbia?

I imagined the LEM was an ornery spider with glittering eyes of gold, peering at the orbiting Mother Ship Columbia piloted by Michael Collins. The Mother Ship floated above the spider's head. Was the Mother Ship Columbia a magical pod woven of burlap sacks by a goddess in a silent chamber of deep space? Was the Columbia a work of gunnysack genius, as spied by the LEM? It planned to leap back up to make its snatch at the Mother Ship Columbia! When it caught its mother, might it accidentally sting her, or would it know enough to behave itself?

Earlier that day as I watched the LEM descend, I grew alarmed. Its crew and the flight controllers in Houston hinted at a bunch of problems. It sounded like the controllers said the computers were overloaded, and they couldn't tell Aldrin and Armstrong the correct angle or rate of descent. How fast should they fly forward? Where could they find a landing spot without boulders? Did the onboard computers fail because they could not keep pace with data pouring into them?

The swaying motion of the televised images told me that Commander Armstrong piloted the LEM at a rapid forward speed. Was that the way someone might fly a helicopter? "Heck fire, if he flies that way, he'll burn a bunch of fuel," I declared as I jumped to my feet.

"Now just hush!" Paul shouted.

"Freak!" Mark added.

"But guys-"

Before I could say another word or even blink, two pillows shot toward me. One headed low and east, catching me near the knees. The other headed high and west near my chest, catching me in a crossfire in a perfectly timed one-two swishing punch to knock the wind plum out of me. I crashed to the floor, my body changing direction in mid-air as the first and second pillow struck me with opposing forces. As I hit the floor, the top part of me skidded to the west while the bottom part of me shot eastward, wrenching me and wringing breath out of me. I simply lay there for a few seconds to catch my breath and my dignity before crawling away.

My brothers' laughter echoed through our living room. Wheezing for breath, I still thought that if Armstrong kept flying at that horizontal speed, he might run clean out of fuel before he could land in the Sea of Tranquility. As Buzz Aldrin quoted angles and their speed of descent, I guessed the crew might be in trouble, doing what they could without computers to find a landing spot. Those calculations whirling through Buzz Aldrin told me he's one fine mathematician! As Aldrin worked to find a solution, I closed my eyes and began to see numbers and equations, fuel consumption and control panels, flickering lights and then no lights at all on computer screens gone dark. Whispering my prayer, I felt my fingers digging into the pillows my brothers tossed my way, and I held my breath.

Finally, The Eagle gingerly touched down, the sprays of lunar dust jetting up from around its landing gear. Fully recovered, I simply could not help myself, and I shouted, "I think they just about ran clean out of fuel!"

In no uncertain terms, the hail of words around the room caught me in another crossfire. "Sit down and shut up, you ninny! They know what they're doing, you fool," red voices thundered at me.

Humans had flown to the moon, and they were all right! Their bravery made me feel cozy inside. Well sir, after puttering around on the lunar surface, they planned to blast off to dock with the Command Module. Then, they'd fire their engines for a return-flight home. But what if that engine didn't work? What if the astronauts couldn't dock with Columbia? With no backup for the LEM's ascent engine, Aldrin and Armstrong wouldn't be able to dock with the Command Module. Michael Collins, the Command Module pilot, would need to return to Earth without them. How sad would that be to abandon his friends?

Everything depended on the whether or not the LEM's engine would fire properly, and that might depend on chance. Something about that idea snatched my imagination. My thoughts whirled, sweeping me into space.

I was sure we all depend upon chance and on the wisdom of a few choices. Again I rose, this time to exclaim, "If we make correct assumptions, then most of the other details don't count for much!"

Annoyed grimaces filled the room. "Oh, Sean hush up now. Just be still," urged my sister Janice whom I reckoned must have thought I'd grown lonesome for attention. Didn't she know I had spoken to help put things into perspective for us all?

Since no one seemed interested in my words, I hushed. If I choose wisely, and if luck is on my side, I might succeed. Otherwise, look out! Maybe the best and most effective things in life are the simple ones, the dependable ones. I prayed that the LEM's ascent engine was simple, one that would improve the odds that it would fire properly so that the astronauts might fly home.

Since the crew of the LEM had only one engine to rocket them into orbit in a docking maneuver with the Command Module Columbia, that engine simply had to work. If it had no backup, then the LEM's ascent engine became the weakest link.

Being raised on a farm, I imagined that simple things in life can cut to the very essence of a problem. If the NASA scientists included fancy designs in the ascent engine, that might add to the chances of failure. By contrast, if the LEM's ascent engine had been designed as a single pulse motor, that might help improve its chances to work properly. But how could I find out if that was the case? The Apollo mission was a closely-guarded secret. No ten-year-old boy could swagger up and ask about such matters.

Next, I thought further about simple things—about how they're better. I remembered some of the city folks parading around the county in their expensive cars, not satisfying them much. Don't humans need to simplify? Don't we need to see a few basic principles that lie at the heart of the matter? The LEM's engine was a case in point. (I also wondered if using controlled burns on forests to clear the underbrush might lower fire danger.) Maybe quarantines (to slow the spread of disease) are another example. If folks choose wisely when it came to one or two critical factors, then the rest might work out all right. Are most outcomes teetering in the balance, resting on the choices made for a few key variables?

Lying on the floor of our living room that midsummer's eve, I said a prayer for the astronauts and for the LEM's ascent engine. If it fired properly, then it would blast the astronauts into orbit so quickly that the LEM might take out like a bloodhound that's caught the whiff of whats being tracked.

As I thought about the designers in NASA, my mind drifted to the photograph I had seen of a famous chef sharing one of his recipes. The caption read that the chef listed all details of the recipe except for one or two secrets. Without two or three key secret ingredients, no one could replicate the chef's masterpiece. Similarly, not knowing the two most important parts of a problem might spell trouble.

Each time I thought about the LEM and its ascent engine, I wondered if there are oftentimes only a few key crucial points, like the fact that engines without backups must be simple. Do tools of science give us a false sense of security by measuring the obvious, as if doing so puts us back into control?

Take Mr. Thomas, a parishioner who farmed several miles north of our church. He struggled with crop failures, and he teetered on bankruptcy. One day he told Dad that he had bought a fancy adding machine to track all of his finances. Who needs a gadget to tell him he's broke? Wouldn't it be better to focus on the few choices that really matter rather than on measuring? Which approach leads to control?

I remembered the tight rope walker I had seen in a dusty big top tent. Could our lives totter on a razor's edge of uncertainty with the outcome shifting one way or the other, just as a tree cut in a forest might sway to and fro with prevailing winds?

"Sean, pay attention," demanded my sister Janice. "Neil Armstrong is stepping down the ladder to walk on the moon!"

In the fall of 1969, I began fifth grade. School interested me because it meant friends to know and books to read. It also meant new puzzles to solve.

Indian summer held its grip that fall, the way a dog gnaws on a prized bone. Although the days stayed warm, the evenings took a chill. Using the evening temperatures as a calendar, Mother began to work on our Halloween costumes for the annual competition at our church.

Mother's sewing skills were well-known in our county. Like Grandmother Kearney and Aunt Laura Lee, she could make our sewing machine sing. I can still see her seated at her Singer sewing machine as she cobbled gunnysacks from our granary into costumes—amazing ones. Gunnysacks work better than duct tape or baling twine to bridge the gap between what a body wants and what they hold in their hands.

Mother crafted most of our outfits with burlap and sturdy twine (rivaling high-test fishing line) threaded on oversized needles. Since the gunnysacks no longer toted wheat, milo, or barley, Mother shook them to free grains that clung to their fibers. No matter how much she shook those burlap sacks, a few grains clung to the burlap.

Once, Mother shook out a daddy long legs as it scampered across our kitchen floor to find shelter in the southwest corner. There it eyed Mother as she wove costumes: cocoons of gunnysack burlap. Like that daddy long legs, we kids waited anxiously to see what our "Gunnysack Genius" might weave.

A gentle smile rested on Mothers lips, and a few beads of sweat moistened her skin above her upper lip. Her face beamed while she labored, and we kids sparked excitement from our pores every time we poured ourselves into our costumes. Our spirits rose high, although the cost of the costumes crept low. Mother joined simplicity and versatility in a happy union. Watching her, I saw genius at work (with her fail-safe design principles). Her first principle called for costumes becoming part of the person who wears them. Dad once told me that any fine actor knows that the costume and the actor must become one. Gunnysacks are pliable and adapt nicely to the body. The burlap mimics me, and we merge together. There is a hinterland between the two, where neither exists but both do in a checkered, blurred reality. That adds to the costume's wonder.

Anyone wearing a Halloween costume knows it must allow air flow. This is Mother's second design principle. The costume's fabric must breathe if it's expected to be worn long. I was always more comfortable in a burlap costume than in a synthetic one that chokes me with suffocating walls. The kids in expensive, synthetic costumes simply sweltered.

Her third principle is key. Costumes must be believable. She created legendary ones: scarecrows, potato heads, creatures from a dark lagoon, and cabbage patch monsters without even breaking a serious sweat, thank you very much.

Her potato head costume featured an oversized spud for a head, about half again as long as the rest of the body. That meant the crotch sank to knee level. Arms radiated way below the hips. The sight of the potato head slogging toward me made me giggle. It looked eerily believable.

Leo and Paul teamed with me for our 1969 parish costume competion. Paul played the part of an escaped abominable ape-man from a local zoo, while Leo and I played trainers who led him to his iron cell. Those times roared! Of course, we took first prize. Mother's costumes always did. Gunnysack genius prevailed.

Mother's designs were the best, and nothing else mattered—not even the gaudy plastic that money can buy, or which plastic may purchase today. All the finery made in high-tech factories and all the showy colors looked great, but they did not look "real".

With her talent and our excitement, we eased ourselves gently into the winner's circle. We delighted our friends who tromped around the gymnasium in their artificial garb. By managing a few first principles, we balanced our lives as we leaned gently into the wind to solve problems.

As Dad had said, "Do your best to improvise, let gravity be your guide, and lean gently into the wind. Don't make false starts, and always remember to take your time. Just lean gently into the winner's circle." Leo, Paul, and I won first prize of ten dollars. Our classmates clapped and cheered their approval, and Mother beamed her pride. Likewise, the NASA scientists achieved what what had been a madman's dream only a century earlier. When humans first walked on the moon, a great cheer rose from the control room in Clear Lake near NASA Road One, echoing all over Houston and rippling throughout the Great State of Texas.

"How did you do it, Mrs. Redmond? What's your secret?" parishioners asked.

"Oh, nothing really. It was simple," she replied. I think she knew it was something, for indeed it was simple.

Slop the Hogs, Momma!

Hogs are all right, not nearly as stinky as people make them out to be, and a heck-of-a-lot smarter than most people think. While it's true they fancy plopping down in cool mud during hot summer days, how many of us might do the same? I whiffed a sense of restlessness about hogs, their piercingly beady eyes showing me that they knew much more than they let on.

Knowing that one day our hogs would end up on my dinner plate did not set well with me. Quietly, I stopped eating pork after we raised our pet hog Wilbur. I slopped him daily, and to see him scurry up to the trough for food misted my eyes. Did he see me as his protector—or as a traitor?

I slinked around the barnyard every morning as Wilbur's butchering day drew near. How could I let someone murder my friend? I thought about freeing him, but I knew he'd be captured. And then, even if he wasn't jailed, he'd wind up with a slow starving death, and I couldn't bear to see him suffer.

Well, I made a compromise, which Grandmother had said is usually the wisest course. I decided that Wilbur's death would be swift. He wouldn't suffer. I also decided that pork was "foul" tasting. Why? Because I couldn't look at a slice of ham, a rasher of bacon, a piece of sausage, or a pork chop without remembering Wilbur and his sad eyes as he drew toward his feeder every day. He may have known he'd be slaughtered, but maybe not—I hope.

The Schlossers moved to their farm in 1961, only a year after our family moved to ours. While we fussed with wheat, alfalfa, sheep, and cattle, they were hog farmers. By the early 1970s they cared for more than two hundred head.

Each fall Mr. Schlosser butchered some of the hogs himself, while he sent the rest off to the slaughterhouse. I puzzled why he didn't send them all off to spare himself the trouble of murdering his hogs. After all, wasn't Mr. Schlosser haunted by their death squeals? I would have been, and that was after I heard a hog's death scream once, which was quite enough for me.

One evening in late October of my twelfth year, Mother and I stopped by the Schlosser's to deliver two cartons of Amway's SOC and a bottle of LOC that Mrs. Schlosser had ordered. "Sean, help me carry these supplies," Mother said.

Well, I thought nothing of carrying supplies up to the Schlosser house—that is, until a hideous squeal stabbed through the barnyard just as the Schlosser's front door flew open. There stood Mrs. Schlosser herself in front of me, fresh blood splattered on her gingham dress. She tossed her head, and her hair whipped around demonically.

I gasped, my heart racing. Had she been helping the mister with his bloody deeds in the barnyard?

Mrs. Schlosser invited us in, explaining, "Don't mind this damn mess. It's that time of the year, you know, and—well, look at me."

Mrs. Schlosser's two daughters (at least three years my senior) were studying in the living room just off of the entryway. They coyly glanced up from their books, and then, without so much as a hello, they looked back down. Although they feigned innocence, I knew better, seeing as how their eyelids commenced moving weirdly—twitching above their bloodshot eyes, that nervous feeling when the small muscles around the eyeballs move without permission. Were their lids aiming to tell me something that their mouths knew better than to squeak? It was clear the girls were hiding "something".

"How much do I owe you, Lola?" Mrs. Schlosser asked.

Mother handed Mrs. Schlosser the invoice that reflected Mother's handwriting on a carbon copy.

Then, with a flurry of scribbles and the thunder of head jerks, Mrs Schlosser whipped the hair over her face and handed Mother a check. "Thanks, Lola. We need these supplies. Just look at this mess." Mrs. Schlosser motioned toward her soiled dress. "It's our time of the year again, and we have a few left to slaughter. Seems like we butchered only a couple of months ago, not one blame year ago. Where does the time fly?"

Walking toward the door to leave, I glanced over my shoulder at the girls sprawled in the living room. They knew better than to look at me this time. But their eyelids labored furiously to hide something. What was it? A murder, maybe?

"Did you notice anything odd in there?" I asked Mother when we were back in the car.

"Like what?"

"Oh, I don't know. Like there's something going on we ought to know about?"

"Like what?" Mother mumbled as she guided our white Pontiac station wagon out of the Schlosser's driveway. I reckoned she only half-listened while she calculated something or other for her next customer.

"Well, I can't say exactly. There was something about the blood on Mrs. Schlosser's dress, and the way she crazily whipped her hair as she wrote your check. What about the way her girls acted all coy and mysterious? I don't know. The house smelled salty, not pork salty, but maybe blood salty. Something's not right."

Mother shook her head. I knew she was thinking I was "at it" again.

I didn't tell her everything, though. I didn't tell her I'd seen a pair of men's shoes (size 9) in their front hallway. Whose were they? That's what I wanted to know. Certainly not Mr. Schlosser's. He boasted of the largest feet in the county—size 13 triple E—and he never hesitated to show it.

I also spied an unusually broad brimmed hat (a sombrero, I later learned) hanging on a hook above the shoes. Had the owner of the hat and the size 9s been murdered? Needing to know the truth, I hatched the perfect plan. I'd spy on the Schlosser's.

Suzie, one of our jerseys, had become an expert at hiding from us at evening milk time. She took a notion to silence her bell by rubbing up against creek mud where the bank rose sharply. That made it hard to hear where she hid. Normally a nuisance, her behavior gave me a prime excuse to be gone awhile. My plan sprouted. I'd report that Suzie and Mum hadn't walked to the barn, and that I needed to find them. To look for them, I'd make a mile-long beeline over to the Schlosser's. Of course, I'd happen to spot them on the way back, and no one would be the wiser.

On Thursday evening, dusk drew nigh, and I found Mum and Suzie melting into the shadows next to a muddy creek bank (not far from the deep spot where the cottonwood slanted). Once again their cowbells were loaded with mud, and I reckoned they'd stew there for a spell. So, I crossed the creek and ran for the Schlosser farm a half mile away. The light of the harvest moon would guide me home.

Within six minutes I slowed to find a spot in the field for viewing the Schlosser's pens. Seeing as how the corn had been harvested, the stubble in the field didn't leave much cover. I trailed back to the west side of the pens, and I crawled through the weeds along the fence to camouflage my light brown jacket.

No one appeared as I slithered close to the Schlosser's main shed. Plopping down, I "staked out" its entrance. A light shone from the doorway, a sure sign that Mr. Schlosser was tending to chores. Then, out of nowhere my spine tingled with the squeals of a hog being butchered. I covered my ears and burrowed my head into the weeds. My stomach felt queasy, and I wanted to heave. I could think only of my poor Wilbur. (Poor, poor, Wilbur . . .) Then, as suddenly as the squeals began, they stopped. All lay still.

Then, "it" happened. A man screamed in bloodcurdling horror. Then, a thud sounded, and Mrs. Schlosser staggered out of the doorway. She wielded a wicked butcher knife that dangled from her left hand. Fresh blood had splattered all over her arm and pasty skin. She looked positively marked! My heart raced, and my breath came in wheezes as I ducked lower into the weeds.

What would I say if she strutted over to me, the butcher knife brandished under the light of the harvest moon? Would I ask if she'd murdered a hog—or a man? I wanted to disappear rather than meet that woman.

Although I tried to keep my head down, I couldn't help myself. I *had* to look, and I grimly inched my head upward, like a periscope breaking the water on a stormy sea. What I saw made me wish I'd resisted looking. Mrs. Schlosser smiled as she let blood trickle off of her arm. She gave her head and stringy, blood-splattered long hair two jerks to whip it around her face. Evil consumed her face, and she looked satisfied. My blood froze. The small hairs on the back of my neck stood on end. Then, to make matters worse, she scanned the field the way a hawk looks for a field mouse. Well, I be go-to-hell if she did not stop as she'd trained her eyes where I hid. Didn't her eyes soar out of her skull to kill me right on the spot? Wasn't she aiming to run me down and slit my throat, leaving me to bleed in the stubble of the cornfield? Okay, okay . . . maybe the murdering Mrs. Schlosser hadn't spotted me. Should I wait to run . . . until she creeps into the house? Yes.

Her eyes glinted in the deepening twilight. Mrs. Schlosser moved her chin from side to side. "You're a goner. There's no escape, little boy!" Then she commenced to cackle and move steadily toward the fence. My stomach jolted as she picked up a three-tined pitchfork. (Did she plan to rearrange a pile of hay for their pet cow, or did she plain to rearrange me?)

With her pitchfork in hand, Mrs. Schlosser walked right up to the fence line to stand within a dozen feet of where I lay. "She's seen me, I know it," I whispered. Tears of terror filled my eyes while a warm wetness hit my britches, soaking my shirt.

Mrs. Schlosser grinned as if bored, like she'd swatted a fly instead of slitting her husband's throat. A cold-blooded killer like her wouldn't hesitate to do away with me—a witness and a trespasser. After all, didn't a sign at her driveway say "Trespassers, Beware! You'll be prosecuted to the full extent of the law". It didn't say anything about killing curious children, though. Couldn't my actions be excused owing to my youthful zeal?

"Dear God, save me," I whispered under my breath. "Save me."

After an eternity, Mrs. Schlosser pursed her lips, wrinkled her nose, and exhaled mightily. She shook her head, and then she walked toward the house. She still carried the pitchfork, and I waited for her to ride it. Wouldn't she cackle in evil delight as she winged into the darkened air?

Halfway up the walkway, she stopped, turned her head to the left and muttered, "I know. I know." Then, as pretty as you please, she sauntered the rest of the way to the front door and opened it.

Shrouded against the curtains in the living room were two shadows the size of Mrs. Schlosser's girls. They'd been watching their mother . . . and me . . . I knew it. As soon as Mrs. Schlosser thudded the door shut, the shadows scattered. Did her girls know what she'd planned to do? Were they watching in horror as she approached? Did they believe she might slit their throats, too? Maybe they ran for their lives when they heard her coming.

I didn't wait to find out about their lives; I was too busy trying to spare my own. Crazed, I galloped over the stubble of the cornfield, my pants soaked and my heart pounding. In minutes I reached the creek, and I splashed into the water to rinse off the amber stains up my shirt and down my britches.

There stood Suzie and Mum where I left them, looking over at me as if to say, "What in the Sam Hill's wrong with you?" I'll bet they wanted to know if I'd taken leave of my senses. I panted and quivered in the cold creek water.

The next two days were hazy—from shock or fright? I really don't know. Either way, I couldn't sleep, and I slid under my covers to keep a vigil through the night. Every shadow in the yard became Mrs. Schlosser riding her three-tined pitchfork. Every branch in our walnut tree crafted a shadow in our bedroom that showed me she'd slash her way to me, her bloody butcher knife in tow. After two nights of vigils, I grew exhausted. Finally, I slept on the third night—not out of choice but out of shear exhaustion. A murderess was on the prowl, and I was the star witness to her crime.

In church the next morning, I was too scared to look at Mrs. Schlosser, and I begged myself not to look in her direction when her family entered their pew. Of course, telling myself that meant I *had* to look, and when I did, "she" was staring at me, a faraway smile on her lips.

Naturally, her two daughters sat with her, their white dresses freshly pressed and their hair tied with pink bows. That was normal enough. What wasn't normal was that only the girls sat with Mrs Schlosser. Mr. Schlosser hadn't missed a Sunday mass with his family in two years, and I suspected the worst. Did he lay dead on the floor of their hog shed, his throat slit? That was unlikely. His body would have reeked by then.

Maybe she buried him on the farm. I probably ought to plan a return to the farm to search for a fresh grave, I thought. But I didn't have the stomach for that, and I asked Mother, "Where's Mr. Schlosser? He always comes to mass."

While I may have been one of the first people to ask that question, I was not the last. When Mr. Schlosser didn't appear at church or anywhere else in town for weeks, a rumor spread: Mr. Schlosser left her, and he was suing for divorce.

While "I" knew the truth, I felt bound to keep quiet. After all, how did I know Mrs. Schlosser wasn't waiting for the right time "do me in"? Would she thank me for hushing? I ached to tell her I hadn't seen anything, not really. Maybe she knew I wouldn't tell anyone what I had seen and heard—or hadn't seen nor heard. But did she need to risk any slip-ups? What to do?

"Now hold on," I told myself. I don't know that she killed anyone. Maybe she dropped a bale of hay on the shed floor. Maybe *that* was what I heard and *not* Mr. Schlosser thudding into his blood. Maybe he screamed after stubbing a toe or whacking an elbow against a post, I thought. That was unlikely. And then, who knows if that scream was even his?

My battle between explaining what I'd heard and what I thought had happened plain tuckered me out. Maybe this was my "day-mare", and when I awakened, I'd feel beads of sweat on my forehead, my shirt damp with fear. And when would Mrs. Schlosser's glowing beams of evil stop chasing me?

Weeks crept into months, and no one spotted Mr. Schlosser. His missus wouldn't answer any questions about him. I heard Sheriff Cantwell drove to their farm one night to huff his questions. The townsfolk gossiped about how Mrs. Schlosser said only, "Things didn't work out, Sheriff. My husband left, and I haven't heard from him since."

I thought that those answers could be equally true whether Mr. Schlosser left her, or if she . . . if she'd murdered him. To come forward with what I'd seen risked people thinking I was a busybody. They'd know I held a wild imagination, what with accusing someone of a crime and all, without evidence—like a body. And if I talked, Mrs. Schlosser would know *for certain* that I'd been spying on her. No, I dare not come forward, but I hoped that Mr. Schlosser magically would reappear.

That didn't happen, and bit by bit the rumors tuckered out altogether. Townsfolk had more pressing business to discuss: weather, baseball, the price of corn, and such. After that, I was probably the only one to dwell on what she'd done . . . or hadn't done.

Mrs. Schlosser's husband had been missing nearly one year when she invited my folks over for supper. Even though I begged not to go, Mother insisted that I tag along. My lips twitched as I crept toward the Schlosser's door. Would she spring out with her butcher knife to finish her work? Nothing of the sort happened; Mrs. Schlosser was as kind as all get out. She served mashed potatoes, peas, applesauce, and pork chops for supper. I hadn't eaten pork in months, and I certainly didn't wish to start then. Mother scolded me though, saying it'd be rude for me not to try the chops. After all, Mrs. Schlosser had worked hard for us.

Mother complimented her by saying, "These pork chops are delicious . . . too bad hog prices are down again this year."

"Yep. I'm looking for ways to cut costs," Mrs. Schlosser said. "I'm slopping the hogs with more scraps and with skim milk from the Knuckle farm. They cut me a reduced price, especially on the days when there's too much milk for the truck to haul to town. Better to sell it to me than to let it trickle away down a gutter."

"Nice," Mother offered.

"Sure is. Still, it hasn't been easy. It's a real struggle to make ends meet, especially since my husband cut and ran."

Mrs. Schlosser looked around the table, fixed her hellish eyes on me and said, "Anyway, eat up. Are those knives sharp enough? I simply can't take a dull knife, can you? Makes me want to stab someone, I declare. Enjoy!" she chortled.

She speared from the table to fetch a pitcher of milk from the kitchen. As she sidled through the swinging door, she paused and turned her head halfway to the side, the same way she'd done that hellish night the past autumn. Was she mocking me, reminding me that she knew I'd been watching her from those weeds?

Horrid thoughts seared my brain: No Mr. Schlosser, not even a trace of him. Well-fed hogs . . . slop. Hmmm . . . My God! Mrs. Schlosser sliced up her husband and fed him to the hogs! And we're feasting on them!

I lurched back from the table. "I'm ill. Maybe it's the flu," I sputtered, racing for the door. The beams of evil flashing on Mrs. Schlosser's face tingled my spine, and I gasped as I clawed open the door. She's serving us shrouded evidence in a demoniac ritual! What better way to purge it, and I'm the only one who knows! My dry heaves stretched into a good five minutes.

Another year passed without word of Mr. Schlosser. Folks—who still cared—assumed he'd left. He might get around to divorce his wife in good time. Then, one day I read in the newspaper that Mrs. Schlosser's divorce papers finally came through.

Ahh . . . My agony finally drew to a close. I had to admit, I should have heeded others' advice. Grandmother and Dad and many others had warned me, "Sean, be careful with your wild imagination." My "wild" imagination was responsible for dragging me through all that needless torture.

As I lay down to sleep that evening, I breathed a heavy sigh of relief. I was nearly asleep when I remembered misty words from an article. Appearing below the paragraph about Mr. Schlosser's divorce filing, I'd seen a report of a migrant farm worker who had disappeared about two years ago. He was last seen working on a farm about five miles outside of town. His description read: "A man of Mexican nationality, 5 feet eight inches tall, 165 pounds, size 9 shoe."

The words sliced through me like a razor, forcing me to bolt upright in bed. Sweat streamed from my face. What happened that fateful night? Would the mystery never end?

Maybe news of my over-active imagination had been wildly exaggerated.

The Deuce, If You Please

My bed sheets spurted into the air as I bolted to my bedroom door. Clawing it open, I sprinted down the first flight of stairs as fast as all get out. I leaped down the last six stairs, a jarring thud sounding my landing. Slightly shaken, I raced to the kitchen to make a snatch at *The Louisburg Herald*. My body looked like a fleeing left parenthesis.

Had I'd seen what I thought I'd seen? Had a missing person been seen last in our area, or did I confuse the news in a whirl of nonsense? My heart throbbed.

While I dashed into the kitchen, two thoughts engulfed me. "Oh, please let it be there; tempered with, Oh, please let it be my imagination." If the article was there, I knew what I must do. I'd confess spying to the police. I'd also tick off all that I'd seen, heard, smelled, and felt that horrid night. I'd need to tell them how Mrs. Schlosser sneered at me, the blood trickling down her pasty white arm. Don't forget the horrid scream, the thump, and about how Mrs. Schlosser taunted me with her evil eye. I'd even let on how I galloped to the creek to find Mum and Suzie, wetness soaking my shirt and britches. I didn't like it, and I'd be ashamed, but I had to do what was right. Still, all that bother would be worth it. It meant I had not fantasized the story. I'd be able to stare Grandmother Kearney down, saying, "Grandmother, your lectures about my active imagination are wildly exaggerated."

Then, again I begged for the article not to be there. I sure didn't fancy telling Sheriff Cantwell what I knew. That was the same as announcing to the world that I'd spied . . . and then some.

In quite a fettle, I felt my hands tremble. My face flushed as I drew wind in loud puffs. Spotting Dad who sat at the table, I watched him sipping coffee as he glanced over his bills. The night was nearly spent, the daylight creeping over the east road that led to our creek.

"Are you in trouble, Sean?

"In a hurry!" I gasped, tearing through that fool *Louisburg Herald* that rested on the table.

"What in the Sam Hill's wrong, Sean?" Dad puzzled, the question sounding from his eyes.

As I opened my mouth to answer, not knowing how to explain my quest, I spotted the elusive article in the social section of our local paper.

LOCAL YOUTH LEAVES FOR MEXICO CITY

"The young man left for Mexico to study abroad for a year in a student exchange program. His parents held a party in his honor at their home. They'll host a student from Mexico City while their son is away. He worked for two years on a farm five miles northwest of town to earn traveling money. This "average" eighteen-year-old American boy left on his not-so-average adventure. He was last seen wearing a sombrero and waving farewell as he boarded a direct flight from Kansas City to to Mexico City. Bon voyage!"

Sweat trickled down my face. Dad repeated, "What in the Sam Hill's wrong?"

Ripping my eyes from the newspaper, I found Dad staring at me.

"I'm mixed up: as mixed up as a dog's breakfast."

"What?" Dad aimed not to laugh, and that made me feel even worse.

"Grandmother was right. I do have a wild imagination." Turning, I rested my chin on my chest. Huffing toward the stairs, I sulked in the dawn's half-light. Thank goodness Dad had the good sense to know when to let me stew.

"Have I learned nothing?" I groaned as I took my spot on the stairs. "Grandmother would swat me for this, and I'd deserve it." In agony, I commenced to shift, pout, sigh, and then shift again before I could register a clear thought. Then, I commenced to whisper, "But please understand, Grandmother. Mr. Schlosser was away for two whole years. Folks jabbered about how the missus did away with him. Sheriff Cantwell even mustered up enough steam to drive out to their farm. It was . . . creepy . . . and suspicious. The whole town heard of it the next morning when Sheriff Cantwell waddled in for his all-morning pie break at the coffee shop and grill." (Grandmother would not be impressed.)

"'Mrs. Schlosser doesn't know where he is,' the sheriff reported. Naturally, she'd say that if she'd butchered him. As for me, I was relieved to hear that Mr. Schlosser divorced her. Oh, not about the divorce—only about how Mr. Schlosser didn't wind up as hog slop."

Grandmother might cut me some slack, but I needed to explain what led me to "The Mystery of the Slaughtered Mexican Migrant Worker".

Oh, she'd have fun with me on that account . . . I guarantee.

"But Grandmother, Mrs. Schlosser hung a sombrero in her hallway, and she lined up a pair of men's shoes— size nine—right below it, as pretty as you please. What's a body to think, knowing that Mr. Schlosser wore size thirteen triple E and all?" (I would not tell her how I knew this. She might cluck at me if I let on how I pestered Mr. Schlosser about his gigantic feet one morning after church. He chuckled and told me, "You're a particularly curious hellion.")

"And then that article appeared saying, 'Student . . . Mexico . . . average . . . farm worker . . . northwest of town . . . sombrero . . . last seen . . . two years.'"

Grandmother was sure to scold me for my mistake, "What have I told you about reading too fast? You invent words and meanings, as if you're rewriting the story."

I might not be able to let on about how my fright from that horrid night at the Schlosser farm clung to me . . . how that scream tingled my spine and raised small hairs on the back of my neck. I also wouldn't be able to tell her how I couldn't cleave the sight of Mrs. Schlosser's blood-driping silhouette (or her "evil eye") from my memory. So what if I filled in a few blanks while smoothing off rough spots on unpolished edges?

"At least I don't need to tell the police I was where I shouldn't have been," I said, resting my chin on upturned palms. I'd wedged my hands between my legs and face. My head cleared.

I thought, murder mystery solved. No more wondering if I was pegged to be murdered next.

My head cleared only briefly before "other" mysteries swished back to take front and center stage. I'd neglected them for quite a spell. Question after question swirled: how, when, why, where, who, what if . . . bubbled and rolled until I got all filmy-eyed. Naturally, Dad noticed.

"Sean, you're wandering around like a Missouri mule hit upside the head."

I toted questions about what a bunch of things meant: my accident, pestering thistles, and Grandfather Redmond's death. And what about

Uncle Jim's demise? What message did that pose? What about Dad's haunted world and his belief that Grandfather's estate had been looted? Mother advised, "Tom, it isn't healthy. Let it go." Might I cipher wisdom from his obsession?

And then there were questions about the side of Dad that told me, "We're all the same, really. All of our atoms were baked in the furnace of stars, and people everywhere are pretty much the same." And another side of that said whenever I spy light from under door sills and through cottage windows in the still of the night, I ought to know we're all an echo or vibration of the same Source. That echo forms tiny bits of matter that pulse everywhere. Matter and energy may be reflections of thoughts in a Grand Mind: reflections of Intelligence."

"Dad?" I asked.

"Maybe all we see and touch came into being from twitching bits of thought . . . from vibrations humming a melody throughout an infinite number of universes."

What in the world did all of that mean? I was too embarrassed to pester him about it. When I did ask Dad about "universes", he only nodded. Then, he huffed away for bed where he pulled the covers over his face.

So, as my thirteenth year drew to a close, I ached to craft some sense out of all that I'd seen and heard, touched and felt, loved and tasted, smelled and imagined in the Kansas of my early youth. What could I do? Maybe I'd draw pictures, paint landscapes, or talk to anyone who'd listen. Or, what if I wrote about it?

Grandmother's advice echoed, "If you fancy yourself a writer, do me a favor, kido. Choose a story that makes sense, one you're readers will understand. Find something worthwhile, and try to keep it simple."

"Yes, Grandmother."

"Write so that everyone will understand it, now and in the future." What a mighty chore. Did she think that I could do that? Did I?

I needed expert advice. Might the winds of Kansas blow mists from my mind to clear it? My days passed in a fog of confusion. Ralph Waldo Emerson had asserted that his heart beat with an iron string that sounded a tale to reveal a common feeling. While I needed folks to understand what I felt, I first needed to decipher it enough to explain it myself. Maybe I could ask Dad for advice. Well, maybe not. Dad toted enough questions all his own.

But what was it that he'd told me a lifetime ago? What might I do with questions when he wasn't available to help? Where did he say I should go? Ahhh, yes: I remembered . . .

Bolting for the door, I hightailed it to the creek. I was a young man of thirteen, and no one dared to pester me about wandering to the creek alone. Once there, I grasped a worn stone, one without a fossil creased in it, and I gently lobbed it into the deep part of the pool fronting our leaning cottonwood.

Aching to understand, I turned to the wisest tutor I'd known or ever could know, the Little Country Deuce. (I'd dubbed him LCD for short.) He knew the score, especially about that which matters. His voice whistled and wafted in a vapor of wispy mists, but that was the only thing about him not as solid as lead or as substantial as a world-class scientist.

What did LCD spout four years ago when he bade me good-bye? Oh, yes: "You'll see my hands pawing at leaves in sycamore trees, my fingers teasing at plants as I waft their seeds on prairie winds. I'll tote those seeds over the windswept prairie with my wispy hands, too fine to be seen, with my fingers hidden from view, stealthily so that clearly your wonder will mend."

After I heard the stone kerplunk in the pool, I waited. Nothing—no answers, not even a hint of one. Dumbfounded, I meandered back to the house. Needing to begin chores that evening, I wended my way to our chicken shed. Where was he? I craved LCD's return.

Then one night, the Little Country Deuce swished into my dreams. Paul and Mark were at a "slumber party", and Leo and Greg were sound asleep. Dad was working the graveyard shift. The coast was clear, our house dark and slumbering.

"You called? Hollered is more like it," LCD sputtered. What's eating you, boy?"

I shook my head to clear my eyes and ears. "Is it you? Can you be real?"

"None other. You lobbed your stone into the deep spot in your creek, didn't you? You also lofted your questions into the wind, and I toted them to the powers that be."

"But that was weeks ago," I half-whined.

"This world's one large place. It takes time to gather up questions and lug them around . . . and, you know, wait for answers before I swish them back to you."

"Yes sir," I patronized.

"What did you expect, special delivery? Do you fancy blowing on a high-pitched whistle for immediate attention?"

"No, but-"

"But, nothing, Sean. Time's a wasting. What's your first question?"

"Well, I'm tickled pink to see you-"

"The question, son. Get to the point." LCD was as prickly as ever.

"All right, don't rush me. My first question is this: Why do thistles make trouble? And why have they pestered me all of my life?"

"Narrow it down a pinch?"

"Well, take the time I was mowing our terrace, and Dad was all set to pay my fifty cents. As I mowed, I planned what I'd buy. I thought about sending away for a special buffalo nickel from the Littleton Stamp and Coin Company in Littleton, New Hampshire—03561. Or maybe I'd blow it all on a rocket booster. Or, did I want to hold a set of Lincoln Logs on layaway? And there was a stamp set with cellophane mounts from Mr. Stockwell's store in Paola, or-"

"Get to the point, Sean. Something to do with thistles."

"Oh yeah. Anyway, I'd nearly finished mowing, and I thought about the meat slicer that our butcher in town uses like an adding machine for weights."

"What?"

"Yes, I reckoned his scale is as an adding machine to tally the weights of the meat slices he lays on top of it. He places a sheet of white paper on top of the metal pan first, and then he lays the meat on top of that. Anyway, I was working out volumes and weights of roast beef slices, when out of nowhere an old poke had its say. The thistle bent the mower's cotter pin, silencing the machine. That shut down my chances to pocket my fifty cents."

"Thistles ruined your mower?" The Deuce asked sternly.

"You're darn right. Listen to what else they did. I was minding my own business and thinking about our wobbly homemade boats while I walked over to the terrace on the south side of our yard. Well, a lovely thistle specimen grabbed me and threw me to the ground just to embarrass me," I accused. Why must they hound me?"

"Ha, ha. Is that what you think. . . . that they're hounding you?"

"Yes, what else?"

"Well, excuse me for living!" LCD creased his eyelids shut, and then he slowly opened them. "Think back to the mowing day. The cotter pin broke, and then what happened?"

"I rushed into the house to look for a new one. So what?"

"After that, what happened?"

"A stranger aimed to put down his dog."

"Yes?"

"A stranger hunted with his hound Champ in the pasture south of the east-west road that runs twenty feet south of our yard. They nosed their way up our terrace, and a diamond back nipped Champ in his snout. The stranger finished shooting up the diamond back, and snake innards blew apart and wrapped around the grasses"

"And then the stranger shot the hound to end his suffering, right?"

"Yep. Hey, I thought we were talking about thistles," I objected.

"Oh, but we are. Tell me, do you think you'd have seen that rattler hiding in the grasses if Champ hadn't sniffed it first?"

"Sure."

LCD wrinkled his forehead.

"Well . . . maybe. I-"

"Don't kid yourself. You were good and gone, marooned in day dreaming about God knows what. As you said . . . something about adding machines and curved volumes of matter. Heck fire, you wouldn't have seen an elephant nesting in those grasses."

"Elephants don't nest."

"In your best judgment, would you have seen the diamond back?"

"I suppose not . . . when I'm daydreaming."

"Do you know what might have happened if that thistle hadn't stopped the mower, thereby stopping you? You were headed straight towards the-"

"Diamond back. I'd have mowed right up to that rattler." I held my breath. "Do you reckon it might have bitten me?"

"What do you think? Didn't that musk thistle save you?"

"No, it didn't save me. Champ did," I snapped.

"No, Champ sniffed that rattler only because the thistle stopped you from finding it first."

"Well, maybe," I said, cradling the palm of my right hand against my face.

"Maybe? Well, maybe that thistle saved your life," LCD huffed. "The rattler's venom shot straight for Champ's heart. It would have been the same for you, too."

"I suppose you're right."

"And you have the nerve to say thistles hound you? They bothered you enough to save your life," huffed Mr. Deuce.

I fell silent for a moment. "Okay, then, how do you explain their delight in embarrassing me?" I crossed my arms over my chest.

"Are you hung up on the time a musk thistle held you, keeping you from strolling in front of a speeding car? That embarrassing time?"

My hands went akimbo. "You mean . . . don't you . . . the time that fool thistle practically threw me in front of a speeding car . . . aimed to make mincemeat out of me?"

LCD never played with words. He came directly to the point. "Sean, you'd have been mowed down by that racing car if that thistle hadn't snatched you by the britches. It saved your life."

Gulping with guilt at not seeing the obvious, I stammered, "All right. I'm grateful it saved me. But why me? Why are thistles tracking me? Did I ask for prickly eyesores as guardians?"

LCD winced. "What in the Sam Hill do looks have to do with anything? Remember, what's in the heart makes the difference, that which rings true."

"Ooops . . ."

"It's what inside that makes the difference. (Dad and Mr. Finesse had said as much.)

"But LCD, there's no denying that thistles are spiny, ornery, and mean. They may have their pleasant moments . . . sure . . . but they're cussed, seeing as how cows won't eat them."

"Cows can't eat thistles, but goats do. Maybe goats know enough to get past thistle barbs to dine on their inner goodness. Maybe goats see what others don't care to see."

With that I chortled. I remembered how our goats made snatches at clothes fluttering on our clothes line. They smacked their lips over thistles—their entree in a five-star restaurant. While thistle prickliness nudges away most animals, it was true that nothing stopped the hellion goats.

"Most folks wince at thistles, don't they? They try to poison or burn them."

"Sure."

"Only goats have much to do with thistles, and I don't see a line of goats forming, either."

"Right, again."

"So, how can we love anything as low as a thistle?"

"Are they low, or is that what folks want to believe? Have they given thistles a chance? Maybe they don't know them, not really."

"You think?"

"I know. Sean, think of thistles any way you like. It's up to you. If you think they're weeds, then that's true. If you think they're blessings, then that's true, too. It's all in the way you see them, all in the way you think about them. Thistles are anything you want them to be. But being tough and resilient to survive doesn't make something cussed . . . or low."

"If you say so."

"I do. Take homeless people. Anyone living in fancy homes may think they're nuisances—cusses if you will. Do shallow people in those snazzy homes know how easy they have it?"

I laughed a little. "Mr. Bentley would say, "Why, those stuck-ups in their fancy homes-'"

"Let's stick to the point. Do those stuck-ups know how brave the homeless must be to live on the streets? They improvise, carving out a way to survive daily. They trust where the winds carry them, even when that means passing the night under a sheet of cardboard or under a rail-road trestle. Do you know anything more courageous? Can anyone try harder?"

"Maybe the thistles-" I blurted out, surprising myself.

"Right. Thistles tunnel into rocky soil, in scorched soil . . . disturbed spots where nothing else dares to try . . . in neglected and abandoned soil. And they bravely keep right on tunneling to survive."

"That's what Dad said."

"He's right. Is there anything more sure of heart—anything that cares less about looks—than a thistle?"

"Well, I reckon they're brave," I sputtered. "And useful," I whispered real low.

"What did you say, boy?" Did LCD ever miss anything?

"Dad once told me that the world would be dotted with a bunch of bald and barren patches if it weren't for thistles, and that means they're useful. They never give up." My voice trailed off. I began to deduce what he meant. "All right. I reckon you're right. Thistles are brave and useful, but they're also invasive. They aim to take over, don't they? They squeeze out innocent plants, and that's wrong. Why can't they stay in their place?" I felt my resolve returning.

The Little Country Deuce stiffened "As I said, they grow only where others more faint of heart cannot grow. And what's their place, Sean? Are they trying to take over the land and to shove other plants away, or are they aiming to help us—to teach us how to live?"

"What do you mean?" I shot back. "They do squeeze out other plants. How is that helping us? How is that teaching us how to live?" I slapped my thigh as I coughed a laugh. My thoughts raced back to the hours I'd spent mowing, chopping, and burning thistles. Why couldn't I have spent those hours surveying our creek for fossils . . . or reading books instead?

"Let me show you how they try to teach us to live," the Little Country Deuce began to explain. "Sean, think about your accident—when you became crippled."

I commenced to pay close attention.

"After you let go of that pipe on top of the swing set, you plummeted

471

to earth with an eye full of business. Why did you let go?" LCD prompted. "More specifically, what made you let go?"

"Absent-mindedness. There was sticky slathered all over the pipe, so I let go to wipe my hands on my britches."

"Can you tell me what made that stickiness . . . that stickiness on top?"

"Not really. What was it? Please tell me, LCD."

"Not so fast," replied the Deuce. "You're almost there. I'll give you a hint. Do you remember what you saw in Mr. Brooks' thicket near his northwest pasture fence line one week before your accident?"

It was eerie that LCD should ask me that question. I'd often wondered about what I saw in Mr. Brooks' meadow that day.

"Hmmm, let me think . . . I know I saw bees massing in that part of his pasture, next to the brambles in the thicket. I also saw some weeds growing there. I saw milkweed, shatter cane and, and . . . Canada thistles. Yes! There were thistles because I saw their purple crowns. I saw bees flitting around milkweed, shatter cane, and thistles! But, how does that figure into my accident?"

By this time my heart was racing because I felt close to an answer and yet far away.

"Patience . . . You'll understand soon enough," began the Little Country Deuce. "Let's now focus on Mr. Brooks' honey business. Consider the labels on his honey cans. Don't they say, 'Clover and wildflower honey'? Do you know how his cans ought to be marked?" asked the Little Country Deuce.

I didn't have a ready answer.

"Think, son. Think crisply," he coaxed.

I hesitated, and then I began, "Well, his cans might have said, clover and wildflower, and . . . thistle honey. Yes, honey from thistles, from their purple crowns oozing with nectar. That is what they should have said," I answered with an air of triumph. I remembered reading in a National Geographic magazine that thistles yield scads of nectar even during droughts. They cling to the soil and produce loads of nectar even while other sweet plants are lost.

"Right, those bees were buzzing around wildflowers and purple crowns of the Canada thistles. The bees mine that nectar in mother lodes. Bees made honey in Mr. Brooks' meadows from clover, wildflowers, and . . . thistles."

I gulped as LCD whispered, "And whose honey do you suppose your brothers and sisters spread onto peanut butter and honey sandwiches? Whose honey oozed over the edges and onto their fingers?"

"Mr. Brooks' honey, of course." Such a simple question from such a complicated Deuce. Then, "it" hit me—hard. I lowered my head to search for a place to heave.

"You mean to say that the thistles made the nectar that the bees used to make the honey, the very honey that sticky-fingered kids forgot to wash off that ended up smeared all over the top bar of our swing set? You mean to say that it was thistle honey that brought me low, crippling me?" I asked incredulously.

The Little Country Deuce nodded nonchalantly.

With surging anger at the absurdly controlling tale, I shouted, "No, It was neither the bees nor the thistles. It was my own absent-mindedness. It was my carelessness. No, no, it was I. It was I who caused my accident, not thistles. I did it." Saying so made me feel more in control.

"The thistles knew what you'd do when your fingers glopped onto stickiness on top. Of course they did," LCD spouted. "You played precisely into their prickly plan, didn't you?"

"Nope, I am not buying that. Not for a moment. It can't be. No way, no how! I made my own mistake. They couldn't be that smart to know what I'd do, to plan my accident," I turned my back to LCD so as not to encourage his insolence.

"They knew enough. They knew about your grandfather and how he had died form 'sticky vessels that stopped his heart.' They knew that your mother had told you this. They also knew that she told you to wash your hands often so that you would not get sick. They knew that you thought that if you did not wash stickiness from your hands, that stickiness might edge its way up your fingers and into your heart to kill you. They knew you'd think of all this in a twinkling as you touched the stickiness on top—slathered on the top pole of your swing set," LCD reported.

"That can't be! Nothing's that smart, and certainly not thistles," I sputtered, my back still turned to LCD.

"It's simple, really. The thistles know this, just as the sun knows it, just as the soil and the sky know it, and just as the streams and the ponds know it. And you know it, too."

"How do they know it?"

"Because all things are one, pieces of a great big picture that we can't see clearly. And because all things are one, everything knows it. They're part of the same Big Soul, of the same Grand Intelligence, that hovers over windswept prairies, that hugs mountain streams, and that beats in the hearts of field mice."

"I don't believe that. Not everything's part of something larger!"

"You're mistaken. All things are one, but our clouded vision confuses us."

"No, that can't be. It simply cannot be."

"It can, and it is! If thistles hadn't interceded in your life, you might have found help from anything else, even other people, who are part of your training as well. It just so happens that thistles played the defining role for you. It's not that important, only a background detail. What matters is what they taught you."

"How could that be true, that thistles are as smart as anything else in the universe?" I snapped.

"Thistles may be anything you wish, and anything you wish may be thistles. It's simple. You were drawn to them, just as other folks are drawn to other pieces of this One Grand universe," LCD hummed. "You spied something special in thistles, and they saw something special reflected in you, maybe something most folks miss. It's smack in front of us, and yet we miss it. You suspected their value, perhaps as a prelude to your accident, or maybe as one way it might happen."

"Now hold on. Even if it's true, even if thistles are as smart as anything else in the universe, why would they plan my accident? What purpose did that serve?" I thundered back at LCD, my anger mounting. "I didn't deserve to be punished because I hadn't done anything wrong!" Now I was booming mad.

"It's true that they nudged you to become crippled, but that was not a certain outcome. There was some chance thrown in. You might have handled all of that stickiness another way. It so happens you did exactly as expected, which made their job simple. They knew you'd think of stickiness and heart attacks and your dead Grandfather Redmond all in one instant. But you did have a choice in the matter, even if you don't think so."

"They did conspire to hurt me, and I reckon those thistles are mean and nasty," I rebelled.

"Now, hold on for one minute. About that idea that they hurt you— hold on. They didn't hurt you. But they did arrange a great gift for you. Becoming crippled, you received one fine gift," LCD offered.

"And what gift was that? Suffering? Excruciating pain? Endless torment? Isolation? How's that a gift?" I demanded to know, my patience fraying to an end.

"First of all they gave you a chance to learn about them by letting you focus. Then, they offered you a chance to grow with wisdom through the pain. They also gave you the insight to heal yourself with the power of imagination, even after the physicians, priests, police, and about anyone else you can name threw up their hands and ran for the hills. They abandoned you, didn't they . . . or worse."

"I reckon so. Some even went so far as to ply more torture to my troubles: spread-eagle cast and all."

"What would have happened without those wondrous, inward journeys you took with Lambda Helios, Omega Bluebonnet and me?"

"I'd have died . . . or worse."

"Worse?"

"Maybe I'd have split into pieces. And horrid things happen when a
body and a mind split."

"True. Thistles also pricked you sufficiently to write, *Thistledown
Rising*. That's an honor, one that'll cheer your heart."

"The thistles honored me when they let me write about them? How's
that any honor at all?"

"You've been given the chance to share their story of hope and imagination. That is truly an honor, even if you don't feel that way right
about now," the Little Country Deuce purred.

"How is writing about a bramble of pushy, prickly, no-account, nosey
weeds an honor? If I do write *Thistledown Rising*, the story won't be
about nasty thistles." Then I paused and began to laugh. Slowly at first,
I laughed, wheezed, and then laughed harder still. It wasn't a wimpy
laugh but a powerful and bold one, one to be proud of, a gut-wrenching
one filled with resolve.

"What's so funny?"

"Ha, ha. That's bizarre. Ha, ha, ha! That's so stupid it's funny. Well,
the joke is on them! No, if I ever write *Thistledown Rising*, it will be
about the Kansas of my early youth. It won't be about thistles. They are
just in the background, not important at all."

"If you say so."

"The story is about people, the ones I knew and loved . . . and lost.
It's about living with hope and dreams, about how imagination heals
body and soul. It's about the mystery of taking an inward voyage to find
courage, persistence and loyalty . . . to find hope to heal. It's about how
we find courage to struggle through trials, how life goes on, how hope
endures. It's not about a bunch of pushy, prickly, no-account weeds."

"Go on."

"It's about farmers who use their bodies, worn and stooped from age
and toil, as tools. It's about folks who eke out a living, and who do so
with skill and grace, creating artwork on living palettes. It's about people reaching for tomorrow even though they might lose today. Now
that's real courage!"

"You said it."

"Mostly, it's about the courage to lean gently into the wind to do the
best we can do, even though our heart aches. It's about how we do the
best we can do, in spite of what happens. No, the story isn't about this-

tles at all. Ha! The joke's on them," I asserted triumphantly.

"Well done. Bravo, Sean. Yes, *Thistledown Rising* is about that and much more. You proved their point. It's a tale of Kansas farmers and a whole lot more. Since the story is really about everyone and everything, it's a tale about thistles as well."

"How so?"

"As I said, thistles are part of the One Big Soul that lives in all places. They knew your accident might happen, and they reckoned how it could happen."

"I'm still not sure how they knew that. Will you please explain it again?"

"Same way they know everything else there is to know, just like everyone and everything knows all of that, too."

"But we don't know that, or at least not most of the time."

"We do know, but we refuse to see."

"How do we refuse to see?" I spied LCD through the space between my thumb and index finger. I longed to pinch the pieces together to find the wholeness—the peacefulness—like the still center of a dirt devil whirling around a plowed field.

"We don't see all there is because our vision is clouded and blurred. We've been told to see only what's clear, only what is provable. Our minds grow dulled. We get stressed out, and we aren't centered. We aren't grounded in the Grand Intelligence that puffs through the universe with wisdom. That Intelligence hovers o'er windswept prairies and along mountain streams. It seeps through forests and from underbrush, and it drifts near desert flowers. That Soul is one Great Big Soul that drifts o'er One Grand Prairie. All things are one! All things are reflections of One Energy!"

"I don't believe that. Not everything is the same! We're certainly different from thistles. I know we are. Just take a look at people, and you tell me we aren't different from thistles."

"You think people are different from thistles? Really, now? Don't folks do the best they can to reach their dreams, only to see them puff away into nothingness? When people reach for their dreams, aren't they often startled with pain from a prickly spine instead of a reward they'd imagined? Don't some people try to shun others with their thorns? And don't folks tunnel down into the rocky soil to find pockets of fertile soil to sustain them, to keep them going even when times loom tough? Don't people keep trying to live even when they are stooped and worn from a lifetime of using their bodies as a tool? And don't some folks like Mr. Fields live on rocky patches where something unwelcomed moved in to kill what grew there, leaving them to wonder why they weren't taken, why they were spared while someone else was taken? No, I'd say that people and thistles are quite a bit alike, even if they don't look the same."

"You're mistaken. Thistles are really obnoxious weeds," I sputtered, my steam running in short supply.

"You're seeing with clouded eyes. *Thistledown Rising* is a tale of this-tles, while at the same time it isn't. Likewise, it's about the majesty of the human spirit to hope when there's nothing left but hope itself. More importantly, it's a story about One Great Big Soul, sung by the wind that whistles over all 'prairies' everywhere . It's a tale about everyone, about us all. After all, what else could it be? Anything else but that One Great Big Soul is only so much background noise. The real meaning is timeless because it's everyone's story."

"Grandmother, Dad, and Mr. Finesse would fancy that."

"Sure they would. Sean, thistledown rises all around us, and it echoes season after season."

"Maybe you're right . . ."

"*Thistledown Rising* is a tale of imagination and of hope, of progress slow and painful toward a better tomorrow, of 'pain falling drop by drop upon the heart until in our sleep against our will comes wisdom through the awful Grace of God,' as Aeschylus stated. It's a story about a tomorrow, bright and free, without a dark, clinging past. It's a tale of sacrifice and of persistence fueled by courage, even when you know you will probably lose. And it's a tale of peace and joy when a body may relax and learn the most important lesson of all. Do you know what that lesson is? Do you?"

"Maybe. Yes, although I may be way off course in the ditch some-where with all of those old pokes, pouting and sullen after being mowed and showered with dust."

"Try me."

"Since we're all part of the same Big Soul, and since everyone shares a common heart beating as one, we are all connected. When anyone suf-fers, I suffer. When I hurt, others feel my pain. How can we help but feel compassion for everyone since we are a part of them, and they are a part of us?"

"Yes, and what does that tell you?" LCD prodded.

"I reckon that the greatest lesson of all, which the thistles ask us to learn with all of our trials, the greatest lesson of all is compassion and love for others, for people of all races and all nations, for plants and animals all over the prairies, and all through the forests and mountains. It's love for the One Great Big Soul that hovers all over the world. I imagine the most important lesson of all—the one that means the most—is love through unity."

"I think you're on to something. That kind of love means something, and it makes all the difference. Sometimes a body needs to be directed to what's important, the way one might need to gain the attention of a Missouri mule. Oh, he's ornery and stubborn, but he does have a decent heart. Once you have his attention, he'll see what's important."

"Yes sir."

With his last point made, the Little Country Deuce bowed his head to rest for a spell.

"Now hold on, Mr. Deuce. Who will show this story, this *Thistledown Rising*?"

"You will."

"Heck, I'm no writer. I'm still not sure about all you've said. I'm still not clear on all that's happened," I stammered as I pinched my thumb and index finger closer together while I peered at LCD through that space. "I feel used by thistles and their swarms of little helpers, the hellion bees. And, I don't want to write the story. As Grandmother Cloddie Kearney said, I might make a darn fool of myself."

"Do you reckon you'll make a fool of yourself?"

"Oh, I don't know. If I do, it won't be any time soon. I'm as mixed up as a dog's breakfast!"

"That's all right. Take your time. Either you will write it or you won't. It's your choice. As for the skill to write it, simply do your best. Remember what your dad told you? 'Lean gently into the wind, and breathe deeply. Let your conscience be your guide, and write from the heart. Notice what others feel. Listen, and tell their story the best way you know how. If the boy is a fine listener and remembers what he feels, and if he relates those feelings to other folks, then there's a fine foundation. After that, it's practicing and watching, dreaming and striving to drive for home. I imagine talent might be involved as well. It's in the blood, waiting to pounce when the time is right.'"

"Yes, he sure said that."

"Wait for a timely moment, and then race the story down the homestretch.'"

"Yes, he said that often. He whispered that in the way he stood hunched and leaned forward."

"And do you recall what Samuel Taylor Coleridge remarked?"

"Yes, I do. He said, 'That which comes from the heart touches the heart.'"

"Right, and that means you won't make a fool of yourself. If you write from the heart, you'll touch the heart of the reader."

"Yes, sir."

"Besides, I'll help you if you get stuck. I'll whisper words. Just do your best, and the words will come. That's all anyone can ask of you, just as your dad showed you by leaning gently into the wind. And I know a thing or two about winds, I guarantee."

"Of course you do."

"And Jane Austen said, 'There's no charm equal to tenderness of the heart.' You won't make a fool of yourself, provided your writing is kind. I reckon it might even be charming."

"I suppose she's right."

"She is right. When you come through with *Thistledown Rising* a silent cheer will echo from the stands. Remember how your dad said that a fine writer is like a skilled jockey on a thoroughbred race horse? That jockey knows the exact time to ask the horse to race home. It takes training and breeding . . . and a bit of mystery. If you spy mystery from the corner of your eye, if you accept it and honor it, if you say yes to the adventure, then you'll know the right time to write this story—to bring home the news of your adventures. It's everyone's tale. You're simply recounting it so that others recall their version of it."

"Yes, that's true. Telling the tale is partly in the timing and partly in feeling what other folks long for in their lives."

"And telling the tale is a fine thing. It fills people with strength . . . and hope. And, about your gifts. Try not to screw them up. Use them! That's why folks are given gifts. They're to be exercised. Gifts are meant to be used," he purred. "Your dad told you so."

"But, LCD, what if I decide not to tell this story, this *Thistledown Rising*? What then?" What if writing it is a powerful reason for me to breathe, but I can't bring myself to do it?"

"Well, let time be the judge of that. Follow your conscience. If you think about it long enough, I know you'll do what's right. And you, like the fabled Missouri mule, have a gracious heart. You'll do the right thing."

"Yes, sir."

"Now good night, Sean. I've other matters to tend. Other children need counseling. You do know that, don't you?"

"I reckon so."

"All right. Good night and good-bye," the Little Country Deuce said as he turned to take his leave.

That was the last time I saw LCD's face clearly. Every time since then, I've made out only his outline as I spied him working his mystery on the trees and on the grasses of the prairie and on thistledown wafting to ports of call unknown. Although he bade me good-bye, I knew that I'd see his shadow often. He'd told me, "You'll see my hands pawing at leaves in chestnut trees, my fingers pulling at plants as I waft their seeds on prairie winds. I'll tote those seeds o'er the windswept prairie with my windy hands, too fine to be seen, with my fingers hidden from view, stealthily so that clearly your wonder will mend." I can see him work his wonder where winds blow and where hope endures, which is naturally everywhere I know.

As The Little Country Deuce took his leave, I gleaned an enchanting life through a blustery childhood—through all the pain and torture— through all the heartache and struggles. Through long thoughts, I'd hunkered down with short prayers. In all of my actions, I reckoned that any fine act is a kind of a prayer, maybe the best kind of all.

On that score, I knew I'd do the right thing, that I'd make it . . . that we'd make it. People are here to bloom. Someday soon, the thistles, their hellion accomplice bees, and the wind might be powerful proud of their off-and-on-again student. They might even smile a pinch at me.

If I could feel what's inside, and if I could write about that to touch others (as Samuel Taylor Coleridge said), then all right. If I could see thistles and writing in a new way, doused in bright sunlight and brimming with hope, then maybe I'd help others see them in a new light, too. If I could see thistles in that new light after I wandered the pastures and left Kansas for a spell, I might return home and "see them again, as if for the very first time," (just as T. S. Eliot fancied). Then, I might have something worth writing.

I might write this tale of *Thistledown Rising*, and I might enjoy doing so: that is, provided the winds prove favorable. Maybe I'll become a writer after all, and maybe thistles are wonders to behold. Don't they echo hope and mystery that teem throughout a Grand Universe—this one and all the Others, just as Dad had suspected?

The Creek Draws Near at Twilight, The Draw Creaks Nigh at Dusk

Well now reader, I'm reaching the late autumn of this story, just as many years ago I reached the fall of my boyhood. You've worked hard enough, what with all of your hoeing. Enough already. Please mosey inside to rest for a spell. I'll put the kettle on for mint tea, and we'll share one more cup of warmth before you skedaddle back to all of the doings in your own life.

Flying past a baker's dozen of years, I inherited most of the chores. That meant milking our cows, feeding the chickens, and slopping the hogs with help from Leo and Greg. Mark and Paul were beyond that bother, and Dad had taken ill. After we sold Reddy to the Knuckles, only Mum and Suzie (one of Mum's offspring) remained.

Clanging feed pails together—dented and rusted on the ends—I beckoned them home from evening pasture. Sometimes my call worked, but most of the time it fizzled. The cows toyed with me. So, hightailing it to the creek, I spied on Mum and Suzie. Often, they lurked in shadows near the banks.

On a few rushed evenings, I sensed the creek drawing near at twilight, strangely different from its midday guise. During that fall that my boyhood ended, Indian Summer graced us. It felt different from most falls, the warmth lingering longer than expected, as if the earth was unwilling to let the season pass . . . the last one of my boyhood.

Standing alone at twilight, I viewed the creek. The others had flooded home. Only I remained as I searched for our stubborn Jersey cows that often hid behind a bush. They'd rubbed against the muddy bank to fill cow bells with mud to muffle them. Although they might not have trekked near the creek, I headed there anyway since I wanted to see, smell, feel, taste, and hear the creek once again. I needed to sense the creek at twilight, a stranger to the creek I knew by day. It grew nearer at twilight, as if it lived in another world.

Whenever I stood on the banks of the creek, I felt like I returned home, even if I hadn't left the farm. I skipped smooth stones across the deep pool west of the leaning cottonwood. Farther down the creek rested the pool south of the cement bridge. There we'd launched home-made ships, and Paul noodled for channel cat nestled amidst branches of fallen evergreen trees.

The creek that I knew in my youth came alive, echoing with sounds of birds and insects. Its waters rippled, shimmering under a setting prairie sun. Bluegill, channel cat, and craw dads—fattened and sassy—swirled through its waters. Water spiders skittered across its surface, and water worms gushed in spongy mud. Ornery bull frogs croaked the creek's praises, and snapping turtles hissed approval. Locusts droned in goose-berry bushes near its banks, and the crickets chirped its whispering won-ders. Stopping to peer into the deep pool west of our cottonwood, I returned home. Meandering to the thicket near the east side of the creek where a mighty cottonwood bent gently over the waters, I gazed at the slab of limestone entombed in the section of its gnarled roots. That slab made a platform to sit and to rest for a spell, a prime spot for viewing the deep pool west of that cottonwood. And wasn't that cottonwood like a gigantic musk thistle, one that had grown partial to tunneling? That cottonwood, like thistles, wafted its seeds on prairie winds. The thistledown was buoyed on faithful winds over the Kansas of my youth, "The land of the Southwind People". A thicket of gooseberries still camped around its base, skirting the tree in which songbirds nested. Lengthening shadows along either bank and in the hollow space between the bank and the cottonwood told me the day was done. Rippling waters reflected light into swaying shadows.

As I advanced, the locusts and crickets lowered their drones to a still nothingness, and an eerie feeling swept over me. Cool waves of air filled my lungs as if I swam in hidden pools, musted with a tinge of mystery. The waves of air felt like those on the creek's surface, each with a charmingly different temperature and fragrance. Moist soils and stones near the creek's edge grew mosses and algae, accenting the spongy steps I took near the creek's bank. Leafs swirled in the deep pool for company. Dwindling light once shimmering on water boasted a meager glow.

A few feet up from the shore, the gravel and dirt bed felt crusty underfoot, sounding like someone munching on too-stiff shredded wheat. The jays and meadowlarks, the starlings and the blackbirds, the sparrows and the quail had long ceased their work. Tuckered out and with no twittering called for, they flitted to their nests.

A still and soothing loneliness seeped into the creek, and a nameless tinge of excitement filled the air. Had a branch fallen into the deep pool near the cottonwood to bob and twist gently downstream? Such a branch hums for any who will listen. Would I move to a new mood in its company? Where might it rest? I couldn't say. No one may say where each fallen branch might lite, just as no knew where the cottonwood fluff might rest.

To view the creek at twilight meant to drink in its sights and sounds surrounded by a windswept prairie. Just as it felt special at eventide, it also felt strangely alive at dawn: breathing life. At dawn the creek echoed the chatter of birds. It streamed air, wafting from its surface to caress weathered hills. To gaze at the gurgling rill and to see the images of times past—my past—meant to return home. I rollicked along its waters.

Tossing a pebble into our deep pool, I gazed at rippling waters, dancing all the way to the banks. Into those small waves I cast large thoughts about all that had been in the Kansas of my early youth. Watching those choppy waves, I felt smooth thoughts of all that had been. Are our lives like that pebble cast into the pool? Don't we touch many others gently—and sometimes mightily—just as the ripples from that pebble nudge rock-strewn banks. . . . just as those tiny waves tease and nip at the creek's silty shores?

A clump of grasses clinged to a patch of soil that I found spackled amongst the rocks near one bank, and a tall musk thistle guarding nearby rocks saluted in the breeze. That stilled me, and I basked in golden reflections. The thistle breathed life's persistence. Who can't hold dear such a mighty survivor? I needed to know when and where its thistledown might waft on currents of water or air to ports of call unknown, misting seeds to mysterious places.

I imagined that countless other beings in distant galaxies may be thinking similar long thoughts. May each of us know one another, recognizing our presence by thinking about each other—however distant and without delay? Maybe by thinking about each other we recognize one another, conveying our warm wishes across light years in a twinkling. Do connections stream across time and space in ways sublime? Might cordial thoughts bend space, rippling it with hope, just as gravity warps space around massive bodies?

As I gazed at the teased surface of the pool, bits of my reflection caught there. Likewise, don't each of us catch reflections of our world—a world aching for company? Do we mirror a tiny piece of the cosmos that yearns to be known? Might my life and memories—all that I'd known in the Kansas of my youth—be a meager reflection of One Spirit that courses through the universe? Isn't that Spirit of vibrations and energy One seeking to know Itself? Perhaps its humming beckons to us with its rhythmic siren call: "Draw near; come home from evening pasture."

As I gazed again at that lone thistle—my nemesis and mentor—I was compelled to remember: Dad with his agitated weariness and excited sadness, his stutter-stepping to the comforts of a morning nap and to a few hours of uneasy peacefulness; Grandfather Kearney dressed in khakis, hemp shirt, and reed hat . . . with a piece of moistened terry cloth tucked under it to help guard the back of his neck from sun rays. With simple genius, he tended to his gardens, enlivening them with a masterpiece of living colors.

I recalled Billy Crinshaw and his timid courage, his halting voice imploring me to remember him in a way that I couldn't forget . . . and Nancy Crawford thanking me for believing that she'd make it in an unkind and unaccepting world—despite her father's sins. I remembered Helen Borden tending a pot of chicken and noodles that grumbled atop the kitchen stove. I recalled her sisters and a hope for freedom. I remembered Mr. Jansen burying his father, and Mr. Fields who, like a thistle, survived in rough patches of earth after death snatched his wife.

Why are all of these people returning to me now? I wondered.

The Little Country Deuce spared no time, wafting back an answer. "They never left. They're reminding you to consider them . . . consider them, and be glad."

Consider them? Heck, I'd do a whole lot more than that. I couldn't forget them—ever!

Mrs. Cunningham appeared with her patient kindness, steeped in graceful honor when she saw my brothers and sisters scurrying about to work on half-started 4-H projects too late to salvage. Mr. Finesse appeared with Mr. Brooks, relating all of the tricks for growing the best-tasting spuds and crafting delicious honey. They demonstrated that life is art. Their handiwork thrives on living canvases of soil.

I had to consider Grandmother's advice to speak clearly and to make my story one everyone felt: to write a universal story. And what about Dad's counsel that even a crippled boy may tell a story in a way that the lights dim and a hush falls. Who's telling it, and who's listening?

I considered Mother's praises for my help in growing glorious beets along with the goats, and I felt her poetic expression of unity: "We're made of one part stardust and three parts sea water, purified and gurgling up from ancient springs." Perhaps we're all reflections of the same Great Spirit, united that way. (Maybe we need to clear our vision to see it.) Mother's wise words and quiet humility remained: "We're connected because all are one . . . already merged." When she whispered those words, I felt the humming of the Universe, wiggling with life.

Friend, who would guess there'd be "so much" to carry with me after a mere thirteen years? Heck, do you remember how I always saw myself as being on the high end of forty years old?

Just as the creek held me at dusk, it enchanted me at dawn, insisting on drawing out memories. I remembered the tortured Mr. Crocker peering at me through his bloodshot eyes, feverish with his need to be loved and respected, and how he finally ran away. I pictured Mr. Bentley slapping his left thigh as he exclaimed, " Son, I'm slap out of chicken feed, and liniment!" as he laughed and then grimaced at my mention of Yankees and uncertainty. I fancied Mr. Knuckle as he tended our garden, milked our Jersey cows, or watered our livestock. A cottony feeling gripped my throat as I reflected on his constant, wise work. Mr. Fields had kept right on going in his own shy way, surviving along a dusty lane and a slumbering meadow after death claimed his wife. He kept on trying in spite of loss.

The stories of Dr. Redmond wafted nigh: how he fled from the Indiana farm of his youth, escaping to medical school and his practice where he longed to run away again—-this time back to a farm. Dreams of freedom and control over brimmed his mind, and his apple orchard blossomed. And there was Mr. Zettle who frightened us kids with his stories, and who had to run back to the Osawatomie State Hospital. Was he afraid of what lay inside? Don't many of us grow enchanted by longings to return to our roots? Yet we also wish to take charge, blotting out and rewriting stories too sad to relate.

Uncle Jim and his inward struggles appeared: how he held onto dignity while letting go silently. No had known he'd passed for a few hours, not until that morning when Dad came calling. A certain songbird soothed Dad that blustery morning as he said good-bye to Jim. The mockingbird carried a special message from Uncle Jim, one who had struggled to share his song of hope in a world gone mad.

And there was the madness and panic in October when we heard, "There are missiles in Cuba!" I thought about the warnings: "This in only a test. In the case of an actual emergency, you will be instructed to tune to the emergency broadcast station. This is only a test!" Not finding a fallout shelter, we found courage instead. Had I felt a connection to another culture—clear across the Atlantic and in the frigid north—gripped in the madness of that dreary October?

More madness . . . more memories flashed of the day my family felt too sad to build a fire. We'd lost our king cottonwood in the northwest pasture, and we'd lost our president, all in parts of two days. I tasted the day that I did not know whether the saltiness seeped from the hot dog or from my on-again and off-again tears. Yet, we'd found hope in grief. Hope remained; by improvising, we'd make do.

The hope of improvising in chaos led me to consider the LEM descending to the moon and then blasting back into orbit with the work of a "simple" engine, as simple as the common gunnysack cobbled into Mother's Halloween costumes. I reckoned that Arachne and Pallas Athene would have envied Mother's handiwork, startled enough to run for cover. Even Velazquez might have spun around in dismay at her gunnysack genius.

Then, I pictured our faithful hound placing his ears and his life in Mother's steady hands. Improvised stitches of dental floss spared PJ's life . . . and a bit of my hope. Backed with cotton cloth, those stitches held. With them our hope held, too. I reckoned that most problems may be solved with the genius of baling twine, gunnysacks, and dental floss. . . . not to mention cotton cloth.

I don't know how much hope Dad's illness allowed while it urged him airborne, soaring his car over a snow-filled embankment. He glided over silent landscapes where snowflakes drifted gently down by his side to rest for a spell. But Dad did the best he could, and that's all I ever need-ed to know about him. He did his best, and knowing that is more than enough for me.

Yet, I recall his fondness for Wordsworth's immortal poem, "Ode: Intimations of Immortality from Recollections of Early Childhood". Dad's murmuring of its tenth stanza echo.

> ' . . . What though the radiance which was once so bright
> Be now for ever taken from my sight,
> Though nothing can bring back the hour
> Of splendor in the grass, of glory in the flower;
> We will grieve not, rather find
> Strength in what remains behind;
> In the primal sympathy
> Which having been must ever be;
> In the soothing thoughts that spring
> Out of human suffering;
> In the faith that looks through death,
> In years that bring the philosophic mind.'

I see you're shaking your head. I know . . . I know. I reckon I've lived an overfilled boyhood, what with all the commotion. But you might find similar events in your childhood . . . leastways, similar themes. Heck, you might be surprised by how much all of us endure as we try to gath-er a certain kind of wisdom "from the awful Grace of God".

I imagined that all of these memories spawned by the creek's ripples might be part of one enormous spirit, and that I was seeing only bits and pieces of the whole, as if I gazed at a mosaic. First, I pinched the view of these images between my thumb and forefinger to swirl them into a wholeness, as if they were a dirtdevil with a stillness in its center. Then, I reckoned, "Step back for a wider view, to see the larger picture." I needed to know that we're all one, perhaps reflections of one universe seeking to know itself, a universe that tends to life and hope, one that laughs with joy.

Presently, genius bees flew about in the dawning light. Don't bees nav-igate by the position of the sun in the sky? When the sun hasn't risen fully, it takes one brave bee to venture out into a mysterious world. It takes courage for anyone to venture into a spectral world at half light if a body doesn't know for sure if he'll make it back, doesn't it? But that's the best time to snatch the mystery that we spy out of the corner of an eye. It's the best time to break for home with news in seasons of discovery.

As the bees began to tend the wild flowers, they hovered around the thistles on a mound of dirt. Even in a drought thistles abound with nectar, the raw primer for honey. The amber ambrosia of thistle honey and the structure of honeycomb inspired my healing, just as drifting snowflakes falling silently on our driveway had helped me picture it. Also, Sisters Helen Marie and Henrietta hoped for a homespun miracle with their holy water from Lourdes. I longed for Omega Bluebonnet, Lambda Helios, and the Little Country Deuce, although they never quite left me and hadn't entirely arrived.

Then, I considered Aeschylus and his magical poem of pain. He wrote, "Pain which we cannot forget, even in our sleep, falls drop by drop upon the heart until in our great despair, against our will, comes wisdom through the awful Grace of God." Those drops reminded me of the rain falling gently to Earth to seep into a spring until they were ready to gurgle forth. In the Earth those waters are purified before they leap over moss-laden rocks and stones. There the drops begin another voyage to ports of call unknown, just as thistledown wafts o'er windswept prairies to points unknown. Thistledown wonder shivers my spine, showing me that the land and hope remain. Both the land and hope endure.

Each season of thistles and each new crop of thistledown offer possibilities too grand to know. I sense its wonder as I tilt my head to one side and squint out of my right eye. I catch a glimpse of that wonder and hope, like a flickering image flashed across a screen: a fleeting image of creation unfolding. And rarely are tales richer in hope ever found than on windswept prairies, quite dusted with down.

With all of those images of the past, I began to laugh at all I had known and had not known, at all I had felt and not felt, at all I had seen and not seen in the Kansas of my early youth. I knew I might glimpse the wonder and never quite catch its wholeness. I'd sense only an image of what might be. I laughed with joy tinged in longing . . . and of loss from which hope may sprout.

With my laughter came tears as I remembered all those I had lost in the Kansas of my youth, of all who had ached to be but had not become. I grieved for Mr. Zettle who could tell a tale in a way that showed it up close and personal, better than anyone else I'd known. I missed his dusty tales. I grieved for St. Joseph, the slumbering town on the banks of the mighty Missouri and all that might have been. I remembered my dad and all of his untapped potential, of his diminished greatness. I grieved for Uncle Jim, wrought with profound sadness. Even that seemed all right as I gazed at the thistles dancing in the early morning breeze. And then, I commenced to laugh again—not an ordinary, puny laugh but a hearty, gut-wrenching one powered by mighty breaths as I drank it all in. I knew only that we'd lived and had done our best, and that we had endured in what had often been rocky soils. We'd tunneled into those soils and had held on with only our hope and the will to do so. Nothing else mattered but the strength of that endurance and the will to hang on as best we could. We'd used our very bodies as tools.

On that score, I remembered dragging my body along as we planted beets on the wind-strewn soil fertilized with goat dung and thistle ashes. That memory reminded me of our connection, a bond to the soil and to the enduring thistles. Such a bond cannot be severed. Knowing that I belonged made the struggles worthwhile, and they all seemed sweet. Omega Bluebonnet's sacrifice flashed, her gift binding me with mystery and intuition. She knitted that into my bones with tiny threads—feathery like thistledown and its hope. Those threads may look flimsy, but they're as strong as spiders' webs. They're dewed with hope, one born of winds toting thistledown.

Once again I turned to the thistles to glimpse a bee flitting by one of its purple crowns. The bees and the thistles had conspired to make honey which had changed the very course of my life the day I fell from that swing set on our farm—the day that I stripped my fingers free from that stickiness on the top metal pipe. The bees and the thistles had changed the very course of my life, and they pollinated this book. Without them there would have been no accident, no healing, and no genesis of *Thistledown Rising*. Who and what controlled whom? I wondered, who's the master, and who's the trainee? Certainly not me. In my case the thistles and the bees were my guardians and inspiration. The hope they breathed lives in me, resounding in my bones. That knowledge tightened my throat, flushing it until it felt knotted.

These thoughts flooded me, just as the ancient inland sea flooded

America's heartland. Glancing down to spy another fossil from those ancient times, I remembered fondly asking Dad again, "Is this one a fossil, is this one? Did dinosaurs live here?"

His answer comforted me. "Sean, if you fancy they lived here, then they did as surely as the Lord made little green apples." I knew then that the power of imagination to entertain and to heal is one to be reckoned with. That long thought primed the pump that surged my short bursts of wonder. That respect rippled through all of the years unabated, as unstoppable as the tides that rolled onto shore on those ancient seas, as crisply as the salty mists rising above the sandy shores where the ancient seas met the thirsty land. Over those briny waters, I saw thistledown rising to pilot our dreams to ports of calls unknown. I knew then that imagination may be my greatest ally. If I could picture and believe that I'd be healed, then healed I'd be. As I'd strained to touch the stars, I'd felt all of the points in-between on my flights of fancy—my inward voyages of discovery.

Thistledown at sunrise on a windswept prairie near a rocky shore plays powerful pranks on a body. I imagine it's a state of mind, when hope sprints unabated across a sea of discovery, when I live once again in the Kansas of my youth. All of those stories and memories sweep back like that ancient sea tide rushing to shore. Tales and dreams of adventure rise crisply over those salty waters, just as the morning mists rose above that ancient sea. Life teems! I become a child as I watch and imagine, as I drink in those wonders. I'm a thirsty traveler who tarries at a desert well for a ladle of cool water.

Thistledown dawning is to reach for the stars and to fly to ports of call unknown as humanity explores a mysterious universe, one that teems with life and with love. It's a state of mind, one dawning, one that I sense in the rustling of tall grasses at dawn on windswept prairies. One Grand Spirit moves over rippling pools, and One Big Soul drinks in the wonder.

Oh, the joy of running free without interruption, of simply being without time, gravity, and constraints, with no duties to corral the spirit. The pleasure of simply being, to dream of healing, can't be described fully.

At such times, I glimpse the wonder and draw closer to that which IS. I do not achieve it. I may only approach it, the way an asymptote draws near a boundary but never quite reaches it.

But let me tell you, I gaze into space and murmur any tale that I fancy. Time, space, and gravity hold no meaning. I tilt my head to one side, and I twirl my forelocks to tightness with the fingers of my right hand as if I am weaving a cloth, just as I weave another tale with mystery and wonder that I puzzle over gently. Heck, I reckon there's no telling where dreams leave off and reality begins, seeing as how dreams held with enough love craft a reality as true as truth itself.

I could marvel at all of those mysteries as my thoughts rise like thistledown toward ports of call unknown. I waft into space, knowing neither boundaries nor gravity. The possibilities are as endless as imagination, as refreshing as springs, as ancient as the Earth, and as unlimited as the will to know the universe. Such possibilities inspire me as much as thistledown itself. It's a spirit of dreams, framed by downy white and glowing embers, powered by hope. And one day soon, gigantic spaceships may head out into the cosmos as they venture to the stars and ports of call unknown. . . If such ships drift like thisthedown, then is the Earth its thistle flower, aiming to go to seed?

That deep spot near the leaning cottonwood at our creek beckons to me to return to the Kansas of my youth, to a world teeming with wonder, mystery and discovery. "Come on! Come on, what's taking you so long? Where have you been?" I hear and feel the whispers as strongly now as I did then. "Come back once more to feel the mystery, to feel the wonder," I hear, and the siren call holds me spellbound. How could I resist? Why would I want to stop?

By writing this book, I hope these stories sound familiar, ones you may recognize from your youth. Our collective stories twitch inside of us, begging to be told: tales of hope and of healing, of wonder and of mystery. I reckons it's everyone's story, timeless in its reach across space, cultures, and the millennia. Grandmother had asked me to write it that way, and I hope I did her proud. It's her story, too. I reckon she'd be partial to the way I've recorded it.

Will, since I began this story at the end of another one, I might as well end it here at its real genesis. I reckon that *Thistledown Rising* is a story of us all, continuing for as long as humans fancy hopes and dreams. Hasn't it only commenced as we reach out into a mysterious and grand universe? And don't we need to reach during the half-light, or even in the pitch darkness of a silent night, when all we trust is that daylight will come? It helps to sing a song while rising. So, its "Thistledown Rising" and then "Thistledown Dawning." I'd be a fool not to say so. After all, there's work to be done before the dawning—what with the cows to be milked, the hogs to be slopped, and the chickens to be fed. That "internal" work comes before the dawning, before a grand and mysterious voyage into the cosmos. Without that, what difference does it make where we voyage—we'll still be the same people without such a transforming inner voyage. Well, I reckon it's always a rising before the dawning. How could it be any other way?

I hope you've enjoyed our sojourn to the Kansas of my youth, one which I'm tickled to share with you. It rested inside of me for quite a spell, and it seeped out as I snuggled up to a font of timeless strength. I listened intently to the winds of Kansas, "The Land of the South Wind People". The wind offers us all a power, one that I harnessed to put this story to paper. It's a strength that pioneers tapped as they settled prairies, and it's also one that Native Americans have held dear for millennia. Its power is both complex and simple, eking from an eternal source, one that I found shrouded in mystery. It nudged me to view the world in misted nuances, where uncertainty is mysterious and hope-filled.

That sense of the unknown stretched me. It's a source of energy that hums through the cosmos, echoing inward, and inviting us to engage . . . to dance with It as we journey on wonder-filled voyages inward.

The wind reflects this mysterious font, giving rise to thistledown o'er heartland prairies. It aches to free and lift us all. It may tease you to grow as you stretch outward to embrace Its Wonders. As for me, I began to see the world—and thistles in particular—in a whole new light.

And now, I feel a truth more strongly than ever before. With all the change that swept over the Kansas prairie of my youth, I surely know that thistles are quite extraordinary. Farewell. As for me, I've grown enchanted by restless thistles on windswept prairies, the Kansas of my youth.

Thistledown Dawning

Stalks rustled and shivered to offer a view,
    Of restlessness moving them slightly askew.
From out of each thistle fresh down gently flew,
    Our hope and our spirits to strengthen anew.
The wind using fingers too fine to be seen,
    Soon wafted the down as if gossamer wings;
The thistledown started to glisten and gleam,
    Ere glowing with ease, much like shimmering strings.

Stalks stretched as if pulled on by hands formed of wind,
    Hands stealthy which clearly our wonder does mend.
Stems lengthened and towered to boast that they knew,
    Of splendors then laden with morning's first dew.
A veil formed of shrouding mist soothed thirsty grounds,
    Respectfully dotted by windswept, damp mounds.
Each clump smelled so fragrantly as if perfumed,
    Each thistle quite regal and brightly festooned.

Morn's dew did move wearily into each tuft,
    Soon oozing through cottony puffs of the fluff;
A sight that brimmed crisply with hope, true enough;
    A scene that does tenderly ill will rebuff.
Light seeped from the east to frame the event,
    Starting a new day, the night being spent.
The sunrise did hasten the thistles' consent,
    To form lovely visions in dawn's firmament!

Bees scouted for nectar, their food to be found;
    Each humming and buzzing amidst purple crowns.
Those curators wisely did seek liquid gold,
    Abounding in thistles they often were told!
The flowers of thistles with green are embossed,
    This even while other sweet plants soon are lost.
The thistles are often survivors, not dross,
    While plants less resilient soon welt and are tossed.

The thistles did brim with small wonders I found,
    On windswept still prairies that hold me spellbound.
On prairies that teem with most whispering sounds,
    There life does so rev'rently thrive and abound.
The feath'ry white tufts as if flicked by a knife,
    Do reach to the sky with a promise of life.
The down seeks to puff t'ward horizons of light,
    The down slowly wafting, unfettered sans strife.

Each tuft of the down often wafts all alone,
    On fair winds and clearly are stealthily blow.
For each mystic voyager what magic is known,
    For each eager traveler what life will be sown!
The down swiftly dances and then with no traces,
    The down drifts serenely toward distant spaces.
I know in that twilight and dear holy place,
    An Unbridled Love doth pervade it with grace.

In one grace-filled moment my hope is renewed,
    In one special instant my spirit's enthused.
A peace that abides is to my soul transfused,
    A peace with no worries, each one is eschewed.
The morning's bright dawning quite freely is cast,
    Each daybreak is holding no dark clinging past.
Our troubles do melt beneath each windy blast;
    Our wounds are all healed and do slip away fast.

You'll find that way down on a prairie of winds,
    A soul will oft glimpse a sweet home of my friends;
A home that may call each in its own fine time,
    A home that lives warmly in memories divine;
A peace that does beckon with whispering sounds,
    On windswept still prairies where life does abound;

A source that is timeless and filled with great truth,
    A font drenched with vast hope and with boundless youth.

For rarely are tales richer in hope ever found,
    Than on windswept prairies: still dusted with down.

Acknowledgments for Thistledown Rising

First of all, to my siblings—Janice, Ann, Mary, Paul, Mark, Jean, Julie, Leo and Greg—thanks for the madcap adventures. The cacophony was delightful . . . sort of. What else might I expect?

I'm thankful for Dad: for his gift of language and flights of fancy. Escaping is one way to survive.

To Jim Colwell, thank you for gritty feedback and well-grounded counsel.

To Dorothy Stauber I extend my heartfelt thanks for steadfast and cogent advice and feedback over many months. Without you, this book might not have been possible.

To Mom for imagining possibilities, I'm grateful. You enhanced what may be.

To Ann Cunningham, I'm forever intrigued by your talent to depict the other-worldliness of a mystical reality with your line drawings, as only you could do. You splendidly melded words with images.

To my editor Faye Quam Heimerl, thanks for helping me unearth the whimsical "voice" of the boy I once was (but which I had somewhat forgotten) in all of his innocent curiosity.

To Rick Brearton, your book design echoes the crinkled essence of the Kansas of my youth.

To Shannon Parish, thanks for a Webpage design to launch *Thistledown Rising* to venues yet to be explored.

Professor Hadi Aly, I shall be forever grateful for encouragement. Thanks for introducing me to the possibilities of the self-publishing world.

To Susan McEachern, P.A., thanks for your contagious laughter and support.

To Grandmother, I'm grateful for your infamous advice: Simplify!

To my Fellowship Writing Group—for years gone by—I'm grateful for feedback I received at the genesis of *Thistledown Rising*.

To all the others whose inquiries and words of enthusiasm helped me all along the way, your support counted, and you know who you are.

Finally, to the farmers and other neighbors in the Great State of Kansas . . . and to their Country Cousins in Missouri . . . I express my heartfelt appreciation. You created artwork on living palettes.

    —Sean Redmond
      Boulder, Colorado
      Fall 2004